PLATE I (*Frontispiece*)

Kynance Cove from the north-west (A 570)

NATURAL ENVIRONMENT RESEARCH COUNCIL

INSTITUTE OF GEOLOGICAL SCIENCES

MEMOIRS OF THE GEOLOGICAL SURVEY OF GREAT BRITAIN

ENGLAND AND WALES

Geology of the Lizard and Meneage

(Explanation of One-inch Geological Sheet 359, New Series)

By

J. S. Flett, M.A. and J. B. Hill, R.N.

SECOND EDITION

By

Sir John Smith Flett, K.B.E., LL.D., F.R.S.

LONDON

HER MAJESTY'S STATIONERY OFFICE

1946

The Institute of Geological Sciences
was formed by the
incorporation of the Geological Survey of Great Britain
and the Museum of Practical Geology
with Overseas Geological Surveys
and is a constituent body of the
Natural Environment Research Council

First published *1912*
Second edition *1946*
Second impression *1954*
Reprinted with additional references *1973*

ISBN 0 11 880618 1

PREFACE TO FIRST EDITION

This memoir deals with the geology of the area represented by Sheet 359 of the New Series Ordnance Map on the scale of one-inch to one mile. The original survey was executed by De la Beche and the results were published by him in 1839 on the Old Series one-inch Sheets 31 and 32, and in his classic Report on the Geology of Cornwall, Devon and West Somerset. The district has now been re-surveyed on the six-inch scale by Dr. Flett and Mr. Hill, and the new geological map, on the one-inch scale, to which this memoir refers, is based on that re-survey.

The area in question is divided into two strongly contrasted geological regions by a fairly well marked line which follows a somewhat irregular course from Porthallow on the east to Polurrian on the west. The southern region is composed of a varied series of igneous and metamorphic rocks and is usually referred to in geological literature as the Lizard District although it forms a part of Meneage, an old Cornish expression for the promontory which lies to the south of the Helford River.

The southern region has been surveyed by Dr. Flett. It presents problems of great scientific interest relating to the sequence of the rocks, their relations to one another and the history of the metamorphism.

The northern region has been surveyed by Mr. Hill. It consists mainly of highly folded and comparatively unmetamorphosed sediments; partly of Devonian and partly of pre-Devonian age. In the old maps these sediments were grouped together under the general term, *killas*; but the Devonian rocks have now been delimited and the pre-Devonian rocks have been separated into four distinct groups.

Dr. Flett and Mr. Hill have written the chapters descriptive of the areas which they respectively surveyed, and have collaborated in the preparation of the chapters on Physical Features, the Lizard Boundary, Recent Deposits and Economics. They have also dealt with the very extensive literature relating to the district.

Dr. W. Pollard and Mr. E. G. Radley have made a number of chemical analyses of rocks and minerals for this memoir, and Mr. D. A. MacAlister has furnished notes on some of the mines. The photographic illustrations are from negatives taken by Mr. T. C. Hall, who also prepared the Bibliography. Dr. Flett wishes to acknowledge assistance received from Mr. Clement Reid with reference to the Pliocene Deposits and the raised beaches, and from Professor Bonney who visited the district when the re-survey was nearly completed and discussed the more obscure problems of the geology of the Lizard District with him on the ground.

J. J. H. TEALL,
Director.

Geological Survey Office,
28, Jermyn Street, London,
26th March, 1912.

PREFACE TO SECOND EDITION

The first editions of the geological map of Lizard and Meneage (one-inch Sheet 359) and of its explanatory memoir have been out of print for some years. The map was reprinted in 1934 with extensive modifications in the Meneage. These changes, involving a new interpretation of the succession and structure, were considered necessary by Sir John S. Flett after the discovery by Miss E. M. Lind Hendriks of fossil wood and plant-remains which were described by Professor W. H. Lang, F.R.S., in 1929. After his retirement as Director of the Geological Survey, Sir John Flett agreed to undertake the preparation of a second edition of the memoir. During 1937 and 1938 he re-examined the principal exposures and all the critical sections, and early in 1939 the revision was completed. Publication, however, was suspended because of the outbreak of war, but during the intervening years some further revisions have been made, mainly of a minor character.

In the second edition advantage has been taken of new information provided by Dr. C. J. Stubblefield's examination of fossils collected by Mr. W. Dewar. Additional field photographs by Mr. J. Rhodes, photomicrographs by Dr. J. Phemister, and rock collections by the late Mr. R. E. Montgomery, have been drawn upon for illustration. The bibliography has been revised and brought up to date by Miss E. M. Guppy who has also read all the proofs and prepared the index.

While the memoir has been passing through the press further contributions to the literature of Lizard geology have been made by Mr. J. B. Scrivenor and Miss Lind Hendriks, reference to which is made in the bibliography, but these more recent papers have not rendered necessary any substantial change in the interpretation of the geology.

The author wishes to express his thanks to Miss Hendriks, Mr. Scrivenor and Mr. Leonard Casley for many profitable excursions and arguments in the field during the progress of the revision. With the late Mr. E. H. Davison also he had much fruitful discussion. It is fitting that in this, the preface to his first geological memoir since retirement, warm appreciation of Sir John's masterly treatment of a complicated area and grateful acknowledgment of his distinguished services as Petrographer and Director should be recorded on behalf of his colleagues of the Geological Survey.

W. F. P. McLINTOCK.
Director.

24th September, 1945.

ADDENDUM TO 1954 REPRINT
In connexion with statements given on pages 140 and 146, we understand that since the issue of the 1946 Edition Miss E. M. Lind Hendriks has found plant remains in the Mylor Beds which appear to her to resemble those found in the basal Gramscatho Beds.

W. J. PUGH,
Director.

23rd September, 1953

CONTENTS

ILLUSTRATIONS

Text Figures

ix

PLATES

—————

x

GEOLOGY OF THE LIZARD AND MENEAGE

CHAPTER I

——

INTRODUCTION

THE district comprised within this Sheet may be divided geographically into two areas, the valleys of the Helford River and the Cober River on the north and the Lizard area in the south. The term Meneage is applied strictly to the whole peninsula south of the Helford River, but in current parlance it is generally used to signify the region north of the Lizard boundary including the parishes St. Martin in Meneage, St. Anthony in Meneage and Mawgan in Meneage. The derivation of the name is variously given but it is generally supposed to mean the country of stones— referring perhaps to the numerous large blocks that formerly were strewn over the surface, now mostly removed and built into the stone walls between the fields. It is often suggested that the Lizard is so called because it formerly contained a ' lazar ' or leper settlement but this is not agreed.

The district is mostly an agricultural one and the country around Mullion and stretching thence to the south side of the Helford River contains some of the best land in Cornwall. Large parts of the Lizard on the other hand are remarkably sterile and are covered with heather and thorn. The principal town is Helston (population 2,500), an old historical market-town, formerly one of the ' coinage towns ' of Cornwall, in which the tin produced in the local mines was assayed and stamped. Helston stands on the banks of the Cober stream which discharges into the Loe Pool. The upper parts of the Cober valley in former years have yielded large quantities of stream tin. The Loe Pool, at one time the harbour of Helston, is the submerged mouth of the Cober River and is separated from the sea by a bar of gravel and stones cast up by the stormy waves of Mount's Bay. In former times the bar was cut across periodically when the water in the Pool rose to so high a level that the mills in Helston had to stop work. The Pool is now drained by an aqueduct cut in the rock at the north end of the bar. It is the largest sheet of fresh water in Cornwall.

The Helford River is famous for the beauty of its wooded banks. It provides a safe anchorage in most conditions of wind and weather and is much frequented by yachts in the summer season. At the head of the estuary is the little port of Gweek which partly serves the town of Helston. It is described in the early chapters of Kingsley's ' Hereward the Wake.' Kingsley was at one time a pupil in Helston Grammar School, and his descriptions of the scenery of the country around Gweek are based on intimate knowledge. The oyster-beds of the Helford River were formerly of considerable value, and an effort is now being made to restore them. The little hamlets of Helford and Gillan are well known to artists.

At the north-west corner of the Sheet is the picturesque fishing village of Porthleven. Though much exposed to the south-west gales which sweep across Mount's Bay, its excellent harbour forms a nucleus for a considerable fishing industry which finds a market principally in Newlyn. In severe weather the entrance to the inner harbour is closed by a bar of wooden beams to prevent damage to small craft by the sea. Porthleven is of increasing importance as a summer resort.

The country around the Helford River and Helston, forming the northern half of this Sheet, is entirely cultivated and there are few large woods and no waste land or commons. North of the Helford River the land slopes upwards towards the Carnmenellis Granite, of which the southern edges just enter the Sheet. Between the granite and the river the clay-slate or Cornish ' killas,' which forms the country rock, has been in many places more or less altered by the heat of the granite. Around Constantine and Mabe the granite has been extensively quarried for many years and a large export trade has been, and still is, carried on, but the most important quarries now being worked are beyond the northern boundary of this Sheet. In the ground adjacent to the granite, mineral veins have been found, as is usual in Cornwall, and have been exploited, though not on a large scale, and are now abandoned. They have left their traces however in the deserted and ruinous mine buildings and the ' burrows ' of waste rock that can be seen on the sides of the road that leads from Penryn to Helston. The large piles of waste granite beside the old quarries also form a conspicuous feature of the landscape in this region but the local industry now is entirely agricultural. The upland granite country north of the Sheet yields an abundant water supply to Helston, and through the streets of the town water runs in open channels by the side of the footpaths, though often turbid from the finer debris derived from the stream works and the tin mines.

The railway terminates at Helston and the country to the south of this is well supplied in summer by motor buses. Most of the northern part of the Meneage is rolling agricultural land enclosed by stone walls of the usual Cornish type. There are no extensive plantations of trees except around Bonython, Trelowarren and Bosahan, and on the west side of the peninsula, especially, owing to the salt-laden gales of winter, the growth of trees is sorely impeded and the landscapes are bare and tree-less.   On the eastern side, where there is more shelter, many of the farms are surrounded by a few weather-beaten elms and ashes, and in the valleys trees grow very well.   The stream courses are seldom deeply incised and the valleys are short, but sometimes remarkably picturesque. In this country there has been no mining of importance and the general aspect contrasts strongly with that of those areas of West Cornwall such as Camborne, Redruth and Scorrier, where ruined mine buildings with their engine houses and chimneys form conspicuous objects in the landscape.

The most impressive characteristic of the physiography of the Meneage is the absence of outstanding hills and the level nature of the country.   Except in the bottoms of a few of the valleys there is little ground less than 200 ft. above the sea.   The highest point

Fig. 1.—*The Lizard Platform as seen from the east side of Kennack.*
At the extreme south is Bass Point with Lloyd's Signal Station on the top of the cliff.   The conspicuous points on the sky-line are Lizard Town, Grade Church, Ruan Minor and Ruan Major.   They stand respectively 238 ft., 248 ft., 212 ft., and 261 ft. above sea-level.   The prominent points in the cliffs are Bass Point, Enys Head and Polbream Point.   The coves are Church Cove and Cadgwith Cove beyond Enys Head, Carleon Cove, Poltesco (about the middle of the view) and Kennack (in the right foreground).   Kennack Sands are divided into two areas by the Caerverracks, a reef of serpentine rock submerged at high water.

is Roskruge Beacon, about 2 miles north of St. Keverne, which has an altitude of 378 ft.   The Dry Tree, which is at the north-west part of Goonhilly Down, is 370 ft. above sea-level.   Considerable stretches of the Lizard and St. Keverne roads are almost dead level. The Lizard and Meneage districts are in fact one of the best examples of an elevated platform to be found in Great Britain. This platform rises gradually from the south to the north but the slope is everywhere very gentle.   Great areas of Goonhilly Down and the Predannack Downs are practically horizontal and in winter the heavy rains drain away so slowly that the surface is almost water-logged. The general altitude is from 250 ft. near the sea coast to about 350 ft. inland. Many areas of flat ground occur in other parts of England at or near sea-level, such as Romney Marsh or Sedgemoor, but the Lizard platform though formed at sea-level has been raised to an average height of 300 ft. at a remote geological period.

Moreover the Lizard platform is not now covered by sand, gravel and other marine deposits, though at a former time there can be no doubt that accumulations of this type mantled its surface. To the geologist it is of special interest because it consists of a great variety of rocks such as serpentine, hornblende-schist, mica-schist, gneiss, clay-slate and quartzite, but none of these projects above the surface or forms eminences displaying their characteristic features. The margins of the different geological formations are practically never accentuated; all the rocks have been reduced to a uniform plane. The terrace or platform accordingly is a ' terrace of erosion '; it has been cut across all the geological structures by some levelling agency which has acted uniformly on all the subjacent rocks.

Very fine views of the outline of the Lizard terrace can be obtained from Old Lizard Head, looking west to Kynance and The Rill, or from Cadgwith looking east over Carrick Luz and the Black Head. In both cases the sky line can be seen stretching almost horizontal for several miles. In these districts the rock constituting the platform is serpentine, which weathers so slowly that the original character of the platform is preserved in great perfection. No other rock is so resistant, and where the gabbro, the schists or the clay-slate form the surface the landscape shows rolling features with many open valleys bordered by gentle slopes. The intervening ridges and water-sheds, however, nowhere rise above the general level. The old platform originally extended north across the Helford River to the southern edge of the Carnmenellis Granite, which projects in such a manner as to show that it formed an island or cape, rising above the sea at a time when the whole of the country to the south was submerged.

The imperfect preservation of the platform in the north part of the Meneage is due to the weathering of the rocks exposed for long ages to the action of the atmosphere and to continuous erosion by the streams. The valleys, with the exception of the Helford River, have been cut down into the old rock table and in this way the present scenery has originated. As might be expected, the platform features are not confined to the district now under description. A very large part of Western Cornwall was submerged and the general level of the sea was from 400 to 500 ft. higher than at present. In the Land's End district the evidence is very complete and shows that the sea stretched for several miles inland from the present coast line, and only a few of the granite hills rose as islands above the waves. The granite of the Land's End district, however, weathers more rapidly than the serpentine of the Lizard and the platform features consequently are not so perfectly retained.

On the surface of the platform there are practically no deposits except the products of the decomposition of the subjacent rocks. As this part of England was never covered by moving ice-sheets there is a complete absence of material transported from a distance by glacial action. Where rocks of different composition adjoin one another their boundaries can often be traced with great precision by means of the debris in the soil even though the solid rocks are nowhere visible. In many places the platform has been deeply weathered and in sinking wells it may be found that for twenty or thirty feet the rock is broken down into a crumbling mass. In this way rich agricultural soils have often been produced, but, on the slopes, the rain may have washed away the finer earth, leaving large undecomposed blocks strewn over the surface. In the country round St. Keverne and Coverack great boulders of gabbro are scattered through the fields and downs. The gabbro weathers very unequally, but often deeply, and these blocks (known locally as ' crusairs ') are exposed when the fine earth between them has been washed away. Similarly in the Meneage the hard, white Ordovician quartzite weathered much more slowly than the other rocks, and great masses and blocks of it were prominent objects in the fields. Many of them however have been broken up by the farmers and used for building the stone walls between the fields. In the country formed of schists, serpentine and clay-slate, residual blocks in the fields are far less common because these rocks decompose in a more uniform manner and are more readily broken down by frost, rain and other atmospheric agents.

There is one superficial deposit on the Lizard platform, however, that is of great interest. On the summit of Crousa Down an area of about half a square mile is occupied by a bed of gravel consisting mainly of white quartz pebbles, often several inches in diameter. This bed may be about 20 ft. thick in places and rests on an eroded surface of gabbro. No fossils have been found in it, and the white quartz pebbles are not of local origin, as such material is very rare in the Lizard. Most of them, however, can be ascribed to the quartz veins that occur abundantly in the killas of the Meneage and the country round the Helford River. It is not possible to interpret this deposit as a gravel terrace laid down by a former river; it is clearly a marine deposit though no shells are found in it; if any were originally present they may have been removed in solution by percolating water. We have in these gravels the pebbles that were laid down on the bottom of the sea that rolled over the surface of the Lizard platform when it was completely submerged and the waves broke against an old shore line situated near the southern margin of the Carnmenellis Granite. That deposits of somewhat similar character were widespread in the Lizard district is proved by the occurrence of traces of them in many places where the original terrace features are still in good preservation. Quartz pebbles are frequent on Goonhilly Down near the Dry Tree and Croftnoweth; and even on Kynance Downs, at a lower level, scattered quartz pebbles up to three inches in diameter are quite numerous and easily found. The gravels of Crousa Down have escaped erosion, firstly because they are comparatively coarse, and secondly because they lie on a water-shed where stream action is at a minimum.

A small patch of similar gravel is known at Polcrebo, about 4 miles north of Helston and about a mile north-east of Nancegollan Station. More interesting, however, are the gravels, sands and clays of St. Erth, between Penzance and St. Ives. These have been worked in several pits for many years and have yielded fossils that prove that the deposits are of Pliocene age and according to the most recent information were deposited about twelve millions of years ago. It may be remarked that in the south-east of England in Kent, Sussex, Surrey and Herts., there are fossili-ferous deposits of approximately the same period, known as the Lenham Beds, and that these occur at elevations up to 700 ft. above present sea-level. Consequently it is inferred that in the south of England there was a general Pliocene submergence amounting to several hundred feet, and the Lizard platform is thus accounted for both in origin and age.

When the land rose and the sea retired from its surface, the streams again began to run and a new drainage system was initiated. Rivers such as the Cober, which had never been com-pletely drowned, merely lengthened their courses towards the sea. The Helford River is in all probability a very old stream channel belonging to an epoch anterior to the Pliocene, when the land stood at a much higher level. Of its original history there is very little evidence but we may suppose that the depression was, to a large extent, completely filled up by Pliocene marine deposits which have subsequently been washed out by the action of streams, tides and storms, restoring the old channel. The Loe estuary may have a similar history. In the Meneage and the Lizard new streams arose and the drainage now took the easiest courses to the sea. A study of the present channels of the Lizard streams shows that many of them follow lines of weakness in the rocks that form the platform. Wherever an important dislocation or fault emerges at the coast its position is marked by a cove and a streamlet. Examples of this are Polurrian, Mullion Cove, Kynance, Pentreath, Housel Bay, Polbarrow, Cadgwith, Porthallow, Porthoustock. Church Cove (Landewednack) and Caerthillian Cove are not exactly on the boundary fault of the serpentine but near it, and perhaps on subordinate faults. Other streams have carved their valleys in easily decomposed granitic rocks bounded on each side by serpentine outcrops : to this type belong Kennack, Cadgwith and Poltesco. Other coves and valleys such as Poldhu, Gunwalloe, Porthleven, cannot be ascribed to any obvious geological structure and this is also true of the inland courses of many of the streams.

In the Meneage and the country around Helston the scenery is of the usual Cornish type, undulating smooth ground with few projecting rocks or escarpments and with stream valleys sharply incised though of no great depth. Much of the land is under pasture and the fields, usually rather small and of irregular shape, are bounded by stone walls often topped with thorn. A few weather-beaten trees occur between the fields and may project above the sky line, and there are occasional patches of thorny waste. South of the Lizard boundary line however the scene is different. There is little cultivation on the Lizard Downs and most of the area is abandoned to the Cornish heath and dwarf thorn, among which a few cattle stray in search of pasture. These downs in summer however are a blaze of colour that delights the eye. Cultivation is restricted to the marginal areas and to the ground which is underlain by hornblende-schist, mica-schist or gneiss. The soils upon the serpentine are usually thin and seem to be exceedingly barren; though part of the area has been enclosed and cultivated at some former period, there is now little of the serpentine ground under the plough.

The rather monotonous character of the inland scenery of the Lizard district is in striking contrast to the variety and interest of the coast. Many of the coves are famous for their beauty and are visited every summer by crowds of tourists. Perhaps the best known are Kynance and Mullion Cove, but Polpeor, Housel Bay, Cadgwith, Kennack and Coverack are very picturesque and are often painted by landscape artists. Sir Frederick Leighton said that Kynance (Pl. I) was the most beautiful cove in Cornwall. The rich variety of the Lizard coastal scenery is due principally to the diversity of rocks forming the cliffs and provides a study of never-ending interest to the geologist. As will be seen from the Bibliography attached to this memoir, the number of descriptive accounts that have been published, essentially based on the examination of the Lizard coastal sections, is very great, probably greater than that of any equal extent of coast in the British Isles. These cliffs are as puzzling as they are attractive. They have given rise to much controversy during the last hundred years, and will afford material for investigation and discussion for many years to come.

The Lizard platform is bounded by cliffs on every side. The only low sloping banks are those of the Helford estuary, Lowland Point, and occasional small stretches in the coves as at Kennack and Coverack. Many of the cliffs rise to a height of 200 ft. The highest are on the west side of the serpentine mass, at Vellan

Head, George's Cove, and south of Mullion. In many places on the west and south sides of the peninsula the high cliffs descend vertically into the sea and there is no beach or shore platform. Even in such situations, however, there are usually small coves such as Kynance, Pentreath and Gew-graze, where footpaths lead down to the sea. These are all famous for their beauty. Many of the cliffs of the western coast line seem quite inaccessible, and can be examined only by boat during exceptionally calm summer days. To those familiar with the cliffs, however, there are many places at which a descent can be made, but the stranger will be wise always to secure the services of a local guide who knows the paths that are practicable. These cliffs are slowly but constantly retreating before the attack of the waves. Every winter there are numerous landslips and those who have experience can recognize that the cliff features have changed between every successive visit. The best evidence of this is perhaps the numerous old footpaths that end suddenly on the cliff-top where a fall of rock has cut them off. A fairly good pathway now follows the top of the cliffs all the way around the peninsula from Porthleven to the Helford River, and in the Lizard district these paths are repaired every year.

The boldest cliffs are those of serpentine that face the west and south. For impressive grandeur no cliffs of serpentine in the British Isles can rival those that range along the west coast of the Lizard from Mullion Cove to Pentreath Beach. They are seldom less than 200 ft. in height and exhibit every variety of jointing, pinnacle and gully. About The Rill, The Horse and Pengersick, the scenery is especially remarkable. These are favourite haunts of artists. Kynance Cove and Pentreath Beach are classic localities. The serpentine cliffs to the east of Kennack Cove and round to Coverack by the Black Head are also very striking, but here the cliffs mostly have a sloping top giving place to a vertical descent at a height of a 100 ft., or less, above the sea. This characteristic is probably due to the presence of great numbers of vertical or inclined dykes of gneiss, epidiorite and gabbro which by unequal erosion give rise to numerous landslips breaking down the edge of the cliff. Intrusions of this type are far less common on the western coast and, where they occur, as at Kynance and Pentreath, the scenery of the cliffs is more diversified and picturesque than where they are few or absent.

The dykes and lines of fault in the serpentine are often eaten out by the attack of the sea, and large caves are thus produced extending inland for many yards. The roofs of these caves may collapse, giving rise to great semi-circular depressions or amphi-theatres in the face of the cliff. Examples of this occur at Lawarnick Pit (west of Kynance), Holestrow (west of Pentreath) and Kildown (north of Cadgwith). In the hornblende-schist none of these 'pits' has formed but at the Lion's Den (west side of

Housel Bay) the roof of a cave subsided in 1866 and gave rise to a cylindrical cavity of 50 yards in diameter, open to the sky, and entered from the sea by a narrow passage. The Devil's Frying Pan at Cadgwith had a similar origin at some distant date, of which there is no historical record.

In the hornblende-schist the cliffs are even more varied in outline and feature than in the serpentine, but they are often covered with grey lichen and lack the sheen and variegated colour that distinguish the serpentine cliffs. From Polurrian to Mullion and on Predannack Head on the west coast the foliation of the schists is nearly vertical and the rocks weather with sharp crests and ridges. Around the Lizard Head, Pen Olver and Bass Point the foliation of the schists is nearly horizontal or gently inclined and the cliffs have a mural or battlemented aspect that is very characteristic. Around Cadgwith and Polbarrow the hornblende-schist with fine parallel foliation, dipping landward, yields nearly vertical cliffs descending abruptly into the sea.

The cliffs of gabbro are never striking and prominent except at Carrick Luz. The gabbro is coarsely crystalline and rich in feldspar which readily decomposes. Where the gabbro reaches the sea from Coverack to Porthoustock there are no high vertical cliffs but sloping grassy banks, with bracken and thorn descending to near sea level, and often marked with large grey residual blocks and occasional projecting knobs of rock. To some extent also the comparatively sheltered nature of this part of the coast and the great toughness of the gabbro have led to less rapid recession of the cliffs and explain the absence of bold, vertical rock features.

From Polmear and Porthleven to Gunwalloe and Polurrian on the west coast the country rock is killas, sometimes much veined with quartz and intensely sheared, though the bedding planes are usually preserved. There is great variety in the killas cliffs, and every little fault and fracture gives rise to coves and crannies. At Jangye Ryn, north of Gunwalloe Church, the killas shows complicated folding which has attracted much notice from geologists and is remarkably picturesque. Along much of this coast there is a beach of small pebbles, mostly well worn flints, derived from some deposit, possibly of Eocene age, that covers the bottom of Mount's Bay. These little flint pebbles are cast ashore in enormous quantities and make the storm beach known as the Loe Bar. They cannot have been derived from any part of the Lizard or Meneage as there are no beds of flint debris from which they might have come. Flints, however, are not uncommon on the beaches at Kennack, Poltesco, Cadgwith and other localities. They might have been glacially transported during the Ice Age or washed up by storms from some Tertiary deposits on the sea bottom. The latter is the only possible explanation of the great banks of flint pebbles that fringe the coast from Porthleven to Gunwalloe.

Elsewhere, on the west and south shores of the Lizard peninsula, beaches are absent except in the coves, and there is seldom any trace of a rock platform at sea level below the cliffs. On the east coast there is usually a beach which in many places is occupied by large angular blocks fallen from the cliffs. Many of these fallen blocks are of great size and quite unrounded, as the waves during storms are unable to move them. The principal extent of sandy shore in the Lizard district is at Kennack Cove where the sand is mostly composed of shell debris with many rounded grains of olivine, tremolite and enstatite. At Pentreath, Polurrian and Poldhu also, at low tide, there are sandy beaches excellent for bathing. At Gunwalloe Cove the blown sand has invaded the land forming the Mullion Golf Links.

An old Raised Beach occurs in many parts of the Lizard shore but is seldom a prominent feature of the landscape. There is an exception, however, at Lowland Point, north of Coverack, where a well-marked flat terrace lies below the weathered gabbro cliff. It is covered with grass and blocks of gabbro and its level surface is only a few feet above high-water mark. This Raised Beach occupies an area of more than a hundred acres and is one of the most notable in the west of Cornwall.   Below the village of Coverack the Raised Beach is everywhere present. It is also well seen at Nelly's Cove north of Porthallow. At Kennack there is hardly a trace of it and at the Lizard Point only one small remnant near the Bumble Rock. On the west coast the Raised Beach is never conspicuous and is best seen at Gunwalloe Fishing Cove. Its general level is about 10 ft. above high-water mark.

It is well known that a Buried Forest exists in Mount's Bay and is sometimes exposed when storms erode the sandy shore deposits near Penzance. In the Cober Valley at Helston buried tree trunks have sometimes been found in excavations below the present sea level. Moreover the stream-tin works at Pentewan and Carnon in the Fal valley have shown estuarine and river deposits to a depth of over 100 ft. below the present surface. These facts prove that at a comparatively recent time, probably after human occupation of Cornwall, the land stood at least 100 ft. above its present level for a period sufficiently long for the rivers to excavate their channels to considerable depths.   Much has been written about the old well-wooded land supposed to have occupied the floor of Mount's Bay and to have been submerged by the rising waters. This—the lost Atlantis—is probably in large part mythical but no doubt in Neolithic times the land extended considerably beyond its present margin. The estuaries of the Helford River and the Loe Pool were probably cleared of their Pliocene deposits during this period of relative elevation.

The Raised Beaches and Buried Forests bring us to the consideration of a period vastly more recent than the other elements of Lizard geology but they have left comparatively few and inconspicuous traces of the circumstances of their time.   When the rest of England as far south as the centre of South Wales was covered with ice-sheets during the Glacial Epoch, the climate of Cornwall must have resembled that of parts of Greenland and Spitzbergen at the present day.   The only Glacial deposit in Cornwall is the ' Head,' a loose stony wash that gathered on steep slopes owing to the disintegrating action of frost on exposed rock surfaces.   In many coves there is an apron of Head on parts of the cliff.   It is seen, for example, near Porthleven and Gunwalloe, but is scarce on the west and south coasts.   From the Black Head to Coverack and Porthoustock it is usual to find that the top of the cliff is mantled with Head which seems to be wasting away under existing conditions.   This Glacial Head rests on the Raised Beach, which consequently is usually assumed to be pre-Glacial, that is to say, the period of depression marked by the Raised Beach was anterior to the arrival of the ice-sheets.   When the ice melted away the land rose and was subsequently covered, down to the coast line, by the forests of which the remains are now found buried beneath the sand of the estuaries and the shores.   Once again the land sank till it reached its present level and this probably took place at no very distant date, for some of the streams wander through valleys which they have not yet been able to floor with alluvium.   Whether the land is rising or sinking at the present day cannot be definitely stated as there is no good evidence of a change of level in historic times.

CHAPTER II

SYNOPSIS OF THE GEOLOGY

IN a general description of the area comprised within this Sheet the rocks may be divided into two series separated by the Lizard boundary. The rocks to the south of that line do not occur on the north of it, except for a few areas of mica-schist and hornblende-

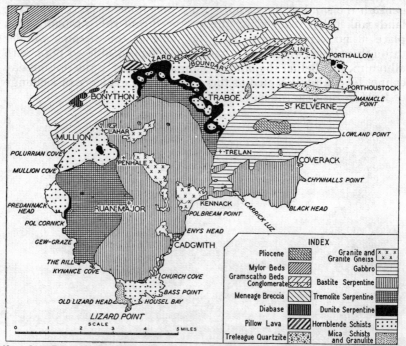

Fig. 2.—*General sketch-map of the Lizard and part of the Meneage, showing the outcrops of the principal rocks.*
(St. Kelverne should be St. Keverne.)

schist situated to the east and west of Manaccan, where they have been brought up to the surface by powerful earth-movements and are much shattered. The typical rocks of the Lizard area are metamorphic schists and gneisses, with plutonic intrusions such as serpentine and gabbro, and numerous basic dykes. All these rocks are in a variable but often intense state of metamorphism. To the north of that boundary are Cornish killas, clay-slates and grits, never highly metamorphic and sometimes fossiliferous, usually well bedded though much folded and intersected by numerous faults. Between these two series, on the east side of the peninsula there is a zone in which the strata are reduced to the condition of a regional breccia, the Meneage Crush-Zone. Intrusive into the killas at the northern edge of the Sheet is the Carnmenellis Granite which extends to Penryn on the east and to Camborne on the north and gives rise to a considerable amount of thermal metamorphism in the adjacent killas. This aureole has a breadth of about a mile and fades away gradually as the distance from the granite increases.

In the Lizard area the oldest rocks are the mica-schists, quartz-granulites and green schists of the Old Lizard Head Series. These extend along the coast from the lifeboat station at Polpeor westwards to Old Lizard Head and thence north to Caerthillian Cove, and are well exposed in the cliffs (Pl. IIA). Another well-known locality for the rocks of this group is south and east of Porthallow where they are seen in the cliffs east of the Five Pilchards inn and in the roads and paths to the south of the village. Inland exposures of the Old Lizard Head Series are few and often obscure. The most notable is that at Polkernogo in the centre of the northern belt of hornblende-schists, but mica-schists and garnetiferous granulites of this group are found occasionally in many places along the Lizard boundary, as at Gwealeath, though their outcrops are usually too small and ill-defined to show on the one-inch geological map.

The rocks of this series are sedimentary, though often containing igneous material. The mica-schists represent clays, the quartz-granulites were sandstones. Mixed with these are certain fine-grained green schists (containing hornblende and chlorite) and quartzose hornblendic granulites exhibiting every transition to the mica-schists and quartz-granulites on the one hand and to the hornblende-schists on the other. These are presumed to represent mixtures of fine igneous material, probably volcanic ashes, with ordinary clastic sediment. Very fine-grained hornblende-schists with a satiny lustre are also common in this series and there is usually much hornblende-schist, fairly coarse-grained and not differing noticeably from the hornblende-schists of normal Lizard type. Nodules and bands of epidote are not uncommon and are usually associated with the green schists and fine hornblende-schists. These hornblende-schists may have been lava flows or intrusive sheets. The Old Lizard Head Series accordingly is an aggregate of sedimentary and igneous rocks and indicates an epoch of volcanic activity, alternating with ordinary sedimentation.

Although the bedding is sometimes not entirely obliterated, these rocks are in a very high state of metamorphism. Their clastic structures have been effaced and they are perfectly foliated and completely granulitised. Minerals characteristic of extreme metamorphism are widely distributed, such as garnet, andalusite, sillimanite, cordierite; and kyanite and staurolite have also been detected. Some of these minerals indicate that the rocks have been at a very high temperature; yet they are not hornfelses but typical schists and granulites, hence it is inferred that their present structures were induced at a time when the rocks were subjected to regional pressure and were also intensely heated—a kind of thermo-regional metamorphism.

There is no direct evidence of the age of the Old Lizard Head Series but from their general character it seems reasonable to infer that they are as old as any rocks in Britain and their counterparts may be sought in Anglesey, the Malvern Hills and in the Highlands of Scotland.

To the south of the Lizard Head there is a group of tide-washed reefs and skerries extending for nearly a mile from the shore and known as the Man of War, Quadrant, Enoch Rock, Vasiler, etc. These consist of a distinctive type of hornblendic gneiss, the Man of War Gneiss, which does not occur on the mainland though large blocks of it can be seen on the beaches at the lifeboat station, Polpeor, and other places between that and the Old Lizard Head. In addition to the presence of hornblende, a distinguishing character of this gneiss is its curious corrugated or undulose foliation, and it is not without significance that a similar corrugation or crumpling can often be observed in the schists of the Old Lizard Head Series. In the shore platform which extends for about 300 yards south of Polpeor and is exposed only at dead low water some very interesting phenomena may be observed. The Man of War Gneiss has injected veins and sills of fine-grained granitic material which permeate the Lizard mica-schist, mostly along the foliation, yielding an injection complex of *lit par lit* structure, in which the mica-schist is so intimately blended with the igneous veins that their mutual boundaries are lost. The gneissic veins may be several feet in thickness or only fractions of an inch, and the thicker ones show pronounced foliation parallel also to the foliation of the schist. It is clear that when the gneiss was being injected there was movement and probably also folding in the schist and that the development of foliation in the schist and in the gneiss was simultaneous and due to the same causes. The breadth of this permeation zone is about 300 yards. It does not extend to the Lizard cliffs at Polpeor, nor is it well seen at the base of Old Lizard Head. It can be examined only in the shore at low water of spring tides.

The hornblende-schists are a very important factor in Lizard geology. They partly surround the serpentine and the gabbro, forming an incomplete ring. On the south they form the larger part of the Lizard and Bass Point district; on the west they occur at Predannack, and a broad belt stretches across the north of the Lizard district from Mullion Cove to Porthoustock and Porthallow. They are absent however on the west from Pentreath to Ogo Dour and on the east from Enys Head to Porthoustock. The mica-schists, granulites and hornblende-schists may be regarded as the country rock into which the serpentine, the gabbro and the Kennack Gneisses were intruded, and probably they originally extended widely on every side, and what is now preserved of them is only a remnant.

They are undoubtedly of igneous origin and were presumably basalts and dolerites or similar rocks. Their close association with mica-schists, green schists and quartz-hornblende-granulites suggests that some of them may have been lavas while others were possibly intrusive sills. In their present state, however, they are completely metamorphic, and igneous structures are rare or absent. Their typical minerals are dark green hornblende and a feldspar that is usually near andesine. Some of them show the effects of high temperature by the presence of pyroxene and garnet. The most abundant accessory mineral, however, is epidote, which occurs in streaks, bands, lenticles and nodules closely following the foliation of the rock and often crumpled or plicated as if the rock had been intensely folded either after or during the formation of the epidotic folia. There is much obscurity about the origin of this epidote, but its abundance is certainly one of the most striking characteristics of the Lizard hornblende-schists.

Two types of hornblende-schist have been recognized in the Lizard peninsula, having a different distribution, character and history, the Landewednack and the Traboe hornblende-schists. The Landewednack hornblende-schists are most abundant near Lizard Town, at Pen Olver, Bass Point, Hot Point and Church Cove. They are also very typically developed at Cadgwith. Much of the hornblende-schist north of the serpentine is of this type, and it occurs also on the shore at Porthallow. The horn-blende-schist associated with mica-schist is epidotic (Pl. IV, 4) : it is intensely foliated usually with a fine parallel foliation so that it splits into smooth-faced slabs. In addition to epidote it contains sometimes pyroxene and garnet. The Traboe schist on the other hand is not epidotic; it is often rich in feldspar and grey in colour. It contains no garnet, and the hornblende is sometimes dark brown. The foliation is rough and interrupted.

The Traboe hornblende-schist has mostly a vertical foliation and at its junction with the serpentine the two rocks are inter-laminated and are folded together. Great infolds of Traboe schist occur in the northern part of the serpentine. The epidotic hornblende-schist, on the other hand, has usually a horizontal or gently dipping foliation, and where it is in contact with the serpentine no common folding has been observed. These features indicate that the Traboe schist is very closely connected with the

serpentine; it was probably a basic intrusive rock preceding the
serpentine and affected by the same movements, and no great lapse
of time separated the two intrusions.

In the mica-schists at Polpeor ellipsoidal bolster-shaped masses
of porphyritic epidiorite or hornblende-schist, several feet or yards
in length, are frequently seen (Pl. IIB).   They are less metamorphic than the epidotic hornblende-schists and possibly represent
dykes injected into the schists when movement and the development
of foliation had nearly ceased.   Dark basic dykes of epidorite cut
the Man of War Gneiss on many of the Lizard skerries and are
obviously of comparatively late injection.   The ' bolster ' masses
at Polpeor may belong to the same phase of intrusion as the basic
dykes of the Lizard skerries.

The serpentine of the Lizard is its most famous rock and is the
largest mass of serpentine in the British Isles.   It covers an area of
twenty square miles and the irregular rounded shape of its outcrop
at once suggests that it is a boss or plug inserted into the
surrounding mica-schists and hornblende-schists.   Since the time
of De la Beche it has been recognized as a plutonic ultrabasic
intrusion.   Direct evidence of this, however, is hard to find.   Its
boundaries at the Lizard are obvious faults, and at Cadgwith also
they are presumably faulted.   The true nature of the boundary of
the serpentine is shown by the western and northern junction with
the hornblende-schists from Pol Cornick by Mullion to Traboe and
Trelan.   In that country although the margin describes a great
semi-circular curve, taken as a whole, it is very complicated in
detail.   The serpentine along that line is everywhere folded with
the hornblende-schists that surround it.   In some places the
margin is sharply faulted and the faults run in straight lines,
but for a large part of its course the boundary describes sinuous
curves.   Numerous areas of hornblende-schist are found in the
serpentine outcrop.   Some of these are only a few yards in length,
others occupy many acres.   The hornblende-schist thus involved
in the serpentine is always of the Traboe type and for a very short
distance at the junction of the two rocks there is a passage between
them—transitional rocks and interlamination of serpentine and
schist.   These are best seen at Pol Cornick and Porthallow.   In
the hornblende-schist areas also there are outcrops of serpentine at
Predannack, Mullion, Henscath, Rosemorder, Halwyn and
Porthallow.   The interpretation of these phenomena is not easy
because the exposures are seldom sufficiently clear to yield
conclusive evidence.   De la Beche expressed the opinion that at
Porthallow the serpentine seemed to have been thrust up through
the hornblende-schist, and all the evidence is in accordance with
the hypothesis that the serpentine, being the later intrusion,
underlies the hornblende-schists through the whole of their
northern outcrop.   In that case the serpentine areas in the
hornblende-schist may be anticlinal and the hornblende-schists in
the serpentine area may be synclinal.   On the other hand it may

be partly true that the serpentine areas in the hornblende-schist are the summits of dome-shaped intrusions and the hornblende-schists in the serpentine are sometimes inclusions rather than infolds. It is also to be kept in mind that no intrusive dykes or sills of serpentine have been clearly demonstrated, but some of the smaller serpentine bosses in the hornblende-schist may quite well be folded sills.

The serpentine is always an ultrabasic rock, and feldspar has been observed in it only in small amount and only in one variety, but there are several kinds of serpentine which are well characterized though transitional forms exist. Next the folded margin the serpentine is very fine-grained and compact and breaks with a lustrous and conchoidal fracture resembling a dark green flint. This rock is a dunite consisting mainly of small rounded grains of olivine. Another type is rich in tremolite which appears as pale green shining specks on the broken surfaces of the rock. The tremolite-serpentine is often distinctly schistose or may have a fibrous appearance. It occurs in abundance on the west coast from Kynance to Mullion and sweeps round the northern boundary in a broad belt. In the centre of the serpentine mass around Ruan Minor, Ruan Major, Goonhilly and Kennack and in the ground between the Black Head and Coverack, the serpentine contains large crystals of enstatite and diallage which by their perfect cleavage and brilliant sub-metallic lustre give a spangled appearance to the rock surface. This rock is a lherzolite (Pl. VII, I) and is much more coarsely crystalline than the other varieties. Most of the serpentine used for ornamental purposes belongs to this type. The chromite-serpentine is usually fine-grained and shows numerous small black specks of chromite or a chrome-spinel. It occurs in fluxion bands, a few inches to several yards in thickness, and is frequent in the bastite-serpentine. In zones of crushing the serpentine may be transformed into schists containing anthophyllite, tremolite, talc and other magnesian minerals but this never takes place on a large scale. The general arrangement of the dunite-, tremolite- and bastite-serpentines indicates that the serpentine mass has a concentric structure and the dunite is the oldest part of the intrusion.

The serpentine of the Lizard is everywhere a metamorphic rock : it never has the poikilitic or poikilo-porphyritic structure of the normal peridotites, though traces of this are sometimes seen. In the tremolite-serpentine there is always a parallel arrangement of the minerals and the rock is often fissile (Pl. VII, 3). In the bastite-serpentine the large crystals are usually almond-shaped and form elliptical ' augen ' very well seen on polished rock surfaces or on the sand-scoured boulders at Kynance or Pentreath. They lie in parallel bands which project on weathered surfaces and give the rock a fluted or ribbed appearance. Moreover where fluxion-structures are visible in the serpentine the ' augen ' structure and schistose banding are always parallel to the fluxion; hence it is inferred that in their origin they are closely connected and that the foliation is a fluxion-foliation induced during or immediately after the intrusion of the rock. Crystallization was complete and the temperature was falling but the rock was still subjected to stress and was in a plastic condition. The development of foliation and the folding of the margin of the serpentine were going on as the rock cooled down.

The serpentine was followed by the gabbro after an interval which was probably not very prolonged. How far the serpentine extends on the sea bottom east of Coverack is not known but the gabbro has the appearance of being a lateral intrusion; the focus of activity had shifted eastwards. There is no gradual transition between the serpentine and the gabbro. The oldest representative of the gabbro magma is the troctolite of Coverack which is rich in feldspar and contains sometimes a small amount of diallage. The dominant type of the gabbro consisted of plagioclase, diallage and olivine and there is not much variation in its composition; its metamorphism however is extraordinarily varied and shows every transition from normal igneous structure to a gabbro-schist with platy foliation, in which the original minerals have been completely transformed. Most of the gabbro is in the ' flaser-gabbro ' stage with broken kernels of the primary minerals surrounded by a schistose matrix of secondary metamorphic products (Pl. VII, 4 and 5).

The marginal relations of the gabbro outcrop are not well exposed on the north and west, as there it is mostly limited by faults, but on the south its original features are often well displayed. In these quarters it injects gabbro dykes into the serpentine in enormous profusion. Nowhere can these be better seen than at Carrick Luz and Coverack. The Carrick Luz gabbro is a large dyke, 50 yards in breadth. In the coves on each side of Carrick Luz gabbro dykes are very numerous. They are still more abundant on the shore at Coverack. In less than half a mile between Coverack Harbour and the North Corner there are nearly two hundred dykes and irregular intrusions of gabbro. These dykes present a most interesting study in metamorphism, for while a few of them are normal, others are perfect schists. The same dyke may be nearly normal in places and schistose in others. Schistose dykes occasionally cut normal dykes and the converse is also common. There is also much variation in the size of their crystals, for some dykes are rather fine-grained and others are gabbro-pegmatites with crystals of diallage several inches in diameter. It is clear that the metamorphism was irregular and spasmodic; it was in progress during the injection of the complex, and periods of rest alternated with periods of movement and crushing.

The next episode in the history of the Lizard complex was the injection of the black dykes. They are very numerous but irregularly distributed; few occur on the west coast but around

Kennack Bay they are fairly common and between the Black Head and Porthoustock there is a very great number. They are well-defined dykes with parallel walls, mostly vertical but sometimes inclined, and vary from a few inches to several yards in breadth. They often cut the gabbro dykes and it is a noteworthy fact that the gabbro dykes are often shifted by small faults that do not affect the black dykes in immediate proximity, though these also are not infrequently faulted (Pl. XIA). This shows that between the injection of the gabbro dykes and that of the black dykes much movement was taking place in the serpentine. The black dykes were originally dolerites and olivine-dolerites and though always meta-morphic they are the least metamorphic rocks in the Lizard. Their augite has been almost wholly replaced by hornblende, so that they are epidiorites or metadolerites but remains of ophitic structure are often visible. Fairly massive in appearance as a rule, they not rarely became schistose, and in some cases have been transformed into fine hornblende-schists where they have been caught in local movements shortly after consolidation. Their uniform fine grain shows that after the injection of the gabbro a period elapsed during which the rocks cooled down, and their well preserved dyke-like character shows that they were injected during an epoch when there was comparative quiescence. In these respects they contrast strongly with the gabbro dykes or veins, which are much twisted, broken and interrupted, and often can be traced for only a few yards.

The banded gneisses came not long after the black dykes. These are the most abnormal rocks of the Lizard and their strange characters have given rise to much controversy. They consist of a dark basic and a light-coloured acid ingredient, the dark being doleritic and probably the last emission of the magma of the black dykes, while the pale-coloured component is the precursor of the Lizard granite-gneiss. Sometimes the basic part was solid when caught up in the gneiss and forms rounded or elongated blocks; for the most part, however, it was plastic or even fluid and the banded structure is due to the fluxion of this heterogeneous and often pasty magma as it was injected into the older rocks of the complex. The basic material was gradually more or less dissolved or permeated by the acid, so that hybrid rocks of intermediate composition, rich in black biotite, are more common than the unmodified basic, and it is invariably the case that the acid rock is later than the basic or the mixed magma. The dark basic masses are surrounded by the acid magma and often penetrated by fine granitic veins. The banded gneisses form dykes (Pl. VIIIB), sills and irregular injections often of large size, and some parts of the serpentine on the west side of Kennack Bay are so filled with intrusions of banded gneiss that the country is composed of these two rocks in almost equal proportions.

The banded gneisses are rare on the east and west coasts but very abundant on the west side of Kennack Bay and along the coast line between Landewednack Church Cove and Kennack Corner. They also have a great extension inland and their areal distribution proves that they are the marginal fringes or offshoots of the Lizard granites.

Granite is seldom seen on the Lizard coasts and is far from prominent in the interior of the peninsula. The reason is that it weathers down very rapidly compared with the serpentine. It forms no ' tors ' or projecting crags, and can be traced only by means of occasional blocks and of the soil and debris in the fields. It yields smooth fertile country as contrasted with the rugged and barren ground occupied by the serpentine and though its boundaries cannot always be sharply defined it certainly covers large areas in the interior of the Lizard and principally in the valleys of the Poltesco stream, the valleys above Kennack and around Gwendreath, and the Cadgwith valley. It is a pale pink to white granite with both biotite and muscovite and has usually a distinct, though seldom pronounced, gneissose structure.

With the banded gneisses, the aplites and quartzose veins, the sequence of Lizard intrusives comes to an end. A complete series of igneous rocks has emerged, from ultrabasic dunites to highly acid felsites and pegmatites. As usual the succession has been from basic to acid types. Between the injections there were pauses but it is difficult to believe that all the intrusives (excepting the Man of War Gneiss) were not the products of differentiation of a single magma.

The phenomena of the Lizard metamorphism, however, are even more interesting than the variety of the Lizard rocks. In the mica-schists and green schists it is evident that the foliation arose in conditions of high temperature accompanied by pressure and movement. This type of metamorphism may be described as ' thermoplastic.' The presence of kyanite and staurolite indicates that the pressures lasted after the climax of temperature had passed and when the rocks were cooling down. The occurrence of andalusite, sillimanite and kyanite in close proximity in the Lizard schists proves a condition of metamorphic disequilibrium.

In the metamorphism of the igneous rocks the most striking feature is its variable and sporadic development. As a general rule the metamorphism is not extreme, but every member of the series shows types which are perfectly foliated and other types in which the original igneous minerals and structures are in quite good state of preservation. The serpentine, for example, is often not very different from a normal peridotite ; in other places it is a talc-tremolite-schist. Adjacent dykes of gabbro may be normal gabbro-pegmatites and gabbro-schists with platy foliation. The banded gneisses have often a close resemblance to the Lewisian gneisses but in the granite areas there are occasionally rocks that look like normal granites. In the dykes the change from dolerite to schist sometimes takes place in a few yards and is apparently connected with planes of dislocation and movement. This is the

Scourie dyke phenomenon as described by Teall. It is not possible to advance a complete explanation of the facts but it is of the first importance to recognize that in each of the main intrusions the foliation was complete (or practically complete) before the next member of the series was injected. The gabbro dykes cut across the banding and foliation of the serpentine. Nearly normal black dykes cut foliated gabbro. The banded gneisses cut the foliation of all the older members of the complex. Another very important fact is that in the dykes the foliation is always parallel to the edges of the dyke and generally to any fluxion-banding that is present. This suggests that the foliation is due to fluxion in a partly crystallized magma—a mush of crystals mixed with liquid. This type of foliation, known as ' protoclastic,' as suggested by McMahon, is probably present, but it is by no means the whole story. In the metamorphic rocks, as Teall pointed out, all the minerals partake in the metamorphism, even those last crystallized. Consequently the rock must have been completely crystallized before the metamorphism ceased to operate. It seems necessary to assume that regional stresses acted at irregular intervals and that certain rocks were more susceptible than others. Those which had recently consolidated and were still hot may have yielded readily, while others also crystallized but comparatively cold may have resisted and retained their original structures. It is a well established fact that most minerals are more plastic at high temperatures than at low temperatures.

At Treleague farm, on the road from St. Keverne to Porthallow, there is a rather fine-grained quartzite of grey or brownish colour which is exposed in pits around the farm buildings and also in a few places at the side of the adjacent roads. By the debris in the fields it can be traced over an area of rather more than a hundred acres. Apparently the outcrop is bounded by faults and there is no other rock like it in the Lizard district. In this quartzite the clastic structure is well preserved but that the rock is metamorphic is proved by the presence of fine needles of hornblende in the cementing material between the quartz grains and by occasional small crystals of garnet. As compared, however, with the Lizard quartz-granulites, which are well seen in the side of the road from Porthoustock to Porthallow, a short distance to the east, the Treleague Quartzite is in a far lower state of metamorphism. But in the pits around the farm greenstone dykes are visible; hence the Treleague Quartzite is older than the Lizard intrusions. This most interesting fact throws much light on the geological history of the Lizard. It proves that the Lizard mica-schists are much older than the serpentine and gabbro and that in the interval the Treleague Quartzite was deposited. It also proves two periods of meta-morphism, the first presumably during the injection of the Man of War Gneiss, and the second after the deposition of the Treleague Quartzite, and probably during the injection of the Lizard intrusive complex. The first period of metamorphism was evidently far more intense than the second, for the Treleague Quartzite is far less metamorphic than the Lizard granulites.

In the country north of the Lizard boundary there is a wide extent of clay-slates of the Cornish killas type with numerous beds of grit and sandstone often traversed by veins of quartz. At the Baulk Head near Gunwalloe on the west coast and at Polnare south of the entrance to the Helford River fossils had been found in slates and grits. They were of too indefinite character to establish the age of the beds in which they occurred but it was generally agreed that they were probably Devonian. On the other hand Charles W. Peach had proved that the massive white quartzite of Gorran near Mevagissey contained fossils of Ordovician type (probably Llandeilo) and on the north edge of the Lizard large blocks of an exactly similar rock were widely distributed. Hence there was a strong presumption that both Ordovician and Devonian strata were present in the northern part of the Meneage but their boundaries and mutual relations were not agreed upon. Collins, Somervail, Ussher and other workers on the geology of Cornwall considered it probable that the unfossiliferous killas of the Camborne and Land's End districts might be largely pre-Devonian (Silurian, Ordovician or even Cambrian) but in the absence of fossils there was no certainty. De la Beche had included the whole series in his grauwacke and regarded its age as undecided. After 1866 Murchison, however, had given the geological maps the Devonian colour except for a small area near Porthallow. Hill, who began revision in the Falmouth and Veryan area in 1899, was much impressed with the resemblance of the Veryan rocks to the Silurian of the South of Scotland.

On the south of the Helford River at Nare Point, Menaver and Gillan Creek there is a thick conglomerate which has been much investigated and frequently described. The conglomerate, probably because with it there occur certain beds containing obscure fossils, was generally assumed to be Devonian. Hill found that it contained blocks of grit which he recognized as derived from the adjacent beds, assigned by him to the ' Portscatho.' Hence he inferred that the conglomeratic base of the Devonian rested unconformably on the Portscatho, which consequently was pre-Devonian, and from its association with the Veryan Quartzite presumably of Ordovician age. Upfield Green, however, maintained that the Portscatho was Gedinnian or Lowest Devonian though he was unable to support this contention by the evidence of fossils.

The work of Lind Hendriks and Lang has proved that Hill's Devonian, Portscatho and Falmouth Beds cannot be separated, and that they are possibly on the same horizon as the Grampound, Ladock or Probus Beds in the Middle or Lower Devonian. They have been called the Hendriksi Beds from their best preserved fossil *Dadoxylon hendriksi* or the Gramscatho Beds. This discovery

necessitated the revision of the geology of the northern part of
Sheet 359 which was published in the second edition of the New
Series geological map (1934).   The Gramscathos occupy the west
coast from Polurrian to the Loe Pool and are there exhibited in
a series of magnificent coast sections.   Thence they stretch across
the peninsula to Gillan Creek and the Nare Point, forming the
shores of the Helford River.   Dark shales and well-bedded grits
are the prevalent types of rock in this group but sometimes they are
pink or buff.   Cleavage is frequent, but rarely obliterates the
bedding, and the rocks are sometimes much veined with quartz.
There is no development of limestone but cherty seams and
dolomitic layers are occasionally present.   Fragments of fossil
plants, mostly indeterminable, are obtained in a few places where
the bedding is especially well preserved.   They have been very
carefully investigated by Lang and seem to indicate a Middle
Devonian age for the strata in which they occur.

All the available evidence leads to the conclusion that Hill's
Mylor Beds are continuous with the Gramscathos.   They contain
many dark, striped shales and thin beds of grit.   They are more
cleaved and contain more quartz veins than the Gramscathos and
may provisionally be placed below that group.   It seems quite
probable that they are Lower Devonian; no fossils have been found
in them.   Around Helston and Porthleven they contain many
greenstones which are all probably intrusive sills.   No lavas and
no tuffs or ashy grits have been found in this series.

Between the Gramscatho Beds and the Lizard rocks the
Meneage Crush Breccia occupies an area of about eight square
miles, stretching from the east coast at Porthallow and Nare Point to
Skyburriowe on the road from Helston to the Lizard.   Its northern
boundary is rather indefinite but on the south it is bounded by the
edge of the Lizard rocks, a line which can be very precisely laid
down as it separates two series differing widely in their lithology
and in their state of metamorphism.   The Meneage Breccia is an
agglomeration of rocks of many different types (Pl. XIB).   Some
of the shales and grits may be, and probably are, Gramscathos and
Mylors.   One lenticular mass, close to the Lizard boundary, has
been assigned to the Dodman Phyllite, a rock occurring at the
Dodman near Mevagissey and probably pre-Ordovician.   A very
characteristic component is the white Ordovician quartzite, the
Gorran Quartzite, which has yielded fossils in a few localities.
It occurs in scattered blocks of all sizes from a few feet to nearly a
hundred yards in length, but it never forms a continuous outcrop,
though its broken masses can be traced along a tract stretching
westwards from the coast for a distance of six miles.   These blocks
are usually embedded in cherty shales and sometimes show grooved
and polished surfaces.   Other rocks of the breccia that can be
identified are the hornblende-schists and mica-schists; they are not
dissimilar to the Lizard schists.   The hornblende-schists are very
fine-grained and full of epidote and chlorite.   They are crushed to

fragments, veined with epidote and quartz, and have perhaps undergone a retrograde or diaphthoritic metamorphism. In the breccia, however, there are many other rocks that do not occur elsewhere in this Sheet or in the country to the north. The little limestone mass of Betty's Cove (half a mile north of Porthallow) has been identified by its fossils as Silurian, probably Ludlow (but see p. 132). The pillow-lavas and radiolarian cherts are probably the same as those of Mullion Island. They occur in a zone stretching along the Lizard boundary from Nelly's Cove, Porthallow, to Trelowarren and Cury and, though often brecciated, they retain their igneous structures in extraordinary perfection. Although the cherts are fossiliferous they have yielded nothing that decisively proves their geological age. The Manaccan Granophyre outcrops in the lane south of Manaccan and fragments of it are also found in the breccia on the coast at the Turwell below Penare. The rock is completely brecciated, but the microscopic structure is well preserved and there is no evidence of shearing. At Gallentreath, on the north side of Porthallow Cove, there is a mass of soda-granite between the killas on the south and pillow-lava on the north. Like the Manaccan Granophyre it is not known elsewhere than in the Meneage Breccia.

Another interesting rock of this region, however, is the Nare Head Conglomerate. At Nare Head it forms a bold cliff and must be two or three hundred feet in thickness. It is found also in separate outcrops at Menaver Beach and Flushing and has been frequently described. From the nature of the associated shales and grits, which contain ill-preserved fossils, the conglomerate has usually been assigned to the Devonian and compared with the conglomeratic beds of the Grampound Grits. Although the outcrops are often faulted the rocks are not brecciated, and whether the conglomerate belongs to the Meneage Breccia or not is open to question. No representative of it has been found in the continuous section of the Devonian on the west coast of the peninsula. Its origin and geological age are problems still unsolved and are discussed in a later chapter (p. 150).

The Meneage Breccia is the result of the Hercynian earth movements that took place at the close of Carboniferous time, when the rocks of Cornwall and Devon were powerfully compressed, crushed and folded by stresses acting from the south. The Lizard crystalline rocks were forced northwards and acted like a plough breaking up and disintegrating the rocks on the north of them, which were mostly well bedded sediments and were splintered into fragments before the advancing Lizard mass. For a breadth of more than a mile the Palaeozoic strata were rent to pieces and driven northwards. Innumerable thrust planes traverse the broken country and rocks no longer exposed at the surface have been propelled upwards in the moving mass. From the nature of its origin this breccia might be expected to contain representatives of the strata of this part of Cornwall from the Archaean Lizard schists that form the basal platform, up to the Upper Carboniferous, but they are so broken, crushed and veined with secondary products that their primary character, especially as very few of them contain recognizable fossils, is exceedingly obscure.   It seems certain, however, that Archaean, Ordovician, Silurian and Devonian elements enter into the complex.

The Carnmenellis Granite is post-Hercynian and was injected after the epoch of folding and crushing had come to an end.   It presents all the usual features of the Cornish and Devon granites and has produced a broad zone of contact metamorphism in the Mylor slates that adjoin it.   The mineral veins of the Constantine and Porthleven districts followed the intrusion of the granite. There are also a few dykes of elvan around Mawgan in Meneage and of lamprophyre, principally on the east coast.   These belong to the granite magma and are posterior to the great earth-movements.   No Secondary or Mesozoic rocks occur within this Sheet and the latest deposits are the Pliocene gravels of Crousa Down which were laid down on the surface of the Lizard platform.

The raised beaches, glacial ' head,' buried forests, alluvium and blown sands represent the deposits of Pleistocene time up to the present and complete the long and intricate geological history of the Lizard, Meneage and Helford River districts.

CHAPTER III

HISTORY OF RESEARCH

FOR a long time it has been known that the rocks of the Lizard district are different from those of the rest of Cornwall. Borlase (1758) mentions the clays of St. Keverne and the asbestos of Landewednack and is specially interested in the Soap Rock of Gew-graze, of which he describes several varieties. It was evidently a well known natural curiosity.

The Royal Geological Society of Cornwall was founded in 1814, under the patronage of the Prince Regent, and the early volumes of its Transactions contain several papers on Lizard geology [see Bibliography at end of volume]. The best of these reports is one by Ashurst Majendie which appeared in the first volume and is entitled ' A Sketch of the Geology of the Lizard District.' It is illustrated by a coloured map and shows a considerable knowledge of the principal outcrops. The mica-schists, hornblende-schists, serpentine, gabbro (diallage rock) are all recognized and some of their boundaries, especially in the coast sections, are laid down accurately. Other contributions by Paris, Berger, Rogers, Carne and Boase contain interesting notes on rocks, minerals and soils. Their attitude, however, is geognostical rather than geological and the authors are concerned mainly with the description and identification of the rocks and minerals, giving them the names then customary and discussing their classification and affinities.

The most important of these early papers is one by Sedgwick (1822) who was then Woodwardian Professor of Geology in the University of Cambridge. His descriptions of the coast sections are luminous and picturesque, and contribute many interesting observations, but he was still a convinced though not a bigoted Wernerian and abjured the theories of Hutton and Playfair. The structural relations of the rocks escaped his analysis.

In 1839 De la Beche published the first edition of the Geological Survey maps of the district (Old Series Sheets 31, 32 and 33) and in the same year his classic Report on the Geology of Cornwall,

Devon and West Somerset. His maps show the geology of the district with considerable detail and accuracy. He knew the coast sections well and had also made traverses of the interior. This was the first account of the geology from a modern standpoint, and, as he was both skilful and cautious, it is of great value.

The boundaries of the Carnmenellis Granite and of the Lizard Complex were laid down accurately. Between these lines the killas was shown as ' grauwacke,' a term employed for all the sedimentary rocks of West Cornwall. In 1839 Sedgwick and Murchison introduced the term Devonian and established this System for rocks intermediate in age between the Silurian and the Carboniferous, but the killas of this district had not been proved to contain characteristic fossils and De la Beche did not use that nomenclature. In his opinion the age of these rocks was uncertain. In 1846 a new edition of the map was issued with changes in the colour scheme, but the old lines and terminology were not altered. After Murchison became Director of the Geological Survey (about 1866) the Devonian colours were given to most of the killas except where it was suspected to be Silurian. De la Beche's map showed the greenstones of Helston, the elvans of Mawgan, and some outcrops of pillow-lava north of the Lizard boundary.

In the Lizard district De la Beche's map is a great improvement on Majendie's. The outcrops of the mica-schist, hornblende-schist, serpentine and gabbro are shown with considerable accuracy. The greenstone dykes were recognized and to the north of St. Keverne an area of greenstone is laid down, stretching east to Manacle Point. This is really gabbro intersected by many greenstone dykes. Possibly De la Beche was misled by the section on the south side of Porthoustock Cove, which is mainly greenstone. The acid veins and banded gneisses intrusive into the serpentine afforded a problem that evidently perplexed De la Beche. Some areas of banded gneiss at Kuggar and Poltesco are shown as hornblende-schist. Others, for example at Pen Voose, appear as granitic intrusions. It is clear that he recognized the intrusive nature of some banded gneisses exposed in the coast sections at Kennack and Poltesco but was unable to make a sharp distinction between this group and the hornblende-schists.

The descriptions contained in the Memoir show that there were many questions on which De la Beche hesitated to arrive at positive conclusions. His discussions are most interesting because these doubtful points are precisely those on which controversy ensued for many years; some of them, indeed, are not yet settled. They prove that he was not only a most accurate observer but also a sage and cautious critic of the evidence to hand and most unwilling to establish hypotheses on doubtful and insufficient grounds.

He was quite convinced that the serpentine was an intrusive igneous rock (and the gabbro also). At some of the junctions there might be appearances which indicated a transition but as a whole the hornblende slate and rock seem to have formed a basin into which the serpentine and diallage rock (gabbro) have been poured in a state of fusion (*op. cit.*, p. 30). In many places as at Cadgwith, Polbarrow, Landewednack and Pentreath, the hornblende-schists seem to dip under the serpentine. At Porthallow he thought it was probable that the serpentine had been thrust up through the hornblende-schist and mica-schist and had given rise to considerable distortion.

He comes to no positive conclusion regarding the relative age of the Lizard rocks and the killas of the Meneage to the north. The Lizard boundary he finds very difficult to define in some of the inland ground especially to the east of Trelowarren; towards Roskruge Beacon the hornblende-schists seemed very mixed up with ordinary greenstone (*op. cit.*, p. 31). At Polurrian Cove a conglomerate of limestone and grauwacke seemed to intervene between the hornblende-schist and the killas and this made it very difficult to consider that the hornblende-schist was of far greater antiquity than the grauwacke. (This conglomerate is really a fault-breccia but the grauwacke seems to underlie the hornblende-schist as the fault-plane dips to the south-east).

In the Nare Head conglomerate De la Beche found fragments of ' hornblende-slate '; this seemed an objection to the hypothesis that the hornblende-schists of the Lizard were ' trappean ash ' of the same age as the grauwacke, or even more recent. In the conglomerate however ' no trace has yet been discovered of either serpentine or diallage rock, though the latter especially is of great hardness.' De la Beche was not aware of the occurrence of both hornblende-schist and mica-schist in the country around Manaccan, and this would have increased his perplexities. Of the similar schists at Start Point, Devonshire, he says that it is safe to assume ' that they form no part of the (grauwacke) series that adjoins them to the north.' But he comes to no conclusion regarding the relations of the Lizard schists and intrusives to the slates and greywackes of the Meneage.

A very important advance in the knowledge of the geology of Cornwall was made when Charles W. Peach discovered fossils in the Quartzite of Gorran and Mevagissey, and Murchison accepted these as Lower Silurian. No doubt was felt that the quartzite masses of the Meneage belonged to the same formation. Peach's discovery was known to De la Beche (*op. cit.*, p. 83) and he regarded the serpentine and ' diallage-rock ' that occur at the Nare Head, near Veryan, as very similar to the rocks of the Lizard. It was not till 1879, however, that fossils were found in the Meneage Quartzite by Collins (1879b, p. 51).

The local geologists continued to take an active interest in the geology of the Lizard and Meneage. Among others Budge wrote on the conglomerates and raised beaches (1841), on the geology of Lowland Point (1842) and on the gravels of Crousa Down (1843). Peach discovered some fossils of obscure character at Nelly's Cove.

Porthallow (1869), and Rogers (1859) gave an interesting account of the alluvial deposits in the Cober Valley near Helston. Pearce (1870) described chromite in the Lizard serpentine. J. Arthur Phillips (1876) and Allport (1876) commenced the microscopic study of Cornish greenstones, and King and Rowney (1876) discussed the origin of Lizard serpentine. None of these contributions, however, was of major importance and there was no general discussion of the special features and problems of Lizard geology till Bonney entered the field in 1877.

Bonney was at that time Fellow and Lecturer on Natural Science in St. John's College, Cambridge, one of the most active petrologists in Great Britain, and widely known for his researches on crystalline rocks. His views are clearly and forcibly expressed. For the next forty years the crowd of controversies which marked the progress of Lizard geology centred mainly on Bonney's theories of the genesis and relations of the Lizard rocks.

He announced that the serpentine was a crystalline igneous rock, a mixture of olivine, enstatite and diallage, in fact a lherzolite, in a more or less advanced state of decomposition. It was intrusive into the hornblende-schists and even the sections at Pentreath Beach and The Balk, which are obviously faults, were simple, intrusive junctions. The serpentine showed a fluxion structure, and was practically in its present condition when the gabbro was intruded into it. The junction with the gabbro at Coverack and Carrick Luz showed that the gabbro was intrusive into the serpentine. He recognized an older gabbro (the troctolite) and a later gabbro, which penetrated it, and gave accurate descriptions of the microscopic composition and characters of both rocks. The black dykes cut the gabbro and serpentine and were originally olivine-basalts : some of them he called ' diorites ' but he suspected that their hornblende was paramorphic after augite. In the best preserved gabbros and black dykes he detected the presence of olivine. He gives full descriptions of the replacement of olivine and diallage in the gabbros by tremolite and serpentine.

The hornblende-schists, mica-schists, green schists and also the banded Kennack Gneisses he regarded as sedimentary rocks, highly metamorphic, which were probably in their present condition when the serpentine was intruded into them. The sections in Pen Voose and Kennack which De la Beche regarded as showing the intrusion of the banded gneisses into the serpentine were considered by Bonney to prove that the serpentine was intrusive into the banded gneiss. The banded structure, now ascribed to fluxion in a heterogeneous viscid magma, was considered to be the survival of bedded layers of sediment in a metamorphic gneiss. A few granitic dykes were observed on the west coast, at Kynance and elsewhere. The numerous lumps of serpentine in the banded gneisses were cross-sections of tongue-shaped intrusions; at the junctions of the serpentine with the hornblende-schists and gneisses a decomposed layer was commonly present.

He thought that the sedimentary rocks of the Lizard peninsula (mica-schist, hornblende-schists and gneisses) were probably ' about Lower Devonian '; the serpentine probably later Devonian; the gabbro and granite late Carboniferous (probably of the same age as the Cornish granites) and he conjectured that the dark trap dykes might be Tertiary.

In 1883 Bonney returned to the Lizard and in a second paper he amplifies and corrects his previous observations and conclusions. He now considers the Lizard schists as obviously pre-Cambrian; describes accurately the boundary faults at Polurrian and Porthallow, and emphasizes the great difference in metamorphic condition between the Lizard schists and the killas rocks to the north of them. As confirmation he cites the presence of hornblende-schist and other metamorphic rocks in the conglomerate at Nare Head, as had been previously reported by De la Beche. Collins, in 1879, had classed the killas of the south shore of Porthallow Cove as Lower Silurian, and the metamorphic rocks adjacent to them as belonging to the same period but greatly altered. There was, in Bonney's opinion, no transition between the Lizard schists and the Palaeozoic slates, but on the other hand the clearest possible evidence of a great dislocation between these two series.

Regarding the age of the serpentine, Bonney reached no positive conclusions. If the Lizard hornblende-schists were Archaean the possible age of the serpentine might be very much greater than he previously suspected. But he saw no reason why some of the granite dykes of the west coast might not belong to the same epoch as the Cornish granites and elvans in the country farther north.

The classification of the Lizard schists now adopted by Bonney was 1. Micaceous; 2. Hornblendic; 3. Granulitic; probably in ascending order. They were all sedimentary, and showed traces of bedding and current bedding. The origin of the term ' granulitic ' is rather curious. He says " I have felt much difficulty in giving this group a name, but think that on the whole it may be best designated as the ' Granulitic Group,' it being understood that garnets are either wanting or very small and inconspicuous." As a matter of fact garnets do not occur in his ' granulitic ' rocks though common in the Mica-schist Group and present also in the intrusive granite-gneiss of Porthallow Cove.

These two papers by Bonney are of the greatest importance in the history of the investigation of Lizard geology and all subsequent work was based on them. They evoked a great deal of criticism and discussion during the next ten years and stimulated research in an extraordinary degree. In 1884 Collins maintained that the serpentine of Porthallow was a stratified rock intercalated in the hornblende-schist. He believed (with Sterry Hunt) that the Porthallow serpentine might have been produced from sedimentary rocks by chemical transfusion or metasomatic processes. Collins returned to the subject in his papers in 1885, 1886 and 1887, but his views received no support. On the other hand he was right in asserting that at Porthallow the serpentine is interleaved and often closely folded with a peculiar variety of hornblende-schist and that transitional rocks are present.

Somervail also joined with ardour in the controversy. He controverted Collins's views on the age of the killas of the Meneage (1883 and 1884) and on the nature and relations of the Porthallow serpentine. With Howard Fox (1885) he published some useful notes on the conglomerates and breccias of the Meneage. He also described the Manacle Point (1889) and the brecciated felsite dyke at Housel Bay (1889). These two authors reported porphyritic structure in the basic facies of the banded gneisses (1888), and Somervail asserted that the ' Granulitic ' masses of the north end of Pentreath Beach were not inclusions but intrusions in the serpentine. While Collins believed in metasomatism Somervail appealed to segregation. If we substitute for ' segregation ' the term ' magmatic differentiation ' now employed, Somervail's views hold good in respect of banded gneiss, black dykes, gabbro, serpentine and part of the hornblende-schist, but it seems probable that the Landewednack hornblende-schists and the Man of War gneiss were derived from other magmas.

Howard Fox made many notable contributions to our knowledge of the geology of the Lizard; he eschewed hypotheses, speculation and controversy and confined himself to the record of facts. He was a diligent and accurate observer and had an intimate knowledge of the Lizard coasts; and he was always willing to place his observations at the service of other geologists. He described mica-schists at Polledan and Pen Olver (1891) and gave an authoritative account (1888) of the rocks of the Lizard reefs and skerries. The importance of the cliff sections at Ogo Dour and Pol Cornick was first recognized by Fox (1890). He also was the first to direct attention to the pillow-lavas and radiolarian cherts of Mullion Island (1893, 1895, 1896, 1898).

Teall's first contribution to the discussion of the problems of Lizard geology was a masterly description of the gabbro and its metamorphism in which he traced all the stages by which the gabbro passes from flaser-gabbro to gabbro-schist (1886). Bonney (1887) protested that Teall had insisted too strongly on dynamometamorphism or regional metamorphism and pointed out that the foliation in the gabbro varies in an extraordinary manner from place to place. Bonney insisted also that the serpentine, except locally, was a normal igneous rock. As usual in such controversies there was truth on both sides.

In his ' British Petrography ' (1888) Teall stated that feldspar occurred in the serpentine of The Rill and Bonney challenged this but Teall maintained his position and proved his assertion. In this work Teall's account of the petrography of the serpentine, gabbro and epidiorites is of supreme excellence.

Teall next took up the problem of the banded gneisses (1887b). He showed that the acid portion formed veins cutting the basic and consequently was of granitic origin. Teall, however, ascribed the banding of the gneiss to a process of rolling out under pressure. It is really a fluxion structure.

In 1893 Fox and Teall described the remarkable sections that Fox had discovered on the west coast at Potstone Point (Pol Cornick) and Ogo Dour. It was shown that hornblende-schist and serpentine are there interbanded so that they form a complex of which it is impossible to say which rock is the older; that there are transitions between them and that the complex is folded. This is one of the most important contributions ever made to Lizard geology. It shows the prime relation between schist and serpentine where the junction is not broken by faults. Somewhat similar phenomena had long been known at Porthallow but the sections there are so confused by faults that their interpretation was not clear. The authors also pointed out that the dolerite dykes were in some places converted into hornblende-schists. In the cove north of the Lion Rock (near Kynance) they described a variety of dyke-like intrusions, especially one flame-shaped mass which had all the characters of Bonney's ' Granulitic Group.' The evidence was very strong, but perhaps not absolutely conclusive and Bonney remained unconvinced. In 1895 Fox and Teall gave the first adequate description of the pillow-lavas and radiolarian cherts of Mullion Island.

McMahon in 1887 brought forward the pregnant suggestion that the foliation of the Lizard gabbro might have been produced ' if gabbro in an imperfectly consolidated or semi-plastic condition were forced into or through an opening in the serpentine rock '; he thought it could not have arisen through shearing movement in the solid rock or by distortion along fault-planes. In 1884, after visiting the Lizard, he thought the hornblende-schists might be ashes and lavas that had been reconstructed through the action of circulating waters. The ' granulites ' he interpreted as being mostly igneous, consisting of an acid magma injected into basic masses which might have been partly ashes and lavas but included also intrusive porphyritic diorite.

In 1890 Bonney and McMahon made a joint examination of the Lizard coast sections. Their paper (1891) shows some important advances in their interpretation of the geology. They admit that the banded structure of the Kennack Gneisses may be due to fluxion in a heterogeneous igneous rock, the dark, basic portion having been softened and drawn out by the injection of the acid matrix so that the whole mass showed fluxion on a large scale. The hornblendic group probably represented basic lavas and tuffs and their banding might be due to either segregation or fluxion, though in certain cases they preferred the hypothesis that it was bedding, and the rock was originally a stratified ash bed. They made a careful study of the fluctuating foliation in the gabbro, especially in the dykes, and agreed that it was not due to a regional metamorphism but considered that it might be best explained as produced by the pressure acting during the injection of a magma ' in which crystals were floating in a magma which was already not very liquid.'

Bonney, in 1895, returned to the discussion of Lizard problems. His opinions had undergone little modification and he still regarded the ' granulitic ' rocks as older than the serpentine. He criticises the opinions of Teall and Fox regarding the folded margin of the serpentine at Ogo Dour and maintains his conclusion that the serpentine is intrusive in the hornblende-schists and that in the Lizard the effects of dynamometamorphism are local and unimportant.

Harford Lowe contributed notably to the discussion of the sequence of the Lizard rocks in two papers (1900, 1901) published in the Transactions of the Royal Geological Society of Cornwall. By this time it was generally recognized that the mica-schists and hornblende-schists were followed by serpentine, troctolite, gabbro, and epidiorite dykes in that order, though Teall was doubtful of the relations of schist to serpentine. Lowe stoutly maintained that the ' Granulitic Group ' was the last member of the sequence and was intrusive into all the others. He appealed to the conformable fluxion-banding, the numerous inclusions of serpentine and (less frequently) gabbro, the contact alteration of included serpentine and the fact that no epidiorite dykes cut the ' granulitics.' As the evidence he cited is easily corroborated and is conclusive, his interpretation cannot be challenged. Others had put forward tentatively and locally a similar sequence, but Lowe was the first to enunciate these views clearly and consistently.

In 1906 Flett began the revision of the Lizard district, which had not been officially re-examined since the survey of De la Beche. The work was done on the six-inch scale and occupied short periods during three seasons. Notes were published in the Summaries of Progress (1907, 1908, 1909) and the Memoir appeared in 1912. As in the present edition of the Memoir the conclusions which he reached during the re-survey are practically unaltered and have been stated in the preceding chapter, it is unnecessary to recapitulate them. He accepted the sequence formulated tentatively by Somervail and Teall and definitely by Harford Lowe and showed the importance of the marginal folding of the serpentine first enunciated by Fox and Teall. The diversity and complexity of the Lizard metamorphism were especially insisted on; in the mica-schists and some hornblende-schists it was regional and thermal; in the serpentine and gabbro it was partly fluxional and partly due to pressure after consolidation; the banding of the Kennack Gneisses was essentially a fluxion structure and the schistosity was impressed during injection or shortly thereafter. For the first time the presence of granite-gneiss masses of considerable size was demonstrated and in the Treleague Quartzite a new component was added to the Lizard sequence.   The presence of epidiorite dykes in the Treleague Quartzite was interpreted as showing that there were two stages in the Lizard intrusions, one anterior to that Quartzite but subsequent to the mica-schists (the Man of War Gneisses) and another subsequent to the Quartzite (the serpentine, gabbro, epidiorites and banded gneisses).   The break between the two series was placed between the Traboe and Landewednack hornblende-schists.

In a final contribution to Lizard geology Bonney (1914) declines to admit that the ' Granulitic Group ' as a whole is later than and intrusive into the serpentine; insists that the metamorphism of the Lizard intrusives is really a paramorphism; and rejects Flett's hypothesis that a gap of importance may have existed between the Landewednack and the Traboe hornblende-schists.

A very interesting addition to the mineralogy of the Lizard was made by Tilley in 1937.   Describing some cordierite-anthophyllite rocks from the Old Lizard Head Series at Pistil Ogo, near Polpeor, he announces the presence of staurolite, while in cordierite rocks of Polkernogo he has found intergrowths of sillimanite and kyanite. These are the first records of kyanite and staurolite in the Lizard schists.

Meanwhile progress regarding the nature and history of the rocks of the Meneage north of the Lizard boundary was being slowly made.   It was known, for example, that at Gunwalloe the dark shales contained ill-preserved fossils of doubtful character. Howard Fox in 1900 gave a full description of them and assigned the fossils to the Devonian genus *Nematophycus*, but it had always been assumed that they were Devonian.   Fossils of similar character had also been reported from Polnare Cove at the Nare Point on the south of the entrance to the Helford River, and it was presumed that these rocks also were Devonian.   Charles Peach's discovery of fossils in the Quartzite of Gorran had been made as early as 1837 and it was generally believed that the white quartzite of the Meneage was the same rock and consequently it was placed in the Lower Silurian (Ordovician) as a member of the Caradoc or Llandeilo.   Collins discovered *Orthis* of Ordovician type in the Meneage Quartzite in 1879.   When Fox and Teall found pillow-lavas and radiolarian cherts in Mullion Island there was a general belief that these rocks also were Ordovician from the analogy with the Ordovician of the Southern Uplands of Scotland from which a similar assemblage had been described.   It was not then known that pillow-lavas and radiolarian cherts are present in all the older Palaeozoic systems of Great Britain.   Howard Fox proved the existence of radiolarian cherts in several places in the Meneage north of the Lizard boundary.   Collins had advanced the opinion that Cambrian (?), Ordovician, Silurian and Devonian rocks were present in the Meneage (1879, 1884) and was criticised by Somervail (1883).   Ussher (1891) placed the whole of the killas and grits south of the Carnmenellis Granite in the same group as the Mevagissey and Gorran slates as pre-Devonian rocks. The base of the Devonian was taken by Ussher at the Grampound Grits and by Collins at the Ladock Beds, which are approximately on the same horizon. A notable advance was made in 1904 when Upfield Green and Sherborn claimed that the limestone of Fletching's Cove or Betty's Cove north of Porthallow contained Ludlow fossils; limestone had been known to occur in this cove from very early times and was shown on De la Beche's maps (1839). Upfield Green now placed the whole of Hill's Portscatho Beds at Helford, Helston and the Loe Pool in the lowest Devonian or Gedinnian (1904b).

Hill started his work on the re-survey of the south of Cornwall in 1897 at Falmouth, and in the Summary of Progress (1898) he divided the killas of the south-west of Cornwall into four series (in ascending order): Mylor, Falmouth, Portscatho and Veryan. Of these, the first three were coloured on the old Survey maps, then current, as Devonian; the Veryan as Silurian. The Veryan contained the Ordovician (Llandeilo) quartzites, pillow-lavas, radiolarian cherts and certain limestones and shales. The other series were older than the Veryan, into which they passed up conformably, but in the absence of fossils their exact age could not be determined. The Nare Point conglomerate formed the base of the overlying Devonian and was considered to be of about the same age as the Grampound Grits (Lower Devonian). A very large area in south-west Cornwall was thus ascribed to strata of Ordovician age or older, but it was recognized that Devonian beds were present in the Meneage on the south side of the Helford River and on the west coast near Gunwalloe. Subsequently Hill was confirmed in this interpretation of the sequence by his analysis of the Nare Point and Menaver conglomerate, which he believèd to contain blocks of Portscatho rocks which were already quartz-veined. and slightly metamorphosed before their incorporation in the conglomerate. In 1909 Upfield Green reasserted his belief that Hill's Mylor, Falmouth, Portscatho, and Veryan (in part) were Gedinnian.

Hill's interpretation became the recognized version adopted by the Geological Survey and represented on the first edition of the revised one-inch map (Sheet 359), though it was never completely accepted by all his colleagues, and on the quarter-inch map, Sheets 21 and 25 (Teall 1909 and Flett 1926), the Veryan was indexed as ' Ordovician,' but not the Portscatho, Falmouth and Mylor, which were left undated.

The weak point of Green's position was that he had no fossil evidence to prove the age of his Gedinnian beds. A strong objection to Hill's system was that it was known that in the Portscatho rocks there were layers of coaly matter that seemed to be derived from ligneous plants, and no such deposits were known from strata older than the Downtonian. Little reliance could be placed on the interpretation of the geological structures as the country was traversed by many dislocations, large and small; the rock junctions were nearly all faulted and regional breccias occurred on a large scale.

In 1925 Miss E. M. Lind Hendriks began a search of the coast sections in the Meneage, Veryan and Mevagissey areas which resulted in the discovery of plant-remains in a number of localities. The plant fossils were submitted to Professor Lang who subsequently collected additional specimens. His report (1929) is of great interest, especially as it shows the occurrence of a species, *Dadoxylon hendriksi,* which is so highly developed that it presumably belongs to rocks not older than the Middle Devonian. The other fragmentary plant-remains lead to a similar conclusion, or at least do not contradict it. These fossils are found in rocks which Hill had mapped as Devonian, Portscatho and Falmouth (but not in the Mylors). The possibility that some of these strata belong to the lowermost Ordovician was at once negatived and Hill's proposed succession and structure had to be discarded. In 1933 Flett issued a new interpretation of the structure of the Meneage based on the work of Hendriks and Lang, and in 1934 a new edition of the one-inch Lizard Sheet 359. The strata in which the Hendriksi flora had been found were called the Gramscatho Group and (with the Mylor Beds) were assigned to the Devonian. The importance of the Meneage Breccia was at the same time emphasized, and a careful study of the lithology of the Menaver Conglomerate was made, revealing the great variety of rocks which it contained, but no positive conclusions were arrived at regarding its origin.

A recent contribution to the geology of the Meneage is Lind Hendriks's paper in the Quarterly Journal of the Geological Society of London (1937). This paper is not confined to the district now under description but contains also many particulars regarding the rocks of the Portscatho, Veryan and Mevagissey country. She believes that the serpentine and gabbro of the Lizard are represented also at Nare Head, Veryan, and that there are two horizons of pillow-lava, the Upper and the Lower Spilite, and the serpentine is intrusive into the later of these (p. 327). Of this there is no evidence in the Lizard as where the serpentine comes into juxtaposition with the spilitic rocks of the Meneage there is always reason to believe that a fault or thrust intervenes. In her opinion also the metamorphism of the Lizard intrusives was due to earth movements that took place in the Lower Carboniferous or Variscan orogeny (*op. cit.,* p. 358). In the Lizard there is evidence that the metamorphism of serpentine and gabbro was posterior to the Treleague Quartzite (which is probably pre-Cambrian) and anterior to the Late-Carboniferous or Hercynian movements, but no evidence has yet been obtained that would lead to a more precise determination of the epoch of crushing and recrystallization.

(A 549

A. Pistil Ogo, near Lizard Point. Metamorphic schists of
Old Lizard Head Series

PLATE II

B. Base of cliff at Polpeor (Lifeboat Station), Lizard.
Epidiorite 'bolster' in green schists

(A 7488

CHAPTER IV

SEDIMENTARY SCHISTS OF THE LIZARD

The Old Lizard Head Series

THE existence of a series of mica-schists at Old Lizard Head and Porthallow has been recognized from the earliest times by all geologists who have described the rocks of the Lizard. They have often been called talcose schists owing to the presence of large scales of pale green chlorite (probably secondary after biotite) but they contain no talc. Their sedimentary origin has never been questioned.

The prevalent types of mica-schist in this group are well-foliated highly crystalline rocks with large plates of muscovite, sometimes half an inch in diameter; less biotite, often weathered into chlorite; subordinate feldspar (principally orthoclase and albite) and no great abundance of quartz. Small pale garnets are almost universally present but rarely visible to the unaided eye. The foliation is often sinuous or undulating and split surfaces are usually curved or crumpled. Feldspathic folia are common and the rock may resemble a micaceous feldspathic gneiss; the feldspar weathers pink and may form elongated lenticles. Veins and segregations of quartz and feldspar often occur, but pure quartz veins are rare. In the hand specimen the mica-schist is brownish or pink, but when chlorite is abundant the rock is pale green.

Alternating with the mica-schists are bands of quartzite or quartz-granulite consisting essentially of quartz with subordinate amounts of muscovite, biotite and feldspar. These rocks also contain numerous, small, pale pinkish garnets. Clastic structure can very rarely be traced and the rocks are usually thoroughly granulitic.

In the mica-schists and garnetiferous quartz-granulites, hornblende may occur in any proportion, and when it is abundant the rocks are green schists and hornblendic granulites. The hornblende is mostly acicular and usually forms discrete folia, though in the granulites it may be disseminated and may penetrate the quartz crystals. Its colour is deep green and the pleochroism strong, but it is often weathered to chlorite. Garnets are not frequent in these

hornblendic rocks.   Where amphibole preponderates the rocks are
fine hornblende-schists often containing folia of quartz or feldspar,
and having a satiny lustre on broken surfaces.   In them the
sinuous or crinkled foliation of the mica-schists is often very
pronounced and the rocks may then be called puckered or frilled
hornblendic schists.   As they pass by all gradations into mica-
schists and quartzites they seem to be undoubtedly of sedimentary
origin, and most writers on Lizard geology have thought it
probable that these rocks contain igneous material and were
originally beds of volcanic ashes (Pl. IV, 2).

Although these rocks are extremely metamorphic and clastic
structures have vanished, their bedding is locally very well
preserved.   This is especially well seen on the south shores of the
Lizard, at Old Lizard Head, Pistil Ogo (Pl. IIA), and Polpeor
(lifeboat station).   The quartzose beds are usually a few inches in
thickness but sometimes more than a foot.   In the cliff faces each
thin bed may be traced for several yards.   At Polpeor the thicker
quartzose beds are sometimes broken up by movement into rounded
blocks, resembling boulders, so that a pseudo-conglomerate is
formed. At Pistil Ogo the beds are sometimes arranged in repeated
folds of no great amplitude, the axial planes of which are nearly
horizontal.   On Old Lizard Head a sill of fine felsitic granite,
probably an offshoot of the Man of War Gneiss, is thrown into a
great S-shaped fold which can be seen from the base of the cliff.
The folds consequently are of all magnitudes, some being several
yards in cross section, others only a few feet, others less than an
inch, till finally we have the fine puckering in the schist.   In the
Man of War Gneiss there is a remarkable corrugated foliation,
very distinctive and characteristic of the rock, and it seems certain
that this type of foliation in the Man of War Gneiss and the folding
in the Lizard schists are closely connected in origin.

There is much evidence that the Lizard schists have at some
period been raised to a very high temperature.   This evidence is
scattered over the whole district.   Andalusite is frequent in the
mica-schists about Old Lizard Head.   Sillimanite occurs at
Polledan, east of.the Lighthouses and in the granulites at Bochym
Lodge on the Lizard road to Helston.   Cordierite-anthophyllite-
gneiss occurs near Polkernogo in an area of mica-schist surrounded
by hornblende-schist north of the serpentine.   Tilley (1937) has
recently described similar rocks at Pistil Ogo and has found that
they contain sillimanite, kyanite and staurolite.   In these two
outcrops he recognizes a variety of rocks consisting of quartz,
feldspar, biotite, hornblende, garnet, cummingtonite, anthophyllite,
cordierite, sillimanite, kyanite, staurolite, etc., and he subdivides
them into a number of classes, all of restricted distribution and
closely connected.   They seem to be derivatives of the Lizard
mica-schists and granulites, among which they occur in the field,
but Tilley is of opinion that some of them may have undergone

metasomatic alteration. It is clear that they are not hornfelses but schists and gneisses, and their wide distribution makes it likely that they belong to a thermal ' aureole ' surrounding the Lizard intrusives. They are gneisses in structure, often perfectly foliated, and the conclusion (with which Tilley agrees) is that the metamorphism of these rocks was both regional and thermal (thermoplastic) and that they attained their present condition by regional pressures acting at a time when the rocks were at a high temperature.

The best known outcrop of the Old Lizard Head Series is at the south-west corner of the Lizard peninsula where they are displayed in a fine range of coast sections from the lifeboat station on the south to Caerthillian Cove on the west coast. The boundary at both margins is a fault which is probably of no great importance as mica-schists occur among the hornblende-schists some distance farther east at Polledan Cove and on Pen Olver. All the typical rocks of the group are represented in this outcrop and there is a complete series of transitions between them. Bedding and folding are remarkably well displayed at Pistil Ogo and Polpeor. The green schists are often traversed by strings and bands of yellow epidote. There are yellow epidotic quartzites and greenish hornblendic quartzites. Small faults are present in every cove but the unity of the series is unmistakable. In the cliff section at Polpeor there are elongated, bolster-shaped masses of porphyritic epidiorite, that seem less metamorphic than the normal hornblende-schists and may be disrupted dykes of basic composition, perhaps belonging to the series of dykes that cut the Man of War Gneiss in the Lizard skerries.

A good deal of hornblende-schist is visible in the outcrops and rocks of this type have been quarried on Old Lizard Head and used for building stone walls. They are dark green schists with occasional porphyritic crystals of feldspar that have not wholly lost their idiomorphic outlines but are mostly altered to secondary minerals. Hornblende-schist also is present in considerable amount to the north of Old Lizard Head. That some of these rocks are probably of contemporaneous origin and were originally lava flows is suggested by their intercalation in the mica-schists, and still more strongly by the mixed sedimentary and volcanic composition of the green schists.

On the shore at Porthallow a short distance east of the Five Pilchards inn the mica-schists outcrop over a limited extent of beach. They are bounded by faults on both sides, and on the west they abut against the breccia which marks the site of the boundary fault. In external characters they resemble very closely the mica-schists of Polpeor; both green and brown varieties are present and there are well marked bands of epidotic green schist and fine hornblende-schist, but the coarser hornblende-schists are absent and there are few representatives of the quartz-hornblende-granulites. Although a strong sill of garnetiferous augen-gneiss is intruded into the mica-schist neither andalusite nor sillimanite has been detected in this outcrop. From Porthallow south to Porthoustock similar rocks occupy a fairly extensive inland area, which has a north to north-east strike. They are not well exposed but may be seen in small quarries to the south of Porthallow and in the roadside to the north of Porthoustock. In the latter locality there are sections showing green schists, mica-schists, granulites and epidosite which have almost a bedded appearance as they are disposed in parallel bands, nearly horizontal or having a gentle dip to the west and giving little sign of folding. The special feature of this section is the thin beds of quartzose and hornblendic granulites often an inch or two in thickness. Although the stratification is perfectly preserved and the beds are hardly even brecciated, microscopic sections show that the quartzites are completely granulitic or mylonitic; the thin quartzose hornblende-schists have perfect linear foliation.

At Polkernogo, on the banks of a little stream flowing north to Tregidden, there is an interesting outcrop of the Old Lizard Head Series surrounded entirely by the hornblende-schists on the north side of the gabbro. The boundaries of this outcrop are very badly exposed, but it certainly has a narrow elongated shape, which, like the strike of the schists of which it is composed, has a northern direction. Several small pits, often badly overgrown with bramble and thorn, afford a fairly good opportunity of collecting specimens. There is comparatively little mica-schist but much granulite and quartz-hornblende-schist and thin bands of epidosite. The banding, which probably represents original bedding, is rather conspicuous. As usual in the Old Lizard Head Series there are rapid alternations in the composition of the rocks, thin quartzose, hornblendic and micaceous layers being frequently repeated. The special feature of this outcrop is the presence of cordierite-anthophyllite-gneisses; they are grey or bluish rocks (Pl. IV, 3) not unlike banded quartzites but showing occasionally the dark blue colour and sheen of large ellipsoids of remarkably fresh cordierite. The anthophyllite is in long thin greyish-green needles arranged parallel to the foliation planes, and giving them a greenish colour. The cordierite often shows strong pleochroic haloes around included zircons. Quartz and alkali-feldspar are both present and some of the rocks are hornblende-schists consisting of dark green hornblende and plagioclase (oligoclase and andesine). Muscovite and biotite are abundant only in the mica-schists; garnets are rare and usually absent. Some of the quartzose bands are so rich in epidote that they become epidosites; the typical epidotic hornblende-schists of the Landewednack group occur in bands alternating with the rocks above described and also form the greater part of the surrounding country.

It is to be noted that Polkernogo and Pistil Ogo are the only localities in Britain for cordierite-anthophyllite-gneiss but similar rocks have been described from several places in Scandinavia and Finland and their origin has been the subject of much discussion (Tilley, 1937).

In the broad belt of hornblende-schist that stretches on the north side of the gabbro from Porthallow to the neighbourhood of Trelowarren, debris of mica-schist may occasionally be found on the surface of the fields, mingled with hornblende-schist and epidosite, but there are few determinable outcrops.   Two may, however, be mentioned, in addition to that at Polkernogo, previously described.   One of these is at Mill Mehal and the other at Tregarne Mill; both are situated in the valley leading down to Porthallow.   They contain the usual assemblage of rocks— brownish, coarse mica-schist, epidosite, granulite, and fine hornblende-schist, but the exposures are not very satisfactory and the area occupied in each case is not extensive.   These are the only outcrops that are sufficiently clear to be indicated on the one-inch Sheet.

Along the Lizard boundary, fragments of garnetiferous granulite and mica-schist are sometimes obtainable and occasionally small outcrops may be seen in pits and roadside ditches.   Of such occurrences mention may be made at the following localities : Bochym, Trease and Gwealeath (on the Lizard road), Skyburriowe, Relowas, Tregidden and Roskruge; also in the quarry beside the Lizard road opposite the east lodge gates of Bochym.   These exposures, however, are rarely satisfactory but they serve to prove that in this northern territory the relations of the mica-schist group to the epidotic hornblende-schists are similar to those that obtain at Pen Olver, Polledan and Polpeor in the vicinity of the Lizard Point.

The Treleague Quartzite

Around Treleague farm, which is half a mile north of St. Keverne, there is a quartzite which is not found anywhere else in the Lizard and Meneage.   The rock in question is a fine-grained grey or sometimes brownish compact quartzite which breaks with a smooth fracture and seems indurated.   It rarely shows obvious traces of bedding or of pebbly structure and does not seem to be accompanied by shales though finer quartzose bands are sometimes present.   In microscopic section it presents very distinctive characters, for the clastic structure is always preserved though the quartz grains are sometimes fractured and often have sinuous or dentate outlines.   There is little mica in the rocks and the only frequent accessories are grains of epidote or zircon.   In some slides (6338), small, pale pink garnets are visible and it seems probable that they are authigenic and not derived from some older garnetiferous rock.   The special feature of the Treleague Quartzite, however, which makes it distinct from any other British quartzite is the presence of a siliceous cementing material which is richly charged with fine needles of hornblende. These acicular crystals are so small that, especially when the rock is somewhat weathered, their nature might be doubtful, but occasionally larger crystals are seen which have the optical properties of dark green strongly pleochroic hornblende, with the characteristic cleavage, and remove any doubt regarding the identity of the finer needles. This curious and unique cementing material seems to imply a certain degree of contact metamorphism accompanied possibly by metasomatism.

A specially interesting feature of this outcrop is the presence of greenstone intrusions apparently in the form of dykes. These are seen in small excavations in the roadsides and farmyard of Treleague, and over the whole outcrop fragments of epidiorite are frequently mingled with those of quartzite. In microscopic characters these greenstones very closely resemble the basic dykes that cut the gabbro on the south side of Porthoustock Cove and at Manacle Point. Their pyroxene has mostly been replaced by aggregates of fibrous hornblende, and some of them are specially rich in feldspar; no olivine is preserved in them.

The boundaries of the Treleague Quartzite can be laid down fairly exactly though all the outcrop is under cultivation. It forms an elongated lenticle about a mile in length from west to east, and a quarter of a mile in breadth. The debris in the fields is abundant and characteristic but there are few actual exposures, though rock *in situ* may be seen on the slopes of the Porthoustock valley, on the road leading down to Mill Mehal and in a few other places. Apparently it is separated by faults both from the hornblende-schists on the north and from the gabbro on the south. In view of the presence of epidiorite dykes and of evidence of contact meta-morphism, its relations to the gabbro are specially interesting, but the southern margin of the Treleague Quartzite is so well defined, and so frequently attended by signs of brecciation in the quartzite that there can be little doubt that it is a line of fault. The gabbro moreover maintains its coarse crystallization up to the junction.

From the presence of the epidiorite dykes it is evident that the Treleague Quartzite is older than that series of intrusions. These dykes, however, may be regarded as the terminal facies of the gabbro magma, with which they are undoubtedly closely connected. The gabbro, in turn, is linked inseparably with the serpentine, which passes at its margins into the coarse hornblende-schist of Traboe type. But the Treleague Quartzite is quite distinct from and far less metamorphic than the garnetiferous granulites of the Old Lizard Head Series, which were evidently highly metamorphic before the Treleague Quartzite was laid down. From this we may infer that when the serpentine and gabbro were intruded the mica-schists, granulites and epidotic hornblende-schists of Landewednack type were already in a high state of meta-morphism, and that the earth-movements which have left their traces on these later intrusives belonged to a second epoch of regional pressures which were distinctly less rigorous than the previous series. In the interval, which was a period of rest, the Treleague Quartzite was deposited.

Microscopic.—Good specimens are obtainable around Treleague farmyard, 6335, 6337, 6345, 6211, sometimes garnetiferous, 6338, 6215. These may be compared with the Old Lizard Head Series of rocks occurring near Trenoweth Mill a little east of the outcrop of the Treleague Quartzite, which are mylonites, 6235, granulites, 6236, and mica-schists 6219.

ANALYSES OF LIZARD MICA-SCHISTS, ETC.

	I.	II.	III.	IV.
SiO_2	55.92	58.10	81.70	65.70
Al_2O_3	22.14	21.33	10.40	14.24
Fe_2O_3	3.75	2.10	} 3.04 {	1.51
FeO	3.72	8.30		6.37
MgO	1.77	1.15	0.70	4.89
CaO	0.30	0.72	0.40	2.39
Na_2O	2.25	} 4.60 {	1.54	1.96
K_2O	4.26		1.33	0.27
H_2O above 105° C.	3.94	} 2.80	0.85 {	1.60
H_2O at 105° C. ...	0.43			0.13
TiO_2	0.88	—	—	0.94
P_2O_5	0.07	—	—	0.17
MnO	0.21	—	tr.	0.09
CO_2	0.21	---	—	—
FeS_2 ...	0.23	—	—	—
(Ni, Co) O ...	0.03	—	—	—
BaO	n.f.	—	—	—
Li_2O	tr.	—	—	(0.03 access.)
Total ...	100.11	99.10	99.96	100.29

I.—Mica-schist, Porthallow, E.6523 (Anal. E. G. Radley)
II.—   do.   do.   (Anal. J. H. Collins)
III.—   do.   do.   (Anal. J. H. Collins)
IV.—Anthophyllite-cordierite-granulite, 250 yds. north of Trelease Mill. Accessories are Cr_2O_3 0.01, BaO 0.02. (Anal. C. O. Harvey).

The chemical analyses, given above, show that the Porthallow mica-schist is a typical member of its class rich in alumina and alkalis. Analysis III contains more silica and is apparently one of the quartzose bands. The cordierite-rock (Analysis IV) contains more magnesia and lime, with less alkalis and alumina and may have been an ashy sediment. The reversal of the alkalis is significant and may be compared with the hornblende-schist (p. 53).

Microscopic.—Good examples of mica-schist are got at Polpeor, 5081, 5082, or Porthallow, 4647; Mill Mehal, 6035; Tregarne Mill, 6209; the greenish mica-schists rich in chlorite as at Porthallow, 5224, pass into chlorite-quartz-schists, 5225, 5245. Andalusite-mica-schist occurs at Venton Hill Point, 5059, and sillimanite-mica-schist at Pen Olver 6830. Pinite after cordierite is present in the garnetiferous mica-schist of Polpeor, 13543. Green schists are present in all localities for mica-schists, *e.g.* Venton Hill Point, 5060; Old Lizard Head, 5067; Porthallow, 5108. At Caerthillan Cove fine granulitic bands contain garnet and biotite, 5153. Examples of epidosite are obtained at Parc-an-tidno, near Porthallow, 5233, and Trenance, 6241. Quartzose hornblendic granulites are found at Pistil Ogo, 5184, at Old Lizard Head, 5066, 5068, and at Trenoweth Mill, one mile south of Porthallow, 6240. Feldspathic micaceous garnetiferous granulites are widespread : examples occur at Gwealeath, Trease and Boscawen, adjacent farms on the Lizard road four miles from Helston, 5271-4, at Bochym House, 5780, and in the quarry east of Bochym east lodge, 5981, containing sillimanite.

From the Polkernogo and Polpidnick outcrop we may cite cordierite-anthophyllite-gneiss, 5988, 5997; cordierite-biotite-gneiss, 6347, 7589; hornblende paragneiss, 5989; mica-schist, 5994; quartzose hornblendic granulite, 6000; garnetiferous hornblendic granulite, 6382; quartz-hornblende-schist, 6373, 6375; and a variety of types mostly sedimentary and often mylonitic. Igneous rocks are represented by feldspathic hornblende-schists, 5996, 6348.

CHAPTER V

HORNBLENDE-SCHISTS

HORNBLENDE-SCHISTS cover a considerable area of the Lizard peninsula, forming an incomplete ring girdling the serpentine. They are typical metamorphic rocks, showing only rarely traces of original igneous structure and, like the mica-schists with which they are associated, they occasionally contain evidence of contact metamorphism. In the district south of Lizard Town they form an area of about half a square mile and are well seen in magnificent coast sections. The boundaries of this outcrop are probably all faulted. On the north these schists abut against the serpentine and the marginal faults are well seen on the east coast at The Balk and on the west coast at the south end of Pentreath Beach; at the latter locality especially, both schist and serpentine are much brecciated and veined with pink dolomite and iron oxides. These faults dip northwards and are presumably thrusts by which the serpentine has been forced southwards over the schists. The relations of the hornblende-schists to the mica-schists and granulites of the Old Lizard Head are less simple. At Polpeor and Caerthillian Cove there is evidence of faulting, though, as mica-schists occur closely intermixed with hornblende-schists to the east of the boundary, and hornblende-schists of fairly normal character are present among the mica-schists on the western coast there can be no reason to doubt that the two series are very intimately connected.

The schists of this area are mostly dark green, almost black rocks, varying in the size of their crystals, but seldom coarse-grained and sometimes fine and silky. Their foliation is perfect, and their split surfaces are often flat and parallel, so that they break up into thin slabs. They are very rich in hornblende but contain also thin folia consisting mainly of feldspar. The most characteristic feature of these schists, however, is the abundance of lenticles and bands of yellow epidote. The epidotic streaks may be as thin as a sheet of paper or may be a foot in thickness. Often they can be traced for several yards and the thicker lenticles may be eight feet long and six to ten inches thick. They curve with the foliation of the schists. By their pale yellow colour, contrasting strongly with the black hornblendic folia, they give the rock a banded and variegated appearance. The origin of these epidotic streaks is not very clear. Apparently they are not the remains of sedimentary intercalations, such as calcareous or dolomitic deposits, converted into calc-silicates, but they seem to be segregations formed during the process of metamorphism (Pl. IV, 4). No calc-silicate bands are known in the sediments of the Old Lizard Head Series. Probably they represent the feldspathic folia normally found in hornblende-schists and their present condition may be due to thermal action at two stages widely separated, firstly by the Man of War Gneisses at the time when the foliation was being developed and, secondly, at a much later stage by the intrusion of the serpentine.

Evidence of thermal alteration is furnished by the presence of pyroxene and garnet, as was remarked by Bonney and McMahon. The pyroxene is not the normal augite of basic igneous rocks but a pale green, almost colourless diopside not unlike the mineral often found in calc-silicates. It shows the usual prismatic cleavage and sometimes traces of crystal outlines. Occasionally it is partly surrounded by green pleochroic hornblende; often it is quite fresh and unweathered. The garnet is pale in colour and recalls grossularite. It is in rounded grains, often showing imperfect crystal faces, and it is less frequent than the pyroxene. The garnet occurs only in the epidotic lenticles and seems to be connected with them in origin. The presence of pale green augite and of garnet in contact-altered greenstones around the Cornish granites is well known and has often been described. These minerals, in the Lizard, are by no means restricted to the hornblende-schists that are in close proximity to the serpentine, but like the cordierite and sillimanite of the mica-schists have a wide but sporadic distribution.

For several hundred yards both north and south of Cadgwith Cove the cliffs are faced by epidotic hornblende-schists that exhibit the closest resemblance to those of Bass Point and Landewednack. The streaky, undulating or contorted epidotic banding is very well seen in the rocks on the beach at the north side of the cove. These schists extend inland for only a very short distance but the junction with serpentine is nowhere well exposed. North of Cadgwith and also at Polbarrow, to the south, the presence of marginal faults is obvious but there is a very obscure section at the entrance to the Devil's Frying Pan, which has puzzled many observers, and seems to indicate an intrusive junction between serpentine and schists. As the banded gneisses enter into the complex, however, the evidence is not absolutely conclusive. No mica-schists or granulites have been observed in the vicinity of Cadgwith but the hornblende-schists have the same perfect and flattish foliation as at Church Cove, and the epidotic lenticles are often very conspicuous. On Carn Barrow massive hornblende-schist occurs and in the cliffs below there are a few quartz veins, an unusual feature in the Lizard hornblende-schists.

(A 7489)

A. Cliffs below Lizard Lighthouse, Polbream.
   foliated horizontal hornblende-schists

B. Church Cove Quarry, Landewednack.
   Folded epidotic hornblende-schists

PLATE III

(A 7469)

The cliffs of hornblende-schist around Cadgwith and at the south-east corner of the Lizard Point have another unusual feature in common. The foliation of the schists dips at a low angle, often about 30° but sometimes much less. On Pen Olver, for example, and on both sides of Housel Bay the foliation is often nearly horizontal and the rocks look from a distance like little-disturbed bedded sediments. This is well seen on the Bumble Rock. At Hot Point and along the east side of the Lizard to Church Cove there is a general dip to east or south-east at 20° to 30°, and at Cadgwith a similar dip to the west. Below the Lighthouses the cliffs of hornblende-schist have mural or battlemented character, resembling (Pl. IIIA) ruined castles and this is also well marked around Housel Bay and on Pen Olver. Of the many hypotheses which might be advanced to account for this there is none that is really satisfactory but the characteristic is general and is seen also, though less clearly, in the other outcrops of the epidotic hornblende-schists. In the neighbourhood of faults the dip is often steeper, probably as a consequence of local disturbances. Near Pen Olver and Bass Point the division planes of the schists show perfect mullioning, their surfaces having grooves and ridges which run in a north-north-west direction. Evidence of folding in these hornblende-schists is often present but never conspicuous. The folds are closely packed and nearly horizontal. Examples may be seen in Church Cove quarry (Pl. IIIB).

On the northern side of the gabbro and serpentine the hornblende-schists (with small outcrops of mica-schist) form a belt extending from Porthoustock and Porthallow on the east to Polurrian and Mullion Cove on the west. These schists are very well exposed in the eastern cliffs north of Porthoustock where they are much worked for road-metal. Excellent specimens can be obtained from the quarries. Epidotic hornblende-schist is abundant in this district and mica-schist occurs on the shore at Porthallow and has an extensive development inland at a distance of about half-a-mile from the cliffs. At Porthallow also the hornblende-schist is invaded by serpentine and the two rocks are closely folded together and can hardly be distinguished at their junctions. The general dip is inland, to west or north-west, at angles about 20° to 30°. Epidotic hornblende-schist is seen at many places along the cliffs but there is also much coarsely crystalline, rudely foliated, hornblende-schist rich in feldspar and free from epidote. Occasionally segregations or veins with larger crystals of hornblende and feldspar occur among these schists and some of these may contain quartz. There are also numerous pink feldspathic or felsitic veins. It may be noted that quartzo-feldspathic veins are occasionally seen in the hornblende-schists as at Church Cove, Pentreath, Mullion Cove, Cadgwith and Pencra Head. They are certainly intrusive but their source and affinities are far from clear.

In the inland districts there are very few good exposures in

the hornblende-schist country.   The rocks are often deeply decomposed and round the farms there are many ' marl ' pits where
the rotten schist has been dug in old times for spreading on the
surface of the fields.   Occasional exposures in the roadsides and
in the banks of streams show that epidotic schists are abundant,
and in the debris in the soil, fragments of fine hornblende-schist
and of yellow epidosite are very numerous.   Where the foliation-
dips can be ascertained they are mostly gentle and rolling or
irregular in their direction, varying from north-east to north-west.
One of the best exposures is in the road-stone quarries on the banks
of the stream north-east of Lower Relowas where the dips are
north-west and west about 20°.   The hornblende-schists are also
well seen on the Lizard road near Bochym Lodge and in an
adjacent quarry.   The strike of the mica-schists at Polkernogo,
as already remarked, is almost due north and south, but near the
Lizard boundary there is a general tendency in the epidotic schists,
which are very prevalent in that country, to have a northerly dip
and to strike parallel to the boundary line.   This may have been
superinduced by movements in Hercynian times, and the original
strike may be that indicated by the mica-schist outcrops at Porthallow and Polkernogo.

The small area of hornblende-schist about Cury Cross Lanes
and Tregadra has on the north the Lizard boundary line and on
the south the powerful fault which runs out to sea at Polurrian
Cove.   There are few satisfactory exposures but epidotic hornblende-schists and epidosites are seen in small pits and roadside
outcrops, usually much decomposed.   Mica-schists and granulites
occur at Bochym, Skyburriowe, Gwealeath and other places, but
are of no considerable extent.   There is also coarse grey hornblende-schist.   The dips are gentle and irregular, often south-west
or north-west.

In the northern part of this area the epidotic hornblende-schists
are the dominant type, but in the south they are comparatively
scarce.   A grey, feldspathic, non-epidotic and more coarsely
crystalline hornblende-schist prevails along the southern edge of
this area of hornblende-schist where it approaches the margin of
the serpentine.   Mica-schists and granulites are confined to the
region of epidotic hornblende-schists.   The coarse grey hornblende-schist is especially common in the district around Traboe
and Polkerth ; formerly there were large blocks of it strewn upon
the downs in this neighbourhood but these have recently been
broken up for road-metal.   The foliation of these rocks is rough
and irregular, as contrasted with the flat parallel foliation of the
epidotic hornblende-schists, and coarse feldspathic veins and lenticles are often to be remarked in it.   Moreover, while the epidotic
schists yield rich agricultural soil, the rocks under description
seem to weather more slowly, producing a shallow soil that is
comparatively infertile though better than the soil upon the
serpentine.   The schists of this type, which have been called the

Traboe hornblende-schists, occur in many patches surrounded by serpentine along the junction of these rocks that extends from Bonython to Kernewas, a distance of about six miles. Some of these patches are quite small; others are as large as several fields, being a hundred acres or more. Their presence can generally be detected by the character of their soil and by the numerous fragments of hornblende-schist in the fields and in the stone walls that enclose them. There are few quarries, however, in these hornblende-schists as the serpentine is more easily worked and serves quite well as a rough building stone. The margins of these outcrops of Traboe schist can seldom be exactly defined as the rough, barren ground is often covered with heather and thorn, but all the larger patches have been cultivated at some former time though now abandoned to coarse pasture and rarely ploughed. By means of the debris in the fields and on the downs, however, it is usually possible to locate the larger outcrops and rudely define their extension.

The small triangular area of hornblende-schist around Mullion is bounded on the north by the Polurrian fault and on the south and east by the Mullion Cove fault and the undulating edge of the serpentine. It is rich agricultural land under high cultivation except in the country adjacent to the serpentine. Exposures are few and much of the schist rock is deeply rotted but in the farm-yards and the roadsides the solid rock is occasionally seen in small pits and local excavations. Along the coast-line, however, between Mullion Cove and Polurrian Cove the hornblende-schist emerges in a fine range of cliffs. These schists are intensely foliated and their dips are practically vertical with a northern strike. Near the great fault in Polurrian Cove the strike tends to run parallel to the dislocation; numerous smaller faults are visible in the little coves to the south. At Mullion Cove and in the roadside quarry four hundred yards east of the cove the hornblende-schists are very well seen. The folding is intense, with a prevailing northern strike, and the rock of the quarry contains many grey folia of feldspar (which is saussuritized) but epidosite is absent.

A special feature of this area is the presence of elongated outcrops of serpentine. Of these there are five. Two occur to the west of the harbour wall, forming the prominent rocky stacks of Henscath and Scovarn; the latter appears to consist entirely of serpentine, the former is mainly serpentine with hornblende-schist upon its eastern side. It seems that the finely jointed and well foliated schist has been removed by the action of the waves exposing a core of serpentine which forms the principal part of these round-topped stacks. At the front of the Mullion Cove Hotel, in the path that descends through a little gully to the harbour, there is an outcrop of serpentine that has been quarried. It is obviously enveloped in hornblende-schist but it is to a large extent covered with debris; its boundaries are not seen. It seems to emerge below the schist in the face of the cliff to the north. About

four hundred yards north of the Mullion Cove Hotel, in the
footpath on the top of the cliffs, leading to Polurrian, serpentine
outcrops for a distance of thirty or forty yards. It is surrounded
by hornblende-schist and, as in the cases previously mentioned,
the streaky banding of the serpentine is parallel to and closely
resembles the foliation of the schist. The serpentine is of the fine,
veined, compact, flinty variety that is the usual marginal facies.
Though none of these exposures is completely satisfactory there
can be no doubt that the serpentine and schist are folded together
and that the streaky banding of the serpentine is similar in origin
and nature to the foliation of the schist. These two structures have
arisen simultaneously apparently by pressure and folding when
both rocks were in a plastic condition. The evidence, moreover,
seems to point to the conclusion that the serpentine is the underlying rock and that its outcrops are the rounded backs of elongated
anticlines. They may be dome-shaped intrusive protuberances
from the main serpentine mass or they may be sills emitted from the
serpentine and folded up with the schist. The evidence is not
sufficient in any one case to be decisive. Another small mass of
serpentine is seen at Meaver beside the road leading from Penhale
to Mullion and is extensively quarried. It consists of fine, banded
and veined serpentine with more or less tremolite and occasional
larger crystals of enstatite. The junction of the main serpentine
and the hornblende-schists at Mullion Cove is a fault well seen in
the cliffs south of the harbour. This fault dies out when followed
inland for less than a mile.

The hornblende-schists of Predannack are bounded on the
north-east by a fault and on the south-east by the folded edge of the
serpentine. On the west they front the sea in rugged vertical cliffs,
nearly two hundred feet in height, with jagged crests and ridges of
very varied though characteristic forms. These schists are all of
the coarse, grey, roughly foliated, Traboe type and in their
lithology as in their scenery they present a remarkable contrast to
the flat, well banded, Landewednack schists of Housel Bay with
horizontal cliff features and flat-topped eminences. The foliation
of the Predannack schists is consistently vertical and the strike is
north and south with little variation. In this area there are two
outcrops of fine serpentine. One of these is at the south-west
corner of Predannack just above the top of the cliff. The exposures
are good and the banding of the serpentine and the foliation of the
schist are perfectly visible and always congruent. The serpentine
seems to rise in anticlinal form and to throw off the schist on each
flank, and, as is often the case with the fine marginal variety of the
serpentine, it is intersected by a network of fine dark veins, between
which the matrix seems often bleached to pale green. About
seventy yards further to the east a small mass of fine serpentine is
seen in the steep grassy slope above the cliff. Its relations are not
quite clear but it may be an intrusive tongue-shaped protuberance.
This is the locality at which veins of datolite were found in the

hornblende-schist at sea-level. The mineral has been fully described by McLintock (1910) and the locality has been practically stripped bare by collectors. It is as yet the only known locality for datolite in the Lizard.

The little cove in the angle of the bay to the south of Predannack is known as Ogo Dour. For four hundred yards farther to the south the cliff is faced with vertical hornblende-schist; then at the promontory known as Pol Cornick or Potstone Point the serpentine first reaches the sea. This locality has been very carefully studied and fully described by Fox and Teall. They showed that the two rocks formed a banded metamorphic complex, with parallel foliation, and were involved in a common system of folding. In a narrow zone at the mutual boundary there were unusual rock facies that indicated a transition. The evidence proved that schist and serpentine came from the same magma and that at some period during or after injection they had been subjected to folding pressures which had stamped on them their concordant and characteristic foliation. As we have seen, the evidence is in harmony with that provided by the serpentine outcrops in the schists along the Predannack and Mullion cliffs, but, as at Pol Cornick the rocks can be examined in a bare cliff-face, the demonstration is perhaps the most convincing in the Lizard district. In one respect however it is unsatisfactory as the complete outcrop cannot be examined on the dangerous rocky cliff without the aid of ropes. Teall and Fox declined to arrive at any conclusion whether the serpentine or the schist was the older rock. In a sense they are, locally at least, contemporaneous but on a wider outlook the great central intrusion of serpentine can only be regarded as subsequent on the whole to the girdle of hornblende-schists which envelops it. Another very interesting feature of this outcrop as described by Fox and Teall is the presence of numerous basic dykes ' which cut the serpentine-schist complex, and which, though partly schistose, are later than the complex and do not share in its foliation.'

In the first edition of this memoir the suggestion was advanced that these two types of hornblende-schist, the Landewednack and the Traboe schists, belonged to two different series, separated in origin by a long period of time. The reasons for this conclusion arise from a number of considerations, their associations, their lithology and the general chronology of the Lizard sequences.

The Landewednack hornblende-schists accompany the green schists, hornblende-granulites, mica-schists and quartzites of the Old Lizard Head Series. These are undoubtedly the oldest rocks of the Lizard assemblage. Some of these hornblende-schists appear to be interbedded or contemporaneous; others may be intrusive. The Traboe hornblende-schists are not attended by mica-schists; on the other hand they are very closely associated with the margin of the serpentine; they seem to be wholly intrusive and to represent à group of basic injections that immediately preceded the intrusion of the serpentine; and between them and the serpentine there are transitional forms. This is well exemplified in the western and northern margins of the serpentine outcrop and must be regarded as one of the most clearly established facts of Lizard geology. The junctions of the serpentine with the Landewednack schists, on the other hand, are in nearly all cases faulted. The serpentine, of course, is also intrusive into these schists and probably in some measure folded with them, but the only sections which might establish this, those in the Devil's Frying Pan and at Porthallow, are so obscure and so controversial that little can be founded on them.

In lithology also these schists represent considerable differences. The epidotic hornblende-schists of the Landewednack group are remarkable rocks representing some unusual characters such as the abundance of epidote and pyroxene (and occasionally garnet). The Traboe schists are more normal, and these accessory minerals are absent; when pyroxene occurs in the Traboe schists it has the characters of a primary igneous mineral, while in the Landewednack schists it seems to have arisen through contact action. It may not always be possible to say whether an individual hand-specimen belongs to one group or to the other but where they occupy a considerable area there is no difficulty in distinguishing between them; the contrast for example between the schists of Pen Olver or Cadgwith and those of Predannack and Traboe is very marked. On the other hand there are districts where the two types of schist seem to occur together and are inextricably mixed, as between Porthoustock and Porthallow, but in that country both the serpentine and the mica-schists are present and confusion might be expected. For this reason, among others, it is not possible to lay down upon a map the regions occupied by each type. To a certain extent it is true that the Traboe schists are less metamorphic than the Landewednack schists because they may contain original augite and olivine but it is more correct to say that they exhibit a different type of metamorphism.

It has been shown that the Treleague Quartzite is a much less metamorphic rock than the garnetiferous granulites of the Old Lizard Head Series and that it is an older rock than the epidiorite dykes which are injected into it. These basic dykes cannot well be separated from the gabbro, which in turn is indissolubly linked with the troctolite and serpentine. The serpentine is closely connected with the Traboe hornblende-schists, which in consequence belong to a period following the deposition of the Treleague Quartzite. The Landewednack schists on the other hand cannot be separated from the Old Lizard Head Series, which, if the evidence is correctly interpreted, is immensely older than the Treleague Quartzite. Hence we are led, on the general interpretation of the sequence of the Lizard rocks, to search for a break in the succession, and the logical conclusion appears to be to place that break between the two types of hornblende-schist.

ANALYSES

	I.	II.
SiO_2	48.64	46.61
Al_2O_3	14.99	15.22
Fe_2O_3	3.42	3.49
FeO	7.76	7.71
MgO	7.76	8.66
CaO	9.60	10.08
Na_2O	3.52	2.43
K_2O	0.52	0.67
H_2O above 105° C.	1.25	2.07
H_2O at 105° C. ...	0.10	1.10
TiO_2	1.90	1.81
P_2O_5	0.16	0.10
MnO	0.30	0.13
CO_2	0.23	tr.
FeS_2	0.06	—
Cr_2O_3	—	tr.
(Ni, Co) O... ...	n.f.	tr.
BaO	n.f.	—
Li_2O	tr.	—
Total ...	100.21	100.08

I.—Hornblende-schist, Lower Relowas Quarry, St. Martin in Meneage Cornwall, E.5797 (Anal. E. G. Radley).

II.—Olivine-basalt lava, Drynoch, Skye, S.8185 (Anal. W. Pollard) ; cited from A. Harker, Tertiary Igneous Rocks of Skye (*Mem. Geol. Surv.*) 1904, p. 31 (Corrected in respect of Al_2O_3).

The analyses quoted above show that the epidotic hornblende-schist of Lower Relowas does not differ essentially in chemical composition from some of the Tertiary lavas of the West of Scotland.

Microscopic.—The Lizard hornblende-schists, consisting as they probably do of a great series of lavas and intrusive sheets, show considerable diversity of minerals and structures. Their characteristic component is hornblende which is usually dark green and strongly pleochroic but may be pale yellowish green, pale green, bluish green. Brown hornblende, which may be pale brown or dark russet brown, is frequent especially in the vicinity of the serpentine, *e.g.,* at Predannack 5187, Mullion 6004, and along the northern boundary in many places 6253, and may be the only variety of amphibole represented in the rock. The hornblende has never crystalline outlines but forms grains of entirely irregular shape : it weathers to chlorite and epidote. In some rocks the hornblende exists as an aggregate of fibres ; ' mossy ' hornblende. Pyroxene occurs also not infrequently (as at Cadgwith 5025, Church Cove 6841) and is mostly a pale green variety, sometimes nearly colourless, often with epidote (Bonython 5928). Like the amphibole it forms grains of irregular shape. A colourless pyroxene, sometimes with the schiller of diallage, is found in some schists near Traboe, 6257, and elsewhere. The pyroxene is often surrounded by hornblende. In some of the schists there are alternate bands consisting of pyroxene with feldspar and hornblende with feldspar (Cadgwith 1716) but the true hornblende-schists greatly preponderate. The abundance of pyroxene seems to indicate that the rocks were foliated at a high temperature. Olivine occurs in some Traboe schists, 6255.

In a number of places the hornblende-schists are injected by veins of pinkish, acid, feldspathic rocks. They never bulk largely in the complex and they seem to be later than the hornblende-schists which look as if they had their foliation well developed before the acid veins were intruded. Instances of this are to be seen in almost every district where the hornblende-schists occur, but the most accessible are at Mullion harbour (south-east corner), Pentreath Beach (south corner), Church Cove (north side), Cadgwith (in the Cove and north of the village), Porthoustock and Porthkerris. The most striking example is in the quarry north of the inn at Cadgwith and on the roadside above Cadgwith leading up to Ruan Minor. Scrivenor has found that at Mullion these feldspathic veins contain tourmaline and many small crystals of pale pink garnet. The age and origin of these veins are problematical. They cannot be distinctly traced to the acid portion of the banded gneisses, but they are certainly intrusive and are not acid segregations from the hornblende-schist. The injected complex has often a considerable resemblance to certain facies of the Kennack Gneisses but in most cases the hornblende-schist has a much more perfect foliation than the dark basic portion of the Kennack Gneisses and there is a conspicuous absence of the phenomena of hybridization.

PLATE IV

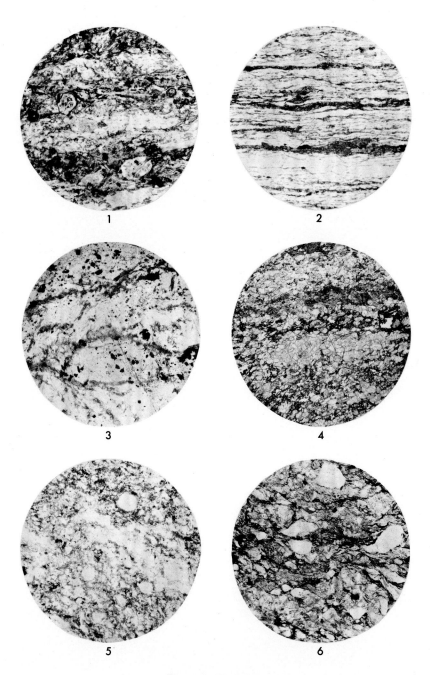

1

2

3

4

5

6

PHOTOMICROGRAPHS

PLATE IV.

FIG 1. Garnetiferous mica-schist, Rose Cottage, Porthallow (E.6201), magnified 33 diameters, ordinary light. Alternating folia of quartz and feldspar (pale) and of muscovite, chlorite after biotite, and rusty iron oxides (dark); a pink, idiomorphic garnet in the top left corner; two rounded porphyroblasts of feldspar below, on right.

FIG. 2. Hornblendic quartz-schist, west side of Trenance, half-a-mile S. of Porthallow (E. 6240), magnified 30 diameters, ordinary light. The rock is intensely foliated and, in fact, mylonitic; the thin dark bands are hornblendic, with iron ores; the pale bands are quartzose; clastic structures have been effaced.

FIG. 3. Cordierite-anthophyllite-gneiss, 450 yds. S. of Polpidnick (E. 7589), magnified 22 diameters, ordinary light. The black grains are iron oxides; the grey crystals are hornblende and anthophyllite; the pale areas are quartz, feldspar and cordierite; a large oval-shaped section of a cordierite crystal is seen below the centre of the field.

FIG. 4. Hornblende-pyroxene-epidote-schist, N. side of Cadgwith Cove (E.5025), magnified 27 diameters, ordinary light. The darker folia are deep green hornblende and feldspar, with some epidote; in the centre of the field a belt of pale green pyroxene, with sphene; at the base a band of pale yellow epidote. The foliation is perfect.

FIG. 5. Hornblendic quartzite, 100 yds. S. of Treleague farm (E. 6337), magnified 25 diameters, ordinary light. The view shows rounded, clastic grains of quartz and feldspar in a matrix which is full of hornblendic needles; the rock is brecciated and intersected by veins of secondary quartz but the clastic structure is well preserved and there is no foliation.

FIG. 6. Greywacke, Porthallow, S. side of cove, adjoining boundary fault (E. 17961), magnified 27 diameters, ordinary light. The rock has perfect clastic structure, with sub-angular grains of quartz and feldspar, and dark flakes of shale, with iron oxides.

CHAPTER VI

THE OLDER GNEISSES

TO the south of the Lizard Point there are a number of reefs and skerries some of which are nearly submerged at high tide, and from their exposed position they can be visited only on favourable occasions when there is a perfectly calm sea. The first descriptive account of these skerries from a geological standpoint we owe to

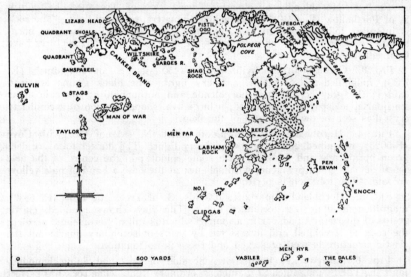

Fig. 3.—*The Reefs and Skerries of the Lizard Point.*

The outer reefs and islands are coarse, corrugated tonalite-gneiss; the inner reefs are finer granulitic gneiss. The cliffs consist of mica-schist, granulite, green schist, etc. An approximate boundary line is drawn across the Vellan Drang, Polpeor and the Wiltshire ledges. There is a fault at Polbream Cove.

Howard Fox, supplemented by petrological notes by Teall. This description was sufficient to show that these reefs contain a group of rocks not well represented, if at all, on the mainland, and different from any other geological formation in Cornwall. As the most prominent of these islets is known as the Man of War rock the general term for the formation is the Man of War Gneiss.

Although the skerries are not easily visited there are many boulders of the gneiss on the beaches at the Lizard Point, Pistil

Ogo and Polpeor, and as they have very distinctive characters they are easily recognized. The gneiss boulders are often of considerable size, being several feet in diameter. As a rule the rock is a grey gneiss with darker folia of green hornblende and chlorite. These folia are clearly and sharply defined and are generally undulating, giving the rock a corrugated appearance which is very uncommon in gneisses. The dark laminae are mostly thin, about a quarter of an inch in thickness, but continuous, and give the rock a wavy, striped appearance. For these reasons the boulders of the Man of War Gneiss are easily recognized. As a rule the undulations or corrugations are an inch or two in length but when they are closer and the rocks are fine-grained they have a distinct resemblance to the crumpled or crinkly folding that is often seen in the Lizard mica-schists and fine green schists.

Other rocks that have come from the skerries may be found on the beaches at the Lizard, such as fine grey granulitic gneisses, often with epidote, hornblende and chlorite, and dark, rather coarse-grained porphyritic hornblende-schists which are somewhat more crystalline and more abundantly porphyritic than the hornblende-schists of the mainland. To the characteristic Man of War Gneiss Teall gave the name tonalite-gneiss as it consists of hornblende, biotite, quartz and feldspar and is a foliated or metamorphic representative of the tonalites or hornblende-biotite-granites.

Fox and Teall divided the islands into two groups, an outer in which the gneiss was more coarsely crystalline and an inner in which finer granulitic types of gneiss preponderate. To the outer group belong the Man of War, Taylor's, The Stags, Sanspareil, Mulvin, Men Par, Quadrant and the Clidgas. The finer-grained rocks characterize the Wiltshire, Canker Drang, Labham Reefs and also the Vellan Drang, Pen Ervan and The Enochs, which are close to the shore or lie to the east of Polpeor. This implies that the northern edge of the igneous gneiss is more fine-grained than the south-western islands and is in accordance with the fact that on the Labham Reefs, which can be reached from the land at dead low water of spring tides, there is evidence of a 'transition' between the gneisses and the Lizard mica-schists and green schists. The 'transition' is really a zone of *lit par lit* injection in which the fine-grained, banded and well foliated gneiss sends many sills and thread-like injections into the schists, forming a complex with concordant foliation and many points of resemblance between the sedimentary schists and the igneous gneiss. It is in fact difficult often to distinguish between the injected veins and the finer bands in the schists and it is easy to believe that there has been assimilation and absorption of schist by the magma. The finer bands of gneiss can be followed for several yards and at their edges appear to blend with the schists, though as a rule they are less rich in mica, hornblende and epidote, and maintain their quartzo-feldspathic character.

These phenomena may be interpreted to mean that the Man of War Gneiss is an intrusive mass that has invaded the Old Lizard Head schists and becomes fine-grained towards the junction, though more coarsely crystalline in the interior. The granitic magma penetrated the schists along bedding and foliation, and either during injection or at a later period the whole complex was much folded and highly metamorphosed. It seems most probable that folding was going on during the intrusion and that it was at this period the Lizard schists attained their metamorphic condition, which seems to imply that they were folded and crystallized at a high temperature. But movement evidently continued after the granite had cooled down and solidified as there is much evidence of granulitization and cataclastic crushing in many specimens of the Man of War Gneiss, and even in the basic dykes which undoubtedly were injected long after the gneiss had attained its foliation.

On Old Lizard Head, at the base of the cliff, there is a mass of fine-grained, light grey, quartzo-feldspathic granulite which is folded in a great S-shaped curve. Its junctions with the schists seem to be intrusive, though the foliation in granulite and schists is concordant. It is probably a sill protruded from the Man of War Gneiss and has all the characters of some of the finer facies of the marginal gneisses on the Wiltshire and the Canker Drang. Another, apparently similar, mass occurs at the base of the cliff a little farther north. At their edges these sills seem to blend with the schists in the same manner as the veins in the mica-schist on the Labham Reefs. These are probably the only representatives of the Man of War Gneiss on the Lizard mainland.

As Fox remarked, the strike of the foliation on the skerries is generally similar to that of the adjacent Lizard schists. On the Man of War and Quadrant the strike is north to north-west. On the Wiltshire the foliation and strike are similar to those of the adjacent schists while the Labham Reefs show gneiss and schists in complete conformity. This indicates that the development of foliation in gneiss and schists belonged to the same period and was induced by the same processes.

On many of the Lizard skerries there are dark basic dykes which, though often shifted by faults and crushed along planes of movement, mostly preserve their dyke-like character. These dykes are not visible from the mainland and are not seen on the Labham Reefs but there are dark hornblendic masses on the Wiltshire which may be basic dykes much crushed. There are two dykes on the Taylor and two also on the Man of War, from five feet to eighteen inches in thickness. Another dyke occurs on the Sanspareil and two on the Quadrant. Two dykes also are seen on the Clidgas. Although none of these dykes can be followed for more than a few yards they are practically all traversed by small faults which interrupt their continuity. These faults show that movement was going on in the gneiss at a very late period and confirm the evidence seen in the Lizard cliffs of small displacements which render it impossible to trace the outcrops of distinctive bands in the schist except for very short distances.

The Man of War dykes are marked by the presence of numerous large porphyritic crystals of feldspar which not infrequently have sharp angular outlines though sometimes they are drawn out into elliptical phakoids. The matrix of these dykes is always metamorphic and consists of hornblende and feldspar with usually a fairly well developed schistosity. Though fine-grained varieties are present, these rocks have usually a more coarsely crystalline matrix than the ' black dykes ' of the Lizard, and it is usually easy to distinguish between these two groups by their microscopic characters. The larger feldspars are often cloudy with decomposition products but when fresh are basic labradorite. No augite or olivine has been found in these dykes; porphyritic feldspar is the only primary igneous mineral, and in no case have they been found to preserve remains of ophitic structure. When they are much crushed and non-porphyritic they form dark bands of hornblende schist in the gneiss which can hardly be distinguished from basic segregations; rocks of this type occur on the Wiltshire (6894) and the Enoch (6869). There seems to be little regularity in the trend of these basic dykes; some of them run north-west like the black dykes of the Lizard (for example, on the Man of War and Sanspareil) but on the Quadrant there are two dykes running east-north-east. Some are nearly vertical while others have a marked inclination. They weather out more readily than the tonalite-gneiss and consequently often form gullies and notches in the skerries. None of the isolated rocks consists entirely of basic dykes; all the smaller rocks are hornblendic gneiss.

The petrographical characters of the Man of War Gneiss have been fully described by Teall (1888). The feldspar when fresh is orthoclase and oligoclase; more basic feldspars are present but often decomposed. The hornblende ranges in colour from pale green (6866 Clidgas) to deep bluish green (1719 Man of War). Biotite is not abundant (6881 Labham) but is often weathered to chlorite. Some rocks are poor in quartz (6868 Enoch). Others are very quartzose and contain little hornblende; these are commonly fine-grained, granulitic and cataclastic (6884 Labham, 6872 Quadrant) ; they rarely contain muscovite (6882 Shag). Dark hornblendic schists are present and may sometimes be basic variations of the gneiss (6869 Enoch). Among the accessory minerals may be mentioned orthite (1720 Man of War), pale pink idiomorphic garnets, zircon and apatite; while epidote, zoisite and prehnite are common secondary products (6893 Wiltshire, 6865 Clidgas).

The Porthallow Granite-gneiss

On the shore at Porthallow to the east of the inn there is a sill of pinkish granite-gneiss in the Lizard mica-schists. It is well seen in the cliff just east of the boundary faults, and great fallen blocks of it, several cubic yards in size, are strewn on the beach below the cliff. Broken masses of it also occur in the fault-breccia mingled with mica-schist, green schist and dark killas. The sill in the cliff is irregular in thickness but has perhaps a maximum of ten feet and it is parallel to the foliation of the mica-schist. It has a distinctly gneissose appearance, with fine undulose folia of quartz and feldspar alternating with pinkish more feldspathic bands, and on fresh broken surfaces it shows traces of ' augen ' structure with larger feldspars scattered in a fine matrix. The rock has been described and figured by Teall (1888). It consists principally of quartz and feldspar. The feldspar is often in fairly good condition and appears to be orthoclase, albite and oligoclase, but the larger crystals are often turbid and cloudy. The quartz forms a fine mosaic. Many of the larger feldspars are rounded by trituration but others retain traces of their crystalline outlines. Biotite has not been abundant and is seldom fresh, having been decomposed into green chlorite. Muscovite is more plentiful and is partly original, in ragged crystalline plates, and partly secondary or metamorphic, in cloudy and feathery aggregates. Teall remarks the presence of tourmaline and of garnet but both these minerals are scanty. The rock has evidently been much crushed and is in places reduced to a fine, almost schistose condition. Secondary muscovite has developed during the shearing of the feldspar, and some parts of the rock resemble a quartzose mica-schist.

ANALYSES OF LIZARD GNEISSES

	I.	II.
SiO_2	74.35	72.95
Al_2O_3	14.70	11.50
Fe_2O_3	0.79	} 5.15
FeO	0.62	
MgO	0.81	0.31
CaO	0.70	1.62
Na_2O	5.29	} 5.41
K_2O	1.67	
H_2O above 105° C.	0.72	} 1.60
H_2O at 105° C. ...	0.11	
TiO_2	0.18	—
P_2O_5	0.12	—
MnO	0.07	—
CO_2	n.f.	—
FeS_2	n.f.	—
(Ni, Co) O... ...	?tr.	—
BaO	0.02	—
Li_2O	tr.	(1.46 loss)
Total ...	100.15	100.00

I.   Granite-gneiss, E.6625, intrusive into mica-schists, shore east of Port-
     hallow (Anal. W. Pollard).

II.   Granite-gneiss, intrusive into mica-schists, shore east of Porthallow
     (Anal. J. H. Collins).

CHAPTER VII

SERPENTINE

THE serpentine of the Lizard is its most famous and characteristic rock. It is the largest serpentine mass in England or Wales and has an area of about 20 square miles, forming a rudely circular outcrop in the heart of the Lizard peninsula. On the north and north-west it is bounded by the hornblende-schists and also on the south near the Lizard, but it reaches the sea on part of its western side and also on the east from Enys Head to Coverack. There is no evidence as to how far it may extend beneath the sea to the east, but serpentine and gabbro occur in the thrust zone south of Mevagissey, twenty miles farther east, and possibly have some connexion with the Lizard serpentine. It passes northwards beneath the schists to the Lizard boundary but there is no trace of it to the north of that line. The general form of its outcrop suggests that it is a rudely circular plug or dome-shaped mass intrusive into the mica-schists and hornblende-schists that surround it. The gabbro of Coverack on the east and the gneisses of Kennack and Erisey in the interior of the peninsula are later intrusions that have risen through the serpentine.

The serpentine ground in the Lizard has many distinctive characters that make it easily recognized. When one travels, for example, along the road from Helston to Coverack, the sudden transition from the well cultivated fields near Trelowarren and Chygarkye to the barren serpentine downs is at once obvious; similarly at Mullion cultivation stops almost precisely at the serpentine boundary. The serpentine forms the greater part of Goonhilly and Predannack Downs, where the level features of the Pliocene terrace are perfectly preserved. It seems to weather very slowly and is covered by a thin layer of brownish, ochreous clay, in which lie kernels of the larger enstatite and diallage crystals. This clay is very barren and is almost impermeable to water so that in winter and after heavy rains the surface of the serpentine downs is practically water-logged. Where streams have cut valleys in the serpentine the rough slopes are diversified by pointed rocky eminences, clustered together, and projecting through the heather and thorn. This type of scenery, so characteristic of the serpentine, is a marked feature of the valleys at Mullion Cove, Kynance, east side of Kennack and at Downas Cove. It is in strong contrast with the smooth slopes of the valleys in the gneiss and in the hornblende-schists.

The serpentine of the Lizard is essentially a crystalline rock consisting of olivine, enstatite and diallage in various proportions. Iron ores and chromite or picotite are also present as original minerals, and tremolite is practically never absent. Feldspar is scarce and local. The rock is never an absolutely fresh peridotite and in not a few places it is completely decomposed to serpentine and secondary iron oxides, and the only original mineral which is left is the chromite or picotite. These decomposed rocks show the rich variety of colours that has made the Lizard serpentine famous as an ornamental stone.

There are three principal types of the Lizard serpentine differing in composition, appearance and distribution. The best known and most widely distributed is the coarsely crystalline enstatite- or bastite-serpentine. In a dull matrix of small olivine grains it has large crystals of enstatite or diallage, that may be half an inch in diameter, and, as they have a perfect cleavage, show smooth, glittering faces on the broken surface of the rock. They also have often a sub-metallic or bronzy lustre which in weathered rocks, rich in bastite, may be pale or silvery (Pl. VII, 1). This type of serpentine occupies the whole central part of the outcrop and is well seen in numerous quarries at Goonhilly, Grade, the Lizard, Kennack and Coverack. Most of the ornamental serpentine is of this variety; the weathered enstatites appear often as darker spots in a matrix of paler colours.

The second variety of serpentine is the tremolite-serpentine. It contains few large porphyritic crystals of enstatite but consists mainly of a rather fine-grained aggregate of tremolite and olivine, with occasionally a little plagioclase (Pl. VII, 3). Owing to the absence or scarcity of enstatite crystals, this rock has a dull appearance. When fresh it is very dark green and when weathered it assumes various shades of brown or red, but it is seldom variegated and is hardly ever used as an ornamental stone. With the increase of tremolite the enstatite and diallage dwindle and disappear. The tremolite forms small prisms with imperfect crystalline faces and usually not very elongated or acicular (about an eighth of an inch in length). They have generally a nearly parallel arrangement and when they are both numerous and well developed they appear on the broken surface of the rock as pale, yellowish green, glittering scales that reflect light simultaneously if their parallel arrangement is pronounced. Occasionally the rock acquires a schistose habit so that it might be called a tremolite-olivine-schist, and such specimens bear much resemblance (Pl. VII, 2) to the darker varieties of the hornblende-schist, but they are not epidotic. The tremolite-serpentine is the characteristic rock of the west side of the Lizard from Kynance by Jolly Town round to Mullion. It occurs also in a broad band forming a semi-circle along the northern edge of the serpentine and passing by gradual transition into the enstatite-serpentine when traced southwards towards the central region of the outcrop. Excellent examples can be got about Jolly Town, Countybridge, Traboe Cross Roads, the Dry Tree and Penhale. It is found also in some of the smaller outcrops of serpentine among the hornblende-schists, as in the roadside quarry at Meaver near Mullion and on Henscath.

The third variety of serpentine in the Lizard is the dunite-serpentine, a fine-grained rock that consists almost entirely of olivine or of serpentine after that mineral. This rock is compact and often breaks with a conchoidal fracture and a greasy or subvitreous lustre resembling the coarser varieties of flint or chert. Its colour is dark green and it is somewhat translucent on thin edges. Although often homogeneous, it is probably equally commonly streaked or banded with pale or dark parallel bands, and may be intersected by numerous veins, dark in colour from precipitation of abundant fine iron oxides which may be blood red when they are weathered. The commonest mineral in the dunite-serpentine, in addition to olivine, is tremolite, which gradually increases in quantity till the rock passes into the normal tremolite-serpentine. Small porphyritic crystals of enstatite or diallage are by no means rare, especially in specimens from the neighbourhood of Mullion.

The dunite-serpentine is the characteristic rock of the margins of the intrusion. It is found principally along the north-west and north boundaries of the serpentine mass where it has been folded with the hornblende-schists. Where the folded margin has been cut out by faults the dunite-serpentine may be absent. The dunite-serpentine is well seen in many small quarries where the north edge of the serpentine describes a great curve from Bonython to Polkerth, Traboe and Kernewas. The width of the outcrop varies but is seldom more than a few hundred yards and very fine tremolitic serpentine often occurs along with the dunite. Along the folded western edge of the serpentine at Pol Cornick, Ogo Dour and Predannack, dunite-serpentine is found occupying a narrow marginal strip. It also occurs in a few places near Mullion Cove. As might be expected, the dunite-serpentine is the prevailing rock of all the intrusions or infolds of serpentine that occur among the hornblende-schists. At Porthallow there are two such outcrops and they consist of dunite- and fine tremolite-serpentine, well banded and often veined. The small outliers at Halwyn and Rosemorder (on the Lizard boundary) have the same character and, as at Porthallow, they are often slickensided through faulting or earth movement. In the Mullion country there is dunite-serpentine and tremolite-serpentine in the infolded mass at Meaver and the four small serpentine outcrops at Mullion Cove Hotel, Henscath, Scovarn and the path to Polurrian are all exceedingly fine-grained. On the south side of Predannack there are several small serpentine masses on the top of the cliffs and all of them belong to the dunite-serpentine.   They resemble the fine serpentine of the quarries near Traboe in being very much banded and veined.

The distribution in space of these three types of serpentine sufficiently proves that the dunite-serpentine was the earliest, the tremolite-serpentine the second and the enstatite-serpentine the last of the ultrabasic intrusions.   As they grade perfectly into one another there seems to have been no interval between them and as it has never been shown that one of them is intrusive into another in the form of dykes or veins, they seem to have consolidated during a comparatively short period and the injection was probably gradual and continuous. The dunite-serpentine, though marginal and fine-grained, is probably not to be regarded as a chilled edge, seeing that it merges completely with the hornblende-schist, though that rock may quite well have been in large measure solidified and consequently at a lower temperature when the serpentine invaded it.   Isolated masses of hornblende-schist are sometimes found in the marginal serpentine, from a few feet to many yards in length. They may be seen at Pol Cornick, Mullion Cove, and in the quarries at Tregadra, Countybridge, Traboe and Kernewas. They have certainly not in all cases been introduced by faulting, and they may be infolds or fluxion bands in a non-homogeneous magma.   Some of them may be inclusions or xenoliths. They sometimes contain augite or enstatite and their hornblende may be of deep brown colour. At Porthallow dark green hornblende-schists in thin layers are folded with the dunite-serpentine but all these rocks are very much decomposed. The tremolite-serpentine has always a strong fluxion structure, amounting in places to marked schistosity. It seems to have been injected under strong regional pressures, by which apparently the surrounding schists were being simultaneously folded.   Whether the tremolite is always an original mineral or has been produced from primary enstatite and augite cannot be positively asserted. In certain peridotites a pale green hornblende is a primary mineral, but in all the Lizard serpentines the passage of pyroxene into greenish amphibole, when subjected to shearing and disruption, is a common phenomenon, and there is much reason to believe that most of the tremolite in the rocks of the Lizard is paramorphic after pyroxene and olivine. At the same time it is clear that when the movements of injection and concurrent folding in the tremolite-serpentine were concluded, the rock had attained its present structure and mineral composition (apart from the results of subsequent weathering). The enstatite-serpentine which occupies the great central area of the intrusion apparently cooled very slowly, developed a coarse crystallization and was less profoundly affected by the regional pressures, though these continued and their effects can be traced in practically every specimen examined.

Fluxion-banding, marked by differences in mineral composition, is common in all the Lizard serpentines. It is perhaps least marked in the dunite-serpentine, though there it is shown by paler streaks which are comparatively rich in tremolite. In the tremolite-serpentine this is often pronounced; the banding in the Porthallow serpentine has often occasioned remark and is due to the relative abundance of tremolite, pyroxene and olivine in the different layers. In the enstatite-serpentine thin bands of pale green colour and rich in pyroxene or tremolite may often be traced for many yards. They are well seen at Pentreath, Poltesco and the eastern side of Kennack. There is another variety of serpentine, the chromite-serpentine, which forms fluxion-bands in the enstatite-serpentine, sometimes several yards in breadth. This variety often has a bright yellow colour and shows few large enstatite crystals, but many small black grains of magnetite, picotite or chromite. Chromite-serpentine is well seen on the Yellow Carn east of Kynance. In the region south of Coverack chromite-serpentine is especially common in well marked bands parallel to the fluxion structure of the enstatite-serpentine. It has in this locality a dark green, brown or purplish colour and has been mistaken for intrusive basic dykes, as it is much finer-grained than the enstatite-serpentine and the bands are very distinct and sharply defined. This variety weathers pale green on exposed surfaces and along cracks and is often cut and polished.

Where the Lizard serpentines have been exposed to weathering in the downs and fields, all varieties show rough, ridged, fluted or braided surfaces. The ridges contain parallel streams of small granular nodules. The hollows between are due to the more rapid decomposition and erosion of the bands that are richest in olivine and serpentine; the nodules in the ridges are crystals of enstatite, or diallage, or clusters of tremolite. Weathering has etched out the primary fluxion-banding of the rocks. This braided structure is coarsest and most prominent in the enstatite-serpentine, finer and more regular in the tremolite-serpentine and often rather indistinct and elusive in the dunite-serpentine. In the tremolite-serpentine of the west coast from the Rill Head to Mullion, the fine, parallel-ribbed structure is very conspicuous in the weathered rocks which form the top of the cliffs. In the coarse enstatite-serpentine it is well marked about Poltesco, Kuggar and the Black Head, but less regular and pronounced in some places on Goonhilly Down and about Ruan Major. In polished surfaces of the serpentine and on the shores, where blocks of serpentine have been scoured by the sand of the beach, it is clear that the large enstatites and diallage crystals are almond shaped; they are pointed ellipsoids, with three unequal axes, and their longest diameters are parallel. In other words, the coarse serpentine has a perfect 'augen' structure. This can be especially well seen in the blocks on the beach at Poltesco, Pentreath and at Kynance

Cove. The parallel orientation is not only due to fluxion in a partly fluid mass, but has been produced also by pressures acting on a plastic solid and sufficiently powerful to grind the crystals into lenticular form (Pl. VB). Microscopic examination confirms this conclusion, for the larger crystals are often broken and have clusters of pyroxene grains and wisps of tremolite at their pointed ends. The pressures which produced folding in the dunite-serpentine and adjacent hornblende-schist, and foliation in the tremolite-serpentine, persisted during the consolidation of the enstatite-serpentine, and gave rise to the ' augen ' structure. The serpentines of the Lizard are not only fluxion-banded, as is frequent in normal igneous rocks, but they are also fluxion-foliated. These two structures are always parallel and concordant; at least very few instances have been observed in which the fluxion-foliation crosses the fluxion-banding; they are part of the same process and if not exactly simultaneous, the one followed the other after no great lapse of time. The extensive replacement of enstatite and olivine by tremolite seems to indicate that the temperature was falling as these changes progressed; but the absence of talc, antigorite and chlorite would show that cooling was not complete. As we shall see later, it is easy to establish that the metamorphism of the Lizard serpentine was complete before the gabbro was injected.

It is doubtful whether there is any serpentine of normal igneous structure in the Lizard. The usual poikilitic or poikilo-porphyritic structure of peridotites has never been observed in typical development, though traces of it are sometimes provided by large enstatite crystals that carry in their interior rounded grains of olivine. Moreover the large enstatites are never idiomorphic but always phakoidal, often broken and embedded in a matrix of olivine, pyroxene and amphibole developed by movement and friction.

The study of the fluxion-banding and braided weathering of the Lizard serpentines leads to some interesting conclusions regarding the mode of intrusion and the action of pressures during and after consolidation. In general there is a tendency for these structures to be parallel with the edges of the intrusion and the junction with the surrounding schists. Along the west coast from The Rill to Mullion Cove, the fluxion structures are nearly vertical and point almost due north. The foliation in the hornblende-schists has the same direction even up to Polurrian. On the east side from Church Cove to Kennack the fluxion structures are mostly a little west of north at very high angles; this is well seen at Carleon Cove. In the Black Head and Coverack district, a north to north-west direction is also very consistently present. Along the cliffs from Carrick Luz to Kennack, the strike varies but is mostly a little east of north, sometimes north-east and often rather indistinct. Similarly between the Lizard and Kynance the strike is north, north-east and sometimes east-north-east for short

distances. On the north side of the serpentine near Traboe the
foliation in the schist and in the serpentine is consistently a little
west of north, but in some of the quarries near Trezise it is west-
north-west. In the large quarry at Countybridge the well marked
fluxion structures are about north-north-west. Along the boundary between Countybridge and Bonython the strike varies near
the junction with the schists, but there is a great prevalence of northern and north-western strikes. Around Bonython and Penhale
the characteristic northern strike is consistently shown. In the

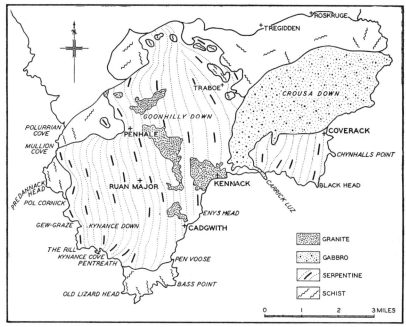

FIG. 4.—*Sketch-map showing trend of fluxion-foliation in the serpentine and
schists.*

The strong black bars indicate places where the fluxion-foliation is often
visible. The dotted lines give the general trend in different localities. There
is a predominance of northerly strikes, with local deviations. In the hornblende-schists and mica-schists the principal strikes are indicated by sinuous
lines.

interior of the serpentine good exposures are not so common and
care must be taken in making observations as the projecting
weathered blocks may have slipped or rolled over : this explains
occasional marked divergences in neighbouring exposures; but
at Predannack Downs, Ruan Minor, Bray's Cot and Croftnoweth,
the fluxion-banding and fluxion-foliation never vary far from a
northern direction and are most frequently a few degrees to the
west of north. These facts seem to indicate that during the injec-

tion of the serpentine, pressures of two kinds were operating. There was a general pressure outwards from the centre of the intrusion forcing the schists apart and upwards, and folding them at the same time : and there was also a regional pressure acting from east-north-east and west-south-west and giving rise to a dominant north to north-west strike where not diverted by local conditions at the junction with the schists.

Another noticeable feature of the fluxion structures is that the dips are usually high, often vertical and rarely more than twenty five degrees from the vertical.   The folded schists and serpentine in the north-west and north of the serpentine have nearly vertical foliation and the folds seem to be very narrow and elongated. There is little evidence of folding in the interior of the serpentine, for horizontal or gently inclined fluxion structures which would indicate the summits of anticlinal arches are practically completely absent.   A very interesting exception to this is seen at a roadside quarry a quarter of a mile south of Ruan Major Church where the fluxion-foliation is practically horizontal. Folding seems to have taken place along the margins and the roof ; the small outlying serpentine outcrops among the schists may be interpreted as anticlinal upfolds of the top of the serpentine intrusion. The great central mass of the serpentine was compressed and sheared but not thrown into repeated folds like the hornblende-schists.

Although the majority of the strikes of the fluxion-banding and fluxion-folding in the serpentine range from north-east to north-west and are mostly a little west of north, it is not without interest to note that in certain regions there are directions which seem to be abnormal.   The principal of these are on the south between Kynance and Lizard Town, where north-east and east-north-east strikes frequently occur though northern strikes are also common.   This may be interpreted as implying that somewhere in this district there was an east-and-west or east-south-east original boundary of the serpentine intrusion.   The actual boundary at present is a fault which runs in a generally eastern direction (though not straight) from the south end of Pentreath Beach to The Balk.   The intrusive edge is cut out by this fault but the occurrence of tremolite-serpentine near the Methodist Church in Lizard Town makes it probable that the margin was not far distant. The deflection of the fluxion-strike to a more easterly direction may be due to the proximity to the original southern edge of the intrusion, just as in the north near Penhale and Polkerth the strikes show everywhere a tendency to conform to the junction with the hornblende-schists. It is noteworthy also that on the west coast from Old Lizard Head to Pentreath the hornblendic and micaceous schists have frequently a north-east strike. Similarly along the coast from Kennack to Carrick Luz the serpentine, which is of the coarse bastite-bearing variety, has by no means infrequently a north-east and sometimes an east-north-east strike. This may indicate that the hornblende-schists last seen

A. North side of Carleon Cove, Poltesco, Ruan Minor.
   Bastite-serpentine with cuboidal joints

PLATE V

B. Same locality as above; base of cliff.
   Bastite-serpentine, fluxion-banded

at Cadgwith and south of Enys Head came round in an eastern direction along an original boundary now covered by the waters of Kennack Bay. Tremolite-serpentine occurs at the Devil's Frying Pan and also north of Cadgwith and in some places near Ruan Minor.

All the serpentine rocks have a grain or ' reed ' which arises from the disposition of their constituent crystals. The grain is not always obvious in the broken specimens but is always emphasized by weathering. The fluted or braided character of weathered surfaces indicates the grain structure arising from fluxion-banding and fluxion-foliation. In polished serpentine ornaments the grain of the rock is also frequently visible. The lenticular or ellipsoidal crystals of enstatite or diallage and clusters of tremolite are arranged in parallel strings like chains of beads and are also aggregated in sheets with definite orientation. If the fluxion-bands, for example, are north and south and nearly vertical, we may imagine three planes at right angles to one another, one of them parallel to the fluxion and the other two perpendicular to it. These will divide the rock into rectangular blocks or box-shaped masses with end-, top- and side-faces (Pl. V). The end-faces might also be called cross-faces because they cut directly across the fluxion; while the side-faces are longitudinal faces parallel to the fluxion. The top or bottom faces are sometimes called ' floors ', being horizontal.

These planes are not purely hypothetical but correspond to a series of joints or divisional planes which, though rarely developed in great perfection, are usually present and may often be perceived in cliff-faces, quarries and as the limiting surfaces of loose blocks of serpentine. They correspond exactly to the three characteristic principal joint directions of the Cornish granites as described by Hill and Ghosh in the Carnmenellis Granite (p. 161). The longitudinal joints in the serpentine as in the granite are parallel to the ' cleaving way ' or plane of easiest splitting. But while in granite these joints dominate, in serpentine they are less pronounced and less important than another set of joints to be subsequently described.

On a cuboidal block of serpentine bounded by these planes the effect of long-continued weathering is to produce a characteristic sculpture depending on and illustrating the grain of the rock. On the end-faces or cross-faces the rough ridges are narrow, continuous, close together and prominent. They correspond to the sharpest edges of the almond-shaped crystals. As a rule they are nearly vertical and parallel to the side or longitudinal joint faces or to the edges between these and the end-faces. On the side-faces or longitudinal faces the fluting is also conspicuous but the ridges are broader and flatter and the intervening hollows less deeply etched. These ridges which may be described as ' lateral ' show the flattest surfaces of the almond-shaped crystals. On the top or bottom of the cuboidal blocks, corresponding to the floor joints and horizontal in the quarries, the prominences due to the weathering out of the larger crystals are often rounded, or sub-rounded ellipses. They are less prominent than on the other faces and have a less marked linear arrangement. They correspond to cross sections of the almond-shaped crystals and clusters of grains, which provide the least elongated and most nearly circular outlines. In a deeply weathered block of serpentine it is not difficult to distinguish these three faces. On weathered rock surfaces in the quarries and on the top of the cliffs the banded structure is often very conspicuous and there are usually also rock faces bounded by one or more of the cuboidal systems of joints above mentioned. Consequently observations may frequently be made of the rock-grain and inferences drawn regarding the fluxion-foliation of the rock.

The cuboidal, rectangular or granitoid system of jointing above referred to, though always present in every kind of serpentine, is often latent, ill developed and inconspicuous. The prevalent system of joints in the serpentine as exemplified in crags, quarries and cairns is of the ' diagonal ' or oblique type. Most frequently the joints slope like the roof of a house, and the ridge angle is usually rather less than a right angle. When two such joints meet downwards they resemble a gully or gutter. In the quarries the most common type of jointing is defined by a ' cross ' joint (vertical

FIG. 5a.—*Pyramidal jointing in serpentine.*

There are two sets of sloping joint planes (B and C) meeting in a point and horizontal (floor) joints forming a base to the pyramid.

FIG. 5b.—*Gable-jointing in serpentine.*

Two sloping sets of joint planes meet in a roof-like ridge (A and B); there are also horizontal or ' floor ' joints, and vertical cross joints perpendicular to the roof joints.

and perpendicular to the fluxion-foliation) capped by two roof joints which meet in a ridge parallel to the fluxion direction. This resembles the gable of a house and may be called ' gable-jointing ' (Pl. VIB). It is very well seen in the large serpentine quarry at Countybridge; also in the serpentine quarry at The Balk; on Carn Caerthillian and in many other places. The cross joints run nearly east and west; the diagonal joints dip to east and west at angles of 60 to 70 degrees and have a northern strike.

Almost equally common is the development of two systems of sloping or roof joints approximately at right angles to each other; when this type of jointing is pronounced it yields four-sided pyramids and may be called pyramidal or steeple-jointing. It

A. The Green Saddle, east side of Kennack Cove.
Pyramidal jointing in bastite-serpentine

(A 748)

PLATE VI

B. Serpentine Quarry, Countybridge, Goonhilly.
Gable-jointing in tremolite-serpentine

(A 749)

is not often perfect, however, and usually gives rise to pointed blocks with three, four, or five faces of unequal size.   Good examples are seen in Poltesco serpentine quarry; at the Green Saddle east of Kennack (Pl. VIA); on the rocky slopes above Poltesco, and in many other places.

Sometimes one set of diagonal or sloping joints is much better developed than the other.   In Mullion Cove there is an apparent syncline in the serpentine.   On the south side are many sloping joints that dip eastwards; on the east side of the cove the most conspicuous sloping joints dip westwards.   The synclinal appearance is delusive, however, because both series of joints are present in either case but they, for some reason not clearly explicable, are unequally developed in different parts of the cliffs.

Fig. 6.—*Diagram of the jointing in the serpentine.*

The rectangular joints bounding the diagram cut the rock into cuboidal masses.   There are three systems of these and the diagram can be held in three positions, (A) horizontal, (B) vertical (right and left) or (C) vertical (front and back).   The plane of the paper will then define (A) a floor joint (B) a cross joint or (C) a longitudinal joint (parallel to the fluxion-foliation). The diagonal joints are indicated within the rectangle and are often more marked than the rectangular joints.   If the diagram is held vertically facing the reader, the paper represents a cross joint, the diagonals are roof joints (see fig. 5a).   If two sets of diagonal joints are well developed, crossing nearly at right angles, the characteristic jointing is pyramidal.

In theory there ought to be other sets of diagonal joints intersecting the rectangular or cuboidal joints in each of their interfacial angles, but so far as the Lizard serpentine is concerned these are of irregular occurrence and of little meaning.   In the quarries and on the cliffs the gable-jointing and the pyramidal jointing are by far the most important.   Though the rectangular jointing is also usually noticeable it is seldom prominent but on the north side of Carleon Cove, Poltesco, it is very well seen and the diagonal jointing there is almost absent.   In many of the

serpentine cliffs of the Lizard the complexity of the jointing and
its irregularity baffle analysis. The joint systems above described

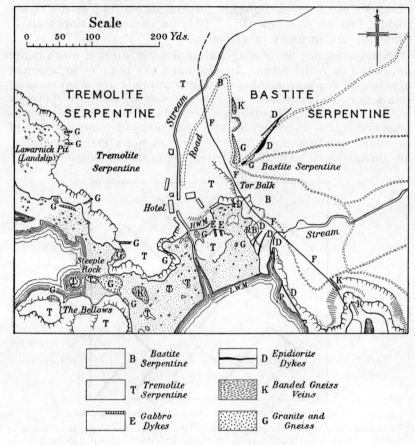

R B. *Raised Beach Platform*
P   *Locality for Pseudophite*
F   *Fault*

FIG. 7.—*Map of Kynance Cove.*

The country-rock is serpentine which is of two varieties, tremolite-serpentine
(T) on the west and bastite-serpentine (B) on the east. These are separated
by a fault (F) which passes in a north-north-west direction from the south-
east corner of the map and is attended by brecciation of the rocks on each
side. In the serpentine there are two small veins of crushed gabbro (E)
visible in the reefs in the shore, south-east of the hotel. Many black dykes
cut the serpentine especially near the mouth of the stream in the south-east
corner of the map; some of these are distinctly schistose, as, for example,
the one near the centre of the map, on the roadside, north of Tor Balk.
Intrusions of banded gneiss (K) and granite (G) are numerous, particularly
in the sandy shore near the Steeple Rock but also below the hotel and in
the roadside north of Tor Balk. Well-marked dykes of granite occur in the
cliffs towards Lawarnick Pit.

are traceable but there is much diversity, and this is probably due
to the intense crushing and movement that attended the Hercyn-

ian folding and produced the numerous thrust planes and crush belts that are visible in most of the coves. At Kynance, Pentreath, Gew-graze, Eastern Cliffs and Pedn Boar, the jointing is too complicated and inconsistent to be separated into well defined categories. In many parts of the Lizard the serpentine is so freely injected by black dykes and sills of banded gneiss that it is easy to believe that movement and displacement have disturbed the original jointing and may have developed new systems of fissuring. This is especially the case in the cliffs on the west and north of Kennack Bay from Pen Voose to Carrick Luz; in these districts the primary jointing is often decipherable but is well preserved only in a few localities.

Analysis of the Lizard serpentine shows that it contains up to 12 per cent of combined water and there has been much discussion regarding the period at which serpentinization took place. Weinschenk and Benson (with others) consider that magmatic water effected the hydration shortly after the rock crystallized or while it was cooling down. But a pneumatolytic or hydrolytic action of this kind took place on a very large scale in the Cornish granites, converting them into kaolin and greisen, and filling their fissures with veins of quartz containing often fluor, tinstone, tourmaline, chlorite and metalliferous minerals of various kinds. In the Lizard serpentine we find no corresponding veins of talc, brucite, magnesite or other secondary magnesian minerals. This might be explained on the hypothesis that the serpentine absorbed water like a sponge and there was no excess to circulate through fissures or to be discharged into the surrounding rocks. As serpentine has a specific gravity of 2.4 while olivine may have a specific gravity of 3.4, the process of serpentinization must have been accompanied by great expansion. That this actually takes place is shown by the radiating cracks which diverge from weathered grains of olivine through the feldspar of the troctolites. Of such expansion, however, there is little evidence in the best cliff exposures of the Lizard serpentine, though it is admitted that there has been much faulting and movement and the gabbro dykes are often crushed, apparently by closing of the walls. But where the gabbro dykes are crushed and even schistose, the adjacent serpentine differs little from normal and shows only slight traces of secondary schistosity, a fact which indicates that the serpentine was at that time a harder or tougher rock than the gabbro.

We must remember that the serpentine at present accessible to inspection is the surface of an old submarine platform which has been exposed to the sea and the atmosphere for about ten million years. There are no deep wells or mines in the Lizard and the condition of the serpentine in depth is quite unknown. Serpentine is a porous rock and the lapidaries who cut bowls and vases of serpentine find that often liquids ooze through them if they are used to contain fluids. Serpentine also is slightly soluble and

the water from wells in this rock is usually very hard.   Hence
it is possible that room for expansion on hydration was provided
by removal of portions of the mass in solution.   If we consider
the immense age of the Lizard serpentine and its long exposure to
weather and percolating water it seems possible that ordinary
atmospheric action might account sufficiently for the serpentinization of its primary olivine.

In all probability serpentinization is still going on and accounts
for some of the properties of the rock.   It is avoided for building
the gables of houses as it is believed to be porous and to allow
the percolation of water.   It is also brittle and liable to develop
cracks or ' shakes '. Hence its use has been discarded for mantels,
lintels, and shop fronts.   This seems to indicate that there is a
state of internal tension in the rock which may be due to expansion

Fig. 8.—*Weathering of Serpentine.*

The photograph shows a block of weathered serpentine from the surface
of Goonhilly Down, near Countybridge Quarry; the prominent ridges are due
to crystals of enstatite with diallage and clusters of tremolite.   The hollows
mark the sites of softer areas of serpentine after olivine.   The ' grain ' of
the rock is etched out by weathering and the fluxion-foliation is well
expressed. (MN 3471).

owing to the conversion of olivine into serpentine.   Much of the
serpentine that is polished and sold in the shops is traversed by
immense numbers of cracks and veins.   These have usually a
central band of black magnetite (which may be oxidized to red
haematite) flanked by edges of pale fibrous serpentine (sometimes

asbestiform). In some cases these veins may be due to fissuring which was the result of faulting movement and then they are usually sub-parallel, or they may be due to folding at the margin of the intrusion (this variety is common near Traboe). But more frequently the cracks run irregularly and form a network which may be very fine, with meshes a tenth of an inch or less. They are always most abundant in serpentine which is very completely weathered and are especially characteristic of the bleached surfaces of blocks long exposed to the atmosphere or adjacent to joints along which water circulated. Perhaps connected with this is the remarkable appearance of some weathered serpentine blocks which are covered by a network of fissures deeply incised into the rock. All varieties of serpentine may show this ' reticulate weathering '. Some of the blocks resemble ' bread-crust bombs ' (Pl. IXB). One could imagine that the interior had expanded and torn the surface layers apart. The network of cracks may have meshes less than an inch or several inches in diameter and when the meshes are large the cracks may be three inches deep. The most probable explanation is that the cracks have been widened and deepened by the solvent action of atmospheric waters. They are not visible in blocks taken from the quarries but they must be latent in the quarried rock. It is not easy to assign the role that expansion and solution may have had in producing this extraordinary and characteristic appearance, but it is reasonably certain that both of these agencies have played a part.

The characters of the Lizard serpentines have been well described by Teall in his ' British Petrography ' (with coloured illustrations). The essential minerals are olivine, enstatite and diallage, with magnetite and chromite as the commonest accessories. Tremolite is practically always present, and there is some feldspar in the tremolitic serpentine. Anthophyllite, talc and chlorite may be added to this list. In the dunite-serpentine the olivine crystals are always small and very abundant : some pyroxene and tremolite are usually also present. The tremolite-serpentine is distinguished by the abundance of tremolite (5005 Cadgwith, 5132 Kynance), which is pale yellow or pale green. Brownish hornblende may also be present (5134 Kynance), but is scarce. There is usually also feldspar (near bytownite) in rounded grains often weathered (5123 Rill). Both enstatite and diallage occur in many specimens of serpentine, sometimes in crystals half an inch in length (5029 Ruan), but enstatite is the more frequent. In all the Lizard serpentines there is evidence of crushing and the large pseudo-porphyritic pyroxenes are lenticular phakoids (5031 Poltesco), often disrupted and sometimes reduced to granulitic aggregates (5957 Trezise) in which tremolite is abundant. The tremolite-serpentine is often distinctly schistose (5945 Countybridge). The chromite-serpentine is fine-grained, devoid of pyroxene porphyroblasts and is spotted with dark grains of chromite (brown), picotite (green) or magnetite (opaque) (5074 Yellow Carn). At shear zones the serpentine passes into thin belts of pale talc-tremolite-schist, and a similar change is induced by pneumatolysis (6668 Kynance, 6387 The Balk). When long exposed to the weather the serpentine bleaches and part of the iron oxide is removed but much is concentrated along the central lines of the material which occupies the cracks in the rock (5904 Tregadra). Secondary products of many kinds occur in veins in the serpentine (tremolite, talc, asbestos, dolomite, limonite, etc.). The most curious of these is a colourless garnet in small rounded grains (Pentreath Road Quarry 5040, Kynance 5133).

ANALYSES OF LIZARD SERPENTINES

	I.	II.	III.	IV
SiO₂	40.12	40.87	39.58	38.58
Al₂O₃	0.98	3.93	3.19	2.72
Fe₂O₃	6.52	6.17	4.70	8.75
FeO	1.21	2.37	2.76	1.02
MgO	35.78	32.86	36.21	35.72
CaO	0.12	2.36	1.09	0.07
Na₂O	0.24	0.39	0.28	0.44
K₂₂O	0.08	0.04	0.06	0.19
H₂O above 105° C.	12.17	8.95	10.79	11.03
HO at 105° C ...	1.69	1.09	0.51	1.42
TiO₂	tr.	0.16	0.10	0.08
P₂O₅	0.10	0.07	0.16	0.03
MnO	0.52	0.29	0.34	0.14
CO₂	0.15	0.11	0.24	0.04
FeS₂	0.01	0.01	n.f.	tr.
Cr₂O₃	0.28	0.25	0.20	0.28
V₂O₃	tr.	tr.	n.f.	? tr.
(Ni, Co) O... ...	0.15	0.17	0.16	0.07
BaO	n.f.	n.f.	n.f.	n.f.
Li₂O	n.f.	n.f.	tr.	tr.
Total ...	100.12	100.09	100.37	100.58

I. Dunite-serpentine, E.5172, 70 yds. W. of Parc Bean Cove, S. side of Predannack (Anal. E. G. Radley).

II. Tremolite-serpentine, E.7590, Lawarnick Pit, west side of Kynance (Anal. E. G. Radley).

III. Bastite-serpentine (Lherzolite), E.5031, Poltesco Mill, Ruan Minor (Anal. E. G. Radley).

IV. Chromite-serpentine, E.5074, Yellow Carn, E. of Kynance (Anal. E. G. Radley).

For other (less complete) analyses, of Lizard serpentines, reference may be made to Teall's ' British Petrography ' (1888) p. 124. The analyses quoted above show the essential similarity between the various kinds of serpentine in the Lizard. All the rocks contain comparatively little silica, and much magnesia and combined water. The dunite-serpentine contains least alumina and very little lime while the tremolite-serpentine contains most of these ingredients. This explains the presence of feldspar in the tremolite-serpentine. The chromite-serpentine contains so little chromic oxide that the black grains visible in the hand-specimens are evidently picotite and magnetite, but chromium is present in all the serpentines. The alkalis and phosphoric acid are very low and this partly explains the barren character of the serpentine soils.

PLATE VII

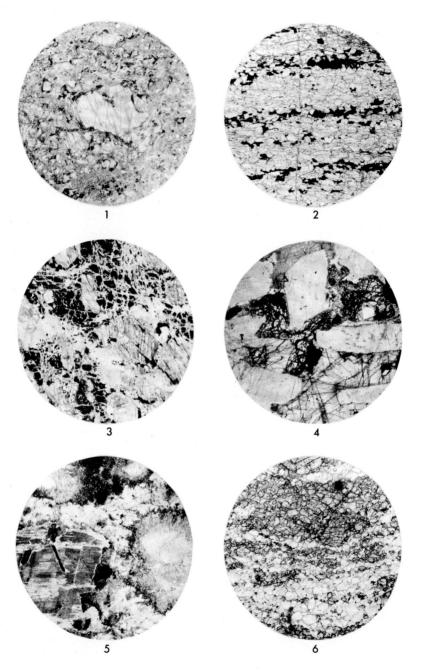

1

2

3

4

5

6

PHOTOMICROGRAPHS

PLATE VII

FIG. 1. Bastite-serpentine, 500 yds. W.S.W. of Trelan (E.6277), magnified 14 diameters, ordinary light. A large irregularly shaped crystal of enstatite occupies the centre of the field, with smaller crystals of enstatite on the left, embedded in a matrix of olivine, serpentine, enstatite and iron oxides (augen structure).

FIG. 2. Tremolite-olivine-schist, 100 yds. S. of Traboe (E. 5954), magnified 16 diameters, ordinary light. A well foliated rock consisting of alternate bands of dark serpentine after olivine and pale tremolite. The schistose structure is very pronounced.

FIG. 3. Tremolite-serpentine, W. side of Devil's Frying Pan, Cadgwith (E. 5005), magnified 24 diameters, ordinary light. The rock is cut across the foliation and shows the amphibole cleavages in the pale tremolite crystals. The dark areas are serpentine after olivine; there is little fresh olivine in the rock.

FIG. 4. Olivine-gabbro, 400 yds. W. of Polcoverack (E. 6709), magnified 5 diameters, ordinary light. A coarsely crystalline rock with olivine, diallage and feldspar. Olivine has dark iron oxides along cleavages and cracks and is locally rimmed by hypersthene. The feldspar has well shaped rectangular outlines. The pale brownish diallage encloses the feldspar and the olivine. The original minerals and structures of the igneous rock are in good preservation.

FIG. 5. Flaser-gabbro, 250 yds. N.W. of Treveddon (E. 5011), magnified 6 diameters, ordinary light. On the right a cluster of pale green actinolite crystals after olivine; on the left a schillerized diallage crystal partly replaced by amphibole along edges and cracks; at the top of the field another mass of actinolite, probably after olivine; the spotty, grey, matrix is feldspar passing into saussurite. The igneous minerals are being converted into metamorphic minerals and the igneous structures are fading away.

FIG. 6. Granulitic malacolite-gabbro, Spernic Cove, W. side of Carrick Luz (E. 7616), magnified 31 diameters, ordinary light. This rock is a granulitic and well foliated aggregate of malacolite (or colourless pyroxene) and feldspar; both minerals are in good preservation.

CHAPTER VIII

THE TROCTOLITE AND THE GABBRO

THE gabbro of St. Keverne occupies an area of about seven square miles on the east side of the peninsula and is well exposed on the coast from Coverack to the south side of Porthoustock Cove. Its southern boundary is an intrusive junction of highly irregular form and the serpentine to the south is penetrated by gabbro veins in great numbers. Elsewhere the gabbro seems to be bounded by a series of powerful faults which describe a great curve from the west side of Kennack to Porthoustock. This junction is nowhere clearly seen but in the course of mapping it proves to be very well defined as it brings together rocks of widely different composition each of which weathers in characteristic fashion. On these sides the intrusive fringe of gabbro dykes is apparently absent. As usual in the Lizard, this line of faulting has given rise to numerous hollows which form the valleys of unimportant streamlets.

The gabbro weathers deeply but irregularly, yielding a strong yellow clay containing small fragments of the primary minerals. In some places this decomposed material is twenty feet deep and it always contains blocks of hard rock which vary from a few inches to many feet in diameter. These blocks are rounded or elongated, with blunt edges and corners; on the higher ground at Crousa Downs where the Pliocene platform is fairly well preserved many great blocks of gabbro cumber the surface. The softer earth between them has been washed away by the rains, and the residual blocks, some of them weighing several tons, gradually emerge as the surface is lowered by erosion. This feature is partly due to the slow decomposition of the coarsely crystalline rock and partly to the wide spacing of the principal joints along which the water percolates and decomposition proceeds. Where the land has been taken into cultivation the large blocks have often been broken up and used for building stone walls or repairing roads, but many are still left in the middle of rich fields. The gabbro does not make imposing cliffs, like the serpentine and hornblende-schist; as a rule there is a gentle slope on which lie many gabbro blocks (known as ' crusairs '), in a tangle of vegetation, with, at the base, a low vertical cliff dropping abruptly to tide level. The shore is often strewn with enormous angular blocks detached from the cliffs.

The gabbro ground around St. Keverne, Rosenithon and Lanarth is famous for its fertility and in former times yielded amazing crops of wheat. It is in high cultivation and near the farmhouses are many old marl pits where the rotted gabbro has been dug for use as a top dressing for the fields. On Crousa Downs, however, north of Polcoverack, there is a considerable area which has not been ploughed and is still covered with heather and thorn, possibly because the abundance of large gabbro residual blocks has made it too costly to clear the ground or because the rotted soil is comparatively shallow.

The gabbro is mostly a coarsely crystalline rock of grey green colour. Its crystals average from a quarter to half an inch in diameter. Fine-grained and very coarse-grained varieties occur but usually only in veins or segregation patches and form only a small part of the rock mass. The feldspar is grey and has a greasy lustre as it is usually saussuritic and its cleavage is no longer evident. The diallage is dark brown with bronzy lustre, but like the olivine is wholly or in great part replaced by aggregates of prismatic actinolite which give the rock its greenish tinge. Like the serpentine of the Lizard the gabbro is practically always metamorphic but the metamorphism is seldom complete; the rock is essentially a flaser-gabbro that has been crushed but has retained many broken residues of the primary minerals, though these are embedded in secondary products such as actinolite (Pl. VII, 5). In the main gabbro outcrop such rocks as actinolite-schist and gabbro-schist are never abundant, but they occur in the gabbro dykes and in zones of special crushing. On the other hand, unlike the serpentine, the gabbro locally retains its original characters. This variety is a coal-black rock with metallic reflections when examined in strong sunlight (Pl. VII, 4). Near Polcoverack there are many specimens of this kind of gabbro in the field walls though they are not seen *in situ*. At the North Corner of Coverack also the black gabbro is by no means uncommon and on the beach about half a mile farther north large masses of the same rock are frequent : in these a kind of rough fluxion-banding may be seen, some bands being richer in feldspar and paler than the remainder of the rock. The dark colour of the normal gabbro is due to the presence in the feldspar of immense numbers of minute inclusions which may be titaniferous iron oxides (schillerization). At the first touch of pressure metamorphism these seem to be absorbed and disappear. The original diallage is also schillerized but the secondary amphibole is not. Hence the degree of metamorphism in the gabbro is sufficiently indicated by the stage of the development of the grey-green colour.

The main gabbro does not as a rule show gneissose, schistose or ' augen ' structure, and cannot be said to have a well developed foliation with a definite strike, though all these phenomena appear in the gabbro dykes. There are few good inland exposures of bare gabbro and the weathered blocks on the downs are mostly covered with lichen ; moreover, there is only one quarry in the gabbro (at Dean Point) and in the cliff exposures it is very difficult to perceive any general orientation in the mineral structures of the rock. Evidence of fluxion-banding is rarely seen and has probably been obliterated in the general crushing which the rock has undergone. The most careful search has not disclosed any symptoms of folding either in the main outcrop or at its edges. Probably the best evidence is afforded by the sand-scoured boulders on the shores at Coverack and Lowland Point (Pl. IXA). In these there seem to be indications that the rock is often a coarse breccia of which the broken fragments have been veined and recemented by later injections, usually paler in colour and more feldspathic than the original mass, and often in turn crushed and torn apart by later movements. Crushing was apparently in progress after a large part of the rock had crystallized but new magma was still being introduced, and this, in turn, was shattered by movement shortly after it solidified. These later veins have no consistent orientation but interlace and intersect one another in all directions.

In the cliffs on the east side of the Lizard between Polbarrow and Pen Voose a remarkable mass of gabbro makes its appearance. Very little evidence of it is seen inland though a few large blocks and many small fragments may be found in the fields on the east side of Trethevas. There are at least two faults which bring in the serpentine and the hornblende-schists at Polbarrow, to the north, and to the south this gabbro makes its final appearance in the cliffs on the north of Pen Voose Cove. In the cliff path past The Chair there are many small outcrops of serpentine, gabbro, banded gneiss and pink granite-gneiss but no continuous exposure of any of these rocks. Much of the cliff is impracticable and the best means of examining the exposures in them and in the reefs is by means of a boat from Church Cove or Cadgwith. The sections are of a very extraordinary character. The serpentine occurs in detached masses, cut and enveloped by irregular veins and sills of gabbro, which in turn is penetrated by many sills and shapeless intrusions of banded gneiss and red felsitic gneiss. The most accessible exposure is that which occurs on the north wall of the north cove of Pen Voose where these four types of rocks are mixed together in great confusion. These sections have given rise to much discussion in the literature of Lizard geology and have been variously interpreted. They are certainly exceedingly complicated but in view of the general facts to be established regarding the sequence of the Lizard rocks in the whole province the succession is sufficiently clear. The gneisses cut the gabbro and the gabbro cuts the serpentine and each rock contains many xenoliths of the types that preceded it. As usual in the Lizard cliffs, there are many faults, with displacements of varying and mostly of unknown magnitude, and this must be allowed for in interpreting the individual sections. This mass of gabbro (and the banded gneisses which are mingled with it) is probably the western edge of

intrusions of considerable size that are covered by the waters of
Kennack Bay to the eastward.

The troctolite of Coverack has long been known and its
macroscopic characters are familiar to most students of British
petrography.   It is restricted to that neighbourhood, where it
occurs in the beach on both sides of the village.   On the north it
is well seen in the shore from the west side of the harbour for a
distance of four hundred yards to the churchyard.   It forms
irregular masses or small bosses with rounded or sinuous margins

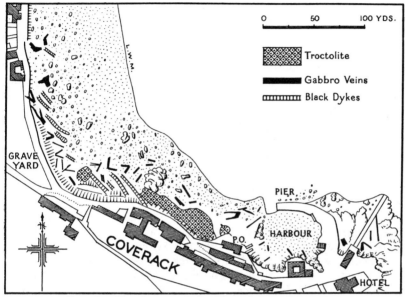

FIG. 9.—*Sketch-map of the Shore below Coverack.*

Coverack stands on serpentine in which there are numerous intrusions of
troctolite, gabbro and epidiorite.   The troctolite occurs in several masses near
the base of the cliffs and occasionally also in veins in the serpentine.   The
gabbro veins are very numerous and only a few of them are shown; they are
in various stages of metamorphism.   There are also about a dozen black
dykes which have a well defined north-west trend, cutting serpentine, troctolite and gabbro and showing only a low stage of metamorphism.   The
edge of the principal intrusive gabbro mass is near the north margin of the
map.

and the best exposures are just below the cliff where it is covered
by raised beach and ' head.'   Dykes of troctolite are also present
and they contain many inclusions of serpentine.   Both the bosses
and the dykes of troctolite are cut by numerous gabbro dykes so
that the sequence is quite clear.   The troctolite is newer than the
serpentine and older than the gabbro; hence it has sometimes been
called the ' older gabbro.'   In the exposures above described the
troctolite is often a dark red rock with white spots of feldspar.
It seems to be very rich in olivine which has weathered to a reddish
serpentine.   The troctolite on the other hand which occurs on the

south of Coverack, in Perprean Cove, has usually a dark green colour. Irregular outcrops of this troctolite may be seen in several parts of the beach in the north-west corner of Perprean Cove. In this locality also it makes little appearance in the low rocky cliff and cannot be traced inland. Instances of troctolite cutting the serpentine are quite common also in this locality.

It may be remarked that all the troctolite is a normal igneous rock. It shows little evidence of fluxion and it is not crushed or metamorphic. The olivine occurs in rounded crystals or clusters of small grains; the feldspar forms a general matrix enclosing the olivine and is penetrated by numerous radiating cracks filled with green serpentine and probably occasioned by the expansion of the olivine consequent on hydration and serpentinization. It is a curious and significant fact that the troctolite shows no evidence of crushing and recrystallization while the serpentine, which preceded, and the gabbro which followed it are practically invariably metamorphic rocks. This leads to the conclusion that the serpentine and the gabbro were injected in periods of stress, crushing, movement (and possibly folding) which were separated by a period of calm during which the troctolite was introduced and completed its crystallization as a normal igneous rock.

THE GABBRO DYKES

Gabbro dykes occur in the Lizard in great numbers but their distribution is exceedingly irregular. West of the Lizard road there are few. No gabbro dykes are known at Mullion but Fox and Teall describe one at Pol Cornick. None is seen in George's Cove or on the coast south to The Rill. There are two small shreds of gabbro dykes at Kynance, difficult to find, and very impersistent. There is at least one dyke in the cliff north of the Lion Rock but none in Holestrow or Pentreath. On the east coast, as previously described, irregular gabbro intrusions are abundant in the cliffs between Pen Voose and Carn Barrow. About Cadgwith no gabbro dykes are known but there are several dykes of saussurite on Enys Head, and in the serpentine cliffs from there north to Carleon Cove several dykes, much dislocated, may be observed. Mere scraps of gabbro intrusions may be seen in the cliff at the south of the storm beach at Poltesco. From that cove north to Kennack Corner gabbro occurs every here and there, one fairly large dyke being just north of Polbream Point. A very well known dyke is seen in the cliff just south of Kennack Gate. It is about nine inches thick and is stepped for a few feet by three little faults, and is also cut across by a two-foot epidiorite dyke. On the east side of Kennack gabbro dykes begin to be numerous especially after passing the Green Saddle. About Poldowrian and Compass Cove several may be seen in many of the little coves. They are numerous in Spernic Cove and Lankidden on each side of the great spectacular dyke of Carrick Luz. Around the Black Head there

PLATE VIII

(A 7426)

B. KENNACK COVE, NORTH-WEST CORNER.
BANDED GNEISS DYKE IN SERPENTINE

(A 7495)

A. COVERACK, BELOW THE CHURCHYARD.
GABBRO DYKES IN SERPENTINE

are many gabbro dykes though the precipitous cliffs of serpentine
are often inaccessible and debar inspection, but at Downas Cove
and Beagles Point there are curious and interesting injections of
gabbro. From the Black Head to Dolor Point there are many
dykes and veins of gabbro, often cut across by black dykes, though
sometimes for a space they occupy the same fissure. From Dolor
Point to the North Corner of Coverack gabbro dykes occur in
extraordinary numbers. In the south side of the little harbour of
Coverack, in a distance of sixty five yards, there are thirteen gabbro

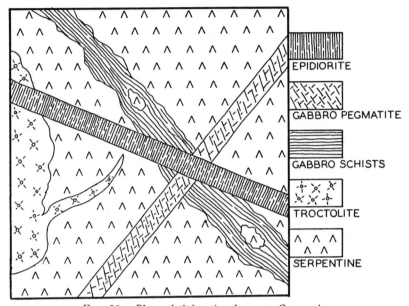

FIG. 10.—*Plan of dykes in shore at Coverack.*

At Coverack the country rock is bastite-serpentine; into this a small boss
(or several bosses) of troctolite are intruded. The troctolite sends veins into
the serpentine. There are also many dykes of gabbro in the serpentine, some
of them foliated or schistose while others are nearly normal igneous rocks.
The serpentine, troctolite and gabbro are cut by black dykes of epidiorite which
show little metamorphism.

dykes or fragments of dykes, some of them only a few feet but
others several yards in length (Pl. XIA). From Coverack pier to the
North Corner, a distance of less than half a mile, there are well
over a hundred dykes exposed in the cliff and in the beach at low
water. North of the junction of serpentine and gabbro at Coverack
no gabbro dykes are known except a small one at Porthallow, of
which fragments are fairly common in the debris on the shore east
of the Five Pilchards inn.

To summarize, it may be said that the gabbro dykes never cut
the hornblende-schists and mica-schists; in a few places there are
coarse feldspathic veins in the hornblende-schists but they do not
contain diallage and they seem to be pegmatitic veins in originally

intrusive dolerites now converted into coarse hornblende-schist. Examples are seen in the quarries at Mullion Cove and Porthkerris; they occasionally contain quartz, which is never seen in the gabbros. No gabbro veins cut the gabbro, but it may be admitted that unless they showed marked chilled edges gabbro veins in gabbro would be hard to distinguish. There are in the gabbro, however, many streaks of gabbro-pegmatite, of late consolidation. The gabbros never cut the banded gneisses, which of course are of later origin. It is only in the serpentine that gabbro dykes are found and they are common only in the district between Coverack and Kennack, that is to say in proximity to the intrusive margin of the gabbro. Taken as a whole it seems probable that they belong to a period following the intrusion of the troctolite and preceding or accompanying the injection of the main gabbro mass.

In breadth the gabbro dykes vary from fractions of an inch to several yards, but most of them range between one foot and four feet. Not infrequently they have straight parallel edges but many of them are wedge-shaped, twisting or irregular in direction. Parallel sets of dykes are occasionally seen and the thicker dykes or veins may give off branches (Pl. VIIIA). As a rule individual dykes cannot be traced for more than a few yards but die out or are shifted by faults. In many respects the great dyke of Carrick Luz is exceptional. It has nearly parallel edges, is two hundred yards in breadth and can be traced for several hundred yards. Like many other dykes it is not strictly homogeneous but the proportion of its minerals varies slightly from point to point though it does not exhibit definite flow-banding. Most of the dykes seem to have the same average composition as the main gabbro, and, like the gabbro, have often later veins which are more feldspathic than the general rock.

As a rule the gabbro of the dykes is rather coarsely crystalline, the minerals being usually from a quarter of an inch to half an inch in diameter. Fine-grained dykes are rare, and in this respect the gabbro contrasts strongly with the epidiorite dykes which followed it. Very coarse-grained gabbro-pegmatites are a feature of the shore below Coverack. Several observers have noted a block on the beach there with crystals of diallage seven inches in diameter, and many of the dykes have diallage crystals which measure from one inch to two inches. Very coarse gabbro belonging to the Polbarrow mass can be seen in blocks at the north end of Pen Voose, and occasional dykes of gabbro-pegmatite have been noted as far inland as Ruan Minor. The gabbros of Porthallow and of Kynance are also coarsely crystalline. It is also to be remarked that the gabbro, even in thin veins, never shows definite chilled edges: dykes half a foot thick are not fine-grained but differ little from the larger intrusions. From these facts it seems a fair inference that when the gabbro mass and the gabbro dykes were intruded the serpentine that forms the country rock was still at a rather high temperature.

By far the most interesting and instructive feature of the gabbro dykes of the Lizard is their metamorphism. In this respect they vary enormously. Practically none of the dykes is absolutely normal. There is a ten-inch gabbro dyke in the rocks on Dolor Point a few yards east of the lifeboat pier which is rather fine-grained and differs little from a normal olivine-gabbro; and some of the coarse pegmatite dykes on the Coverack shore are remarkably free from signs of recrystallization, but the great majority of the Lizard gabbro dykes are in a condition very similar to that of the grey-green gabbro, that is to say their olivine has vanished, the diallage is to a large extent replaced by sheaves of actinolite, and the feldspar is cheesy and saussuritic. In the Carrick Luz dyke a very beautiful augen structure has been produced and has been admirably figured in Teall's ' British Petrography ' (Pl. XXVI). The diallage usually forms the ' augen ' round which the feldspar flows, and the ellipsoids of diallage have a parallel orientation which in the field is steeply inclined or nearly vertical. A further stage in the development of foliation is reached by the production of a gabbro-schist with a perfect linear or plane arrangement of the constituent minerals. In this stage the diallage has disappeared, and actinolite and epidote or zoisite are the characteristic minerals. The gabbro-schist seldom forms the whole of a dyke but mostly occurs as streaks and bands in the flaser-gabbro; sometimes these are visibly connected with planes of movement and displacement but often they appear in a sporadic manner as if movement induced by pressure had been concentrated in certain parts of the rock mass and the remainder had in some measure escaped crushing.

In a schistose gabbro dyke the schistosity, foliation or augen structure is always, in a general sense, parallel to the walls of the dyke. If the dyke is straight, like the Carrick Luz dyke, the augen structure also is pretty uniform in direction; if a dyke bends or branches the foliation also is diverted. Where some dykes taper to an end the foliation tends to converge. The bounding walls seem to have closed together and compressed the dyke mass; no doubt also the plastic matter of the dyke was squeezed forward and may have been forced into cracks in the adjacent rock. The development of schistosity may vary greatly in different parts of the same dyke. Still more extraordinary is the fact that adjacent dykes differ greatly in metamorphism. On the Coverack shore highly schistose dykes are seen side by side with dykes in which the original minerals and structures are in good preservation. Nearly normal gabbro dykes may cut highly schistose gabbro dykes, and in some cases the converse may be observed. Apparently each dyke passed through a stage in which it was especially susceptible to pressure (probably after crystallization was completed but before cooling down) and after that stage it became more resistant. There is much evidence that rock-making minerals tend to become plastic at high temperatures. It is also probable that the pressures were intermittent or spasmodic and that the dykes were not all injected at the same time, so that when increase of pressure supervened some dykes were comparatively cold while others were still hot and in a sensitive condition.

All the dykes of gabbro definitely cut across the flow-banding and also the fluxion-foliation of the serpentine. Obviously the metamorphism of the serpentine belonged to a period anterior to

Fig 11.—*Boulder of Gabbro, Pen Voose.*

This boulder shows contorted banding of dark pyroxenic or actinolitic and pale feldspathic or saussuritic folia, with augen structure in places. The boulder measures two feet six inches, by two feet. (A 7451).

the injection and crushing of the gabbro. Even more remarkable is the fact that the serpentine adjacent to the gabbro dykes usually shows little sign of the development of a new foliation parallel to the dyke. A little secondary foliation of this type is occasionally observable in the serpentine walls of gabbro dykes at Compass Cove and Lankidden Cove but it is never conspicuous. It seems clear that the serpentine was a much tougher rock than the gabbro when the latter was crushed, and possibly the gabbro passed through a stage in which pressure acted on it very readily and this stage lasted only a short time.

(A 749

A. Coverack Shore. Block of gabbro, showing
        brecciform structure

PLATE IX

B. Coverack. Block of bastite-serpentine, with
        reticulate weathering

(A 749

The next episode in the history of Lizard geology is the intrusion of a great series of dolerite dykes and these cut clean through the gabbro and all its structures and foliation. But in the interval the serpentine and gabbro had been subjected to numerous movements which are mostly of the nature of faults or thrusts, with displacements of a few yards. The outcrops of gabbro dykes are shifted laterally and sometimes in the fault fissures the dolerite dykes are intruded. This is the reason why so few of the gabbro dykes can be followed for any distance. Sometimes the gabbro dykes are wrenched across and separated masses may be scattered in the plane of movement; at other times they are severed completely and their continuations are lost. In these movements the dolerite dykes do not share : neither do they partake in the foliation of the gabbro. Excellent examples of this can be seen in the Coverack shore. From these phenomena we are led to infer that after or during the intrusion of the gabbro dykes, and the production of the major part of their metamorphism, but before the injection of the dolerite dykes, there was a period when much movement of the nature of faulting was going on in the serpentine. The reason for this is not easy to assign; possibly it was connected with the intrusion of the main masses of gabbro, but it is not confined to the vicinity of the principal gabbro masses as it occurs also on the west side of the Lizard and at Kynance. The gabbro veins appear as scraps and shreds but the black dykes maintain their dyke-like character and, except locally where they have been involved in movements and pressures of special intensity, preserve their original igneous structures much better than the gabbro dykes.

The petrography of the Lizard gabbros has been very fully described by Teall (1886, 1888). The following are the principal varieties of the gabbro.

(a) The black gabbro, a massive, coal-black rock of unmodified igneous structure; fairly coarsely crystalline; often rich in fresh olivine; all the minerals feldspar, diallage and olivine are intensely schillerized—hence the black colour. The black gabbro is found at Polcoverack (6709), the North Corner of Coverack (6368) and the coast for half a mile north of this (6735).

(b) The grey-green gabbro, a flaser-gabbro in which the minerals are wholly or partly metamorphosed; actinolite replaces olivine completely and diallage, more or less; feldspar is often crushed and permeated by actinolite; schillerization is preserved only in the residual kernels of diallage; the feldspar is often saussuritic; sphene grows around the iron ores. This is the prevalent type in Crousa Down, St. Keverne and Coverack. The minerals seldom have a pronounced parallel arrangement.

(c) The augen gabbro. This is especially characteristic of the Carrick Luz intrusion but is developed locally in all districts of the flaser-gabbro. The 'augen' are diallage crystals with rims and tails of actinolite; the surrounding matrix is feldspar, often saussuritic and charged with prismatic actinolite.

(d) The gabbro-schist, consisting of crushed feldspar and actinolite, with iron ores, sphene and apatite, having a straight or curved schistosity; this appears often in dykes and in crush-zones, but though common is never developed on a large scale (6365 Compass Cove, 6686 Poldowrian).

(e) The gabbro-pegmatite, very coarsely crystalline and generally of nearly normal igneous structure though seldom perfect. It may show weathered olivine. Common in dykes on Coverack shore and not infrequent at Pol-barrow and elsewhere. In the grey-green gabbro pegmatitic streaks or segregations are widespread.

(f) The white gabbro. This unusual rock may be as white as marble. It consists of feldspar and white pyroxene (malacolite) and is not schillerized. The best locality is Spernic Cove (7448) on the west side of Carrick Luz. It occurs also near Gwenter but is scarce.

(g) The granulitic gabbro. In this variety the minerals, feldspar and pale diopside (or malacolite) are crushed to a granulitic mosaic. Actinolite is not developed and the feldspar is clear and fresh. Probably the crushing took place at a high temperature. The only localities are Spernic Cove (7616) and Gwenter (Pl. VII, 6).

(h) The saussurite-gabbro. Veins of a dull, greenish white substance, sometimes with a little diallage, occur in serpentine at Enys Head, Little Cove, Polbream and in many other places. The saussurite is a fine-grained aggregate of zoisite and a reddish brown granular mineral which may be garnet but has not been identified. In some dykes on Enys Head, colourless, rounded garnets are present.

(i) The brecciform gabbro. On the shore at Pen Voose, Coverack and Downas Cove, blocks of gabbro may be seen (Pl. IX A) which have been scoured by the sand of the beach. They often show a complicated structure as if the rock had been broken up and then injected by new magma which cemented the fragments together; the process may have been several times repeated; the earlier fragments are usually fine-grained; the latest veins are pegmatitic. All components show shearing and metamorphism but in varying degree. Possibly these brecciform gabbros come from dykes or veins which have been subject to repeated crushing and injection. They are not known in the interior parts of the St. Keverne gabbro.

ANALYSES OF GABBRO, TROCTOLITE, ETC.

	I.	II.	III.	IV.
SiO_2	50.69	45.73	46.39	42.20
Al_2O_3	20.56	22.10	26.34	17.56
Fe_2O_3	1.55	0.71	2.02	1.20
FeO	3.10	3.51	3.15	6.33
MgO	6.84	11.46	4.82	20.38
CaO	11.99	9.26	15.29	9.61
Na_2O	3.36	2.54	1.63	1.11
K_2O	n.f.	0.34	0.20	0.11
H_2O above $105°$ C.	0.94	} 4.38 {	0.48	1.13
H_2O at $105°$ C ...	0.18		0.10	0.06
TiO_2	0.42	—	0.26	0.09
P_2O_5	0.05	—	—	—
MnO	0.16	—	0.14	0.18
CO_2	n.f.	—	—	tr.
FeS_2	0.11	—	—	0.02 S
Cr_2O_3	0.08	—	tr.	0.06
V_2O_3	0.02	—	—	—
(Ni, Co) O... ...	n.f.	—	—	0.13
BaO	n.f.	—	—	—
Li_2O	tr.	—	—	0.04
CuO	—	—	—	0.04
Total ...	100.05	100.03	100.82	100.21

I. Fresh olivine-gabbro, from blocks at roadside about 400 yards west of Polcoverack, near Coverack [E.6709]. (Anal. E. G. Radley.)

II. Troctolite of Coverack (Anal. F. T. S. Houghton), *Geol. Mag.*, 1879, p. 505.
III. Olivine-gabbro, Cuillin Hills, Skye [S.8043] (Anal. W. Pollard), cited from A. Harker, ' Tertiary Igneous Rocks of Skye ' (*Mem. Geol. Surv.*), 1904, p. 103.
IV. Allivalite (anorthite-olivine rock), Allival, Rum [S.10464] (Anal. W. Pollard), cited from A. Harker, ' Geology of the Small Isles ' (*Mem. Geol. Surv.*), 1908, p. 80.

ANALYSES OF MINERALS FROM GABBRO, TROCTOLITE, ETC.

	I.	II.	III.	IV.	V.
SiO$_2$	49.65	49.9	49.4	48.8	52.8
Al$_2$O$_3$	29.35	6.2	29.8	10.6	2.8
Fe$_2$O$_3$	} 0.59 {	1.7	1.2	1.7	1.8
FeO		3.9	—	4.7	—
MgO	0.46	16.1	1.7	18.6	16.6
CaO	12.18	20.4	12.6	12.2	25.2
Na$_2$O	3.61	—	3.3	—	—
K$_2$O	0.48	—	0.4	—	—
H$_2$O	3.19	0.9	1.7	1.8	0.5
TiO$_2$	—	—	—	—	—
MnO	—	0.4	—	—	—
Cr$_2$O$_3$	—	0.6	—	tr.	—
Total ...	99.51	100.1	100.1	98.4	99.7

I. Feldspar from the troctolite of Coverack (Anal. F. T. S. Houghton), *Geol. Mag.*, 1879, p. 505.
II. Chrome-diopside from gabbro of Coverack (Anal. J. H. Player), quoted from J. J. H. Teall, ' Notes on some Minerals from the Lizard.' *Mineral. Mag.*, vol. 8, 1889, p. 116.
III. Labradorite from the same rock as II. (Anal. J. H. Player), *ibid.*
IV. Hornblende from gabbro-schist, Pen Voose (Anal. J. H. Player), *ibid.*
V. Malacolite from gabbro, Carrick Luz (Anal. J. J. H. Teall), *ibid.*

The analysis of the gabbro I. shows abundance of lime and alumina, which makes a striking contrast with the composition of the serpentine. The Skye gabbro III is evidently a much more basic rock. The feldspar analyses indicate that the principal feldspar is labradorite (approaching bytownite). The malacolite pyroxene of the ' white gabbro ' contains little iron or alumina and has a very exceptional composition for the pyroxene of an igneous rock.

CHAPTER IX

THE EPIDIORITE DYKES

THE dykes of epidiorite, or ' black dykes ', are in some respects the most normal igneous rocks in the Lizard. They occur typically as vertical dykes with parallel walls and as they often have columnar cross-jointing they are not unlike the Tertiary dykes of the west of Scotland. As a rule they take a straight course across country and in the rocky shores they can sometimes be traced for a hundred yards or more. They seldom branch and though they may contain inclusions of serpentine or gabbro they are mostly free from xenoliths. Their average width is perhaps three or four feet; dykes a few inches thick are rare but some of the dykes near Manacle Point may have a breadth of five to ten yards. No large intrusions, laccolites or thick sills, belonging to this group have been observed. They are not always vertical but may occur as inclined sills sloping at an angle of forty-five degrees, or less, to the horizon.

In colour they are always black or very dark green in strong sunlight and they are invariably fine-grained, in which respect they contrast very strongly with the gabbro dykes and veins which they often intersect. It seems clear that after the injection of the gabbro a considerable period elapsed during which the rock masses cooled down, and when the black dykes were injected they crystallized rapidly. Chilled edges, though never glassy, are quite common. Residual igneous structures are often visible, usually porphyritic crystals of feldspar with sharply rectangular outlines, but the rocks are very rarely vesicular and as a rule they do not show flow-banding.

The microscope, however, reveals that practically all these dykes are metamorphic. Although many sections have been cut, hardly one of them is a normal olivine-dolerite. Remains of olivine and of augite have been seen occasionally and the feldspar crystals often have lath-shaped sections; but between them there is a dense matrix of bright green pleochroic amphibole which occurs in fine fibres densely clotted together or in small prisms which rarely show the characteristic outlines of hornblende. Sometimes these fibrous aggregates surround the feldspar in a manner which seems to indicate an originally ophitic structure, but equally commonly there is a tendency to parallel orientation and the development of an inconspicuous schistosity. This may be especially pronounced where fault planes displace the dykes or where they are locally bent out of their normal course. In a special group of these dykes, which will be described later, they have been converted into typical hornblende-schists, but the vast majority at first glance in the field seem little different from normal basic igneous rocks. The period during which these dykes were injected appears to have been one of comparative quiescence, when movement took place only on a small scale and locally. It is difficult to reconcile the almost perfect preservation of their dyke-like character, in relation to the rocks around them, with the not inconsiderable alteration of their original mineral constitution.

Like the gabbro dykes, the black dykes show great irregularity in their distribution in different areas of the peninsula. On two parts of the coast they occur in great numbers. From the Black Head north to Chynhalls, black dykes are seen in every little creek : in a distance of five hundred yards south of the Headlands Hotel, there are seventeen black dykes (one in every thirty yards) and they are even more common on the east side of the Black Head. In the foreshore at Coverack there are six or eight black dykes which can be seen in the low cliff and traced across the shore; in regularity of direction, in continuity and in state of metamorphism, they offer a striking contrast to the numerous dykes of gabbro at that locality (Pl. XIA). For a mile north of the North Corner of Coverack there are not many black dykes in the gabbro but before Lowland Point is reached they increase in number and from thence by Dean Point to Manacle Point they are very numerous. About Godrevy Cove, Manacle Point and the south shore of Porthoustock Cove the black dykes occur every few yards; in some cases two of them occupy the same fissure. They range from six inches up to thirty feet in breadth, are mostly straight and parallel and have often finely crystalline chilled edges. The centres of the thicker dykes are more coarsely crystalline than usual but in this respect never approach even the thinnest of the gabbro dykes. Along the south shore of Porthoustock Cove the black dykes seem to occupy as much space as the gabbro. In the road-stone quarries there the epidiorite forms at least one half of the mass. In the inland district about Rosenithon and St. Keverne, there are few good exposures of solid rock. The gabbro weathers in large conspicuous blocks while the epidiorites are finely jointed and break down into small angular fragments, and there are few outcrops of epidiorite, but an examination of the debris in the fields and of the local exposures in farmyards, roadsides and old ' marl ' pits shows that epidiorite is everywhere present in great abundance. De la Beche seems to have been so much impressed by the abundance of epidiorite in this district that he coloured this ground as ' greenstone ' in the first edition of the one-inch geological map.

In the rest of the Lizard district the epidiorite dykes are not so common as on the eastern shore from Porthoustock to the Black Head. On the south coast from the Black Head to Kennack they occur in considerable numbers though not so commonly as the gabbro dykes. Black dykes are seen at Beagles Point and the mouth of the Downas Stream. On both sides of Carrick Luz black dykes are present in the serpentine. From Carrick Luz to Kennack there are many dark dykes exposed in the cliffs though gabbro dykes are more numerous from Compass Cove eastwards.

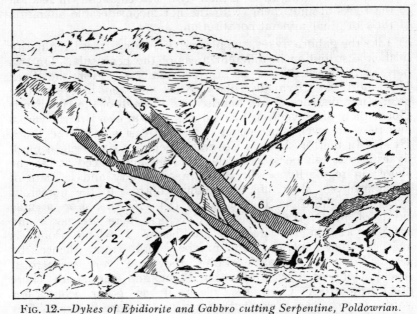

FIG. 12.—*Dykes of Epidiorite and Gabbro cutting Serpentine, Poldowrian.*
The cliff consists of coarsely crystalline bastite-serpentine in which fluxion-banding is visible at 1 and 2. This banding is cut by gabbro veins (3 and 4). These gabbros are distinctly schistose. The gabbro veins are transected by two slanting epidiorite sills, connected by a branch (5, 6, 7), which are slightly schistose in places.

In this district many of the dykes take the form of inclined sills which may be seven to ten feet in thickness. An excellent example is visible about four hundred yards south-west of Poldowrian, where two slanting sills are connected by a branch and cut the gabbro dykes and the flow-banding of the serpentine. Other inclined sills occur between Poldowrian and the east side of Kennack and there is a well known example where the cliff path joins the storm beach at the east end of the sands. This dyke is about five feet thick and contains a large slab of serpentine; it dips east-south-east at less than forty degrees and appears very

massive with only slight traces of schistosity; in the beach below
the cliff it is shifted by a fault but reappears among the boulders a
short distance to the east. There is much faulting in the serpentine at this locality. Kennack Cove is divided into two parts by
a projecting knoll of serpentine which passes seawards into the
tidal reef known as the Caerverracks. On the west side of the
serpentine knoll there is a thin inclined sill, two or three feet thick,
rather irregular and branching. In places the dark rock is
schistose. It appears also in a little cove on the south-west corner
of the knoll and has been shifted by small faults. This dyke also
dips nearly east at an angle of thirty-five degrees and evidently
belongs to the same group as the one at the east corner of Kennack.
On the west side of Kennack from the Gate south to Carleon Cove,
black dykes are not uncommon. In the cliff about sixty yards
south of the Gate there is one which has often been described. It
is from two to three feet thick and vertical, running nearly north
and south, and cuts across a little headland. A thin gabbro dyke,
about nine inches thick, is cut clean through by the black dyke;
the gabbro has been faulted by three small faults which do not
seem to affect the black dyke. The gabbro is rather massive but
not fresh. On the south of the little headland the black dyke is
crossed by a small fault and the separated ends have developed an
incipient schistosity. The black dyke ceases abruptly to the south
where it is cut across by an intrusion of banded gneiss. Another
black dyke is seen in the cliff a few yards farther south. It is
mixed up with a reddish feldspathic intrusion of banded gneiss.

About Polbream Point there are several black dykes in the
serpentine and also not infrequent veins of gabbro. At the base
of a grassy slope about 300 yds. north of Polbream Point there is
an injection of epidiorite into gabbro which cuts the serpentine
and the whole series is in turn injected by banded gneiss. At the
south corner of Carleon Cove there is a black dyke cutting serpentine with many veins of gabbro spattered through the rock. This
dyke is about five feet thick and though not fresh it is very much
of a normal dyke in its behaviour; its direction is a little north of
west. Other dykes occur in several places between Carleon and
Enys Head and on that headland, below the grassy slope, several
black dykes are seen in the serpentine. They are in a rotten condition such as has usually been described as ʻpotstone.ʼ No
black dykes are known at Cadgwith or in the hornblende-schists
to north and south of the cove, but at Polbarrow and between there
and The Chair there are intrusions of this group, mostly as veins
and streaks in the *mélange* of intrusive rocks (serpentine, gabbro
and gneiss) rather than discrete and individual dykes. At Pen
Voose there is no black dyke, and in the hornblende-schists and
mica-schists forming the cliffs thence to Pentreath, the basic intrusions belong to a special group to be afterwards described.

Where the serpentine reaches the coast again at the south end
of Pentreath Beach the black dykes reappear, though they are not

so numerous as on the east coast at Kennack.   One is visible a little
north of the middle of the Beach and at the north end there are two
or three in a bold cliff of serpentine. They cannot be followed to the
top of the cliff.   The most interesting, however, occurs in a little
cove about fifty yards north of the steps at the south end of the
beach.   Here is a slanting sill, partly converted into schist, and
in the adjacent serpentine cliff there are several large separate
masses that look like xenoliths, and might easily give rise to mis-
interpretation.   These masses are not visibly schistose and the
slanting sill probably occupies a plane of movement.

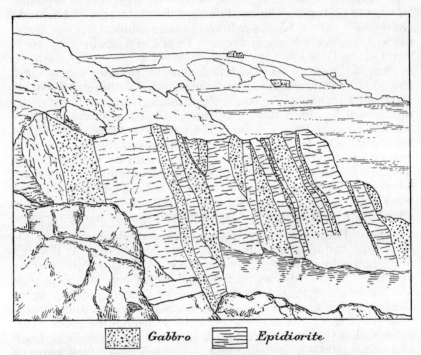

Gabbro   Epidiorite

FIG. 13.—*Epidiorite dykes cutting gabbro at Porthoustock Point.*

The gabbro is coarse-grained and is the country rock.   The epidiorite dykes
are fine-grained with chilled edges, range in thickness from seven feet to
nine inches or less, and have suffered comparatively little metamorphism.
Occasionally two dykes occupy the same fissure.

From Pentreath Beach to Kynance the serpentine cliffs contain
several basic intrusions, some of which have been described by
Fox and Teall in the cove north of the Lion Rock.   At Kynance
Cove there are no black dykes but in little notches in the cliffs to
the east two such dykes are seen but cannot be traced for more than
a few yards.   Along the west coast by the Rill Head, basic dykes
are scarce or absent.   They occur again at Pengersick, and, where
the junction of schist and serpentine forms the face of the cliffs at
George's Cove and Pol Cornick, black dykes make their appear-

ance and were described by Fox and Teall (1893). They are interesting because they cut the interbanded complex of serpentine and schist and the black dykes are apparently absent from the country that consists of hornblende-schist. In the wide stretch of ground between Mullion and Porthallow no black dykes have been identified, and as there are excellent coast sections of this tract on both sides of the peninsula, they must be scarce if present. It is a striking fact that these basic dykes are so numerous in the gabbro south of Porthoustock Cove and absent from the horn-blende-schist on the north of the Cove. In the inland areas of serpentine and gabbro there are probably many black dykes, as fragments that undoubtedly belong to them may often be picked up on the surface though there are no outcrops. Occasionally, however, they are seen in the quarries, as at Countybridge, the roadside south of Trevassack and near Kernewas.

A very marked feature of this system of dykes is the prevalence of a north-westerly trend. This is very characteristic of the great series of dykes around Manacle Point and throughout the northern part of the gabbro. It is also very consistent in the Coverack dykes and is again exhibited in the numerous dykes injected into the serpentine between Coverack and the Black Head. The great majority of the dykes along this eastern coast have a trend which ranges from north-north-west to west-north-west. Along the coast from the Black Head to Church Cove, Landewednack, there are exceptions but they are not very numerous. Some of the inclined sills have a strike which is nearly north and south. Along the west side of Kennack and on Enys Head some of the dykes are tortuous and many are exposed for only short distances, but their general direction varies between west and north. On the west side of the peninsula the same tendency is well marked and the dykes described by Fox and Teall at Pol Cornick have a north-west direction.

The black dykes of the Lizard might be regarded as a ' swarm ' in the sense in which that word has been used in descriptions of the Inner Hebrides. They occur in large numbers, often close together, and have a very consistent orientation. Unlike the Scottish swarms, however, they are not very persistent, for the majority of the dykes of the east coast must have died out before reaching the west coast. In this respect they have more resemblance to the basic dykes of Lundy Island which are not represented on the adjacent mainland.

That the black dykes are occasionally schistose was pointed out by Teall on several occasions (1888, 1893). In the great majority of them the schistosity is far from conspicuous. When examined microscopically they prove to have undergone many changes, and in particular the replacement of olivine and augite by amphiboles, but these changes might be described as paramorphic rather than metamorphic. In certain instances, however, they have been transformed into perfect schists with complete oblitera-

tion of original minerals and structures. These highly schistose
varieties may occur in a dyke otherwise nearly normal, especially
when the dyke suddenly narrows or changes its direction.   But
in not a few localities the black dykes in the serpentine are schistose
throughout : such dykes are usually very thin (only a few inches
in thickness).   That they are dykes and not inclusions of hornblende-schist is proved by the fact that they branch and sometimes
form an interlacing network.   They are not at all conspicuous
and easily escape observation, because they look like thin seams
of decomposed material in the crevices of the serpentine.   A few
readily accessible examples may be cited ; one is at the Kennack
Gate, in the serpentine on the south side ; another is in Carleon
Cove in the serpentine cliff immediately south of the storm beach.
Perhaps the best example is on the old road leading down to
Kynance Cove from the east where the road makes a hair-pin
bend a few yards north of the prominent cliff known as Tor Balk.
The road runs through a cutting in the serpentine about eight
feet deep, and, in the west side, veins of hornblende-schist may be
traced for thirty yards, never more than a foot in thickness and
thinning down to a mere thread.   These veins branch and bend,
and enclose in one place a lump of serpentine.   The hornblende-
schist is very rotten and crumbles into powder in the hand.   A
little further south, nearer the bend of the road, there is a mass of
dark, fine-grained rock on the east side of the cutting, probably
the source from which the thin veins proceeded, and several yards
farther south outcrops of pale feldspathic gneiss are seen in the
serpentine.

The occurrence of schistose and of nearly massive facies of the
black dykes is quite on a parallel with the phenomena that have
already been described in the gabbro dykes.   These thin veins of
hornblende-schist look as if the basic rock had suddenly been
squeezed when in a plastic condition.   It cannot have been liquid
or the veins might have been tachylytic.   Although crystallized
it was still soft and probably a sudden spasm of pressure forced
the yielding material into the cracks in the serpentine and stamped
on it a pronounced schistosity.

Although typical dykes with parallel vertical walls do not occur
in the hornblende-schists, there are in the mica-schists and hornblende-schists around the Lizard Point, certain basic igneous
rocks that may reasonably be regarded as intrusions.   These are
best seen in the brown mica-schist at Polpeor and between that
cove and Pistil Ogo a few hundred yards to the west (Pl. IIB).
They assume the form of bolster-shaped masses several times as
long as broad, with rounded or tapering ends and from sixteen
feet down to one or two feet in length.   As they are not vesicular
they are clearly not volcanic bombs, and as they occur sometimes
in discontinuous series they seem to be dykes or sills that have
been disrupted by movements in the mica-schists ; adjacent
'bolsters' have very much the same petrological characters.

Similar disruption can be seen in the beds of gritty granulite in the schists. They consist typically of porphyritic dark epidiorite; many feldspar crystals occur in them and have usually not lost their crystalline outlines though sometimes drawn out into lenticular shapes. The surrounding matrix is rich in fibrous or acicular hornblende and usually more or less schistose. In the epidotic hornblende-schist in Pen Olver or on Old Lizard Head, masses of similar porphyritic epidiorite are not infrequent and contrast with the epidotic hornblende-schist in several characters, such as the marked porphyritic structure with abundant feldspar phenocrysts, the absence of epidote and the comparatively ill-developed schistosity. In all probability these are later intrusions of similar origin to the 'bolster' masses at Polpeor. On Venton Hill Point in a small quarry a badly exposed mass of basic rock has ophitic structure with residual augite and is probably an intrusion of the same group though it does not carry porphyritic feldspar.

Many of the gneissic reefs and skerries south of the Lizard Point are traversed by dark dykes of porphyritic epidiorite. These are obviously later than the foliation of the tonalite-gneiss, which they cut across quite sharply, but they are usually metamorphic though in a less degree than the gneisses. In many respects they are not unlike the black dykes of the Lizard, previously described, especially in their basic composition and in their variable though usually not high degree of metamorphism. Their feldspars are usually decomposed and original augite has not been preserved; hornblende or actinolite is the usual dark mineral, with some epidote; in structure they may be fairly massive but some of them are perfect actinolite-schists. They are often shifted by small faults and are not very constant in direction though some of them on the Taylor and the Sanspareil have a north-west trend. Their most striking characteristic, however, is the presence of numerous conspicuous phenocrysts of feldspar; this distinguishes them from the Lizard dykes in which porphyritic feldspars may occur but are by no means so common. These dykes seem to have partaken in the later movements that affected the mica-schists though not involved in the earlier disturbances that produced the full schistosity. On the whole it seems reasonable to assign the Man of War dykes and the epidiorite ' bolsters ' in the Polpeor schists to the same period of intrusion, and to consider them as distinct in age and origin from the basic dykes that penetrate the serpentine and the gabbro of the Lizard and St. Keverne.

The least altered black dykes are found at Coverack (Pl. X, 3). Some of them e.g. 6851 Coverack Corner, 6849 Coverack shore, contain olivine filled with dark grains of iron ore. In others olivine has vanished but some augite remains — 9164 Coverack and 6848, North Corner. Some of the Coverack dykes, however, are schistose epidiorites, 5636 Coverack and 6740 Dolor Point. The usual type of dyke on the east coast has feldspar fairly idiomorphic, sometimes porphyritic, enveloped in a fibrous, clotted or mossy aggregate of secondary green hornblende, strongly suggestive of original ophitic structure, *e.g.* 7686 Ebbor Rocks, 6704 Dean Point, 6681 Beagles Point, 6697 Kilter.   This type is common elsewhere; 5181 George's Cove, 5183 Ogo Dour, 1727 Pol Cornick, 1730 Lion Rock Cove.   Schistose types are equally prevalent, 6208 Carleon Cove, 5176 Kennack west corner, 5155, 5160 Pengersick, 5974 Pentreath Beach, 6679 Lankidden Cove.   The Manacle Point and Porthoustock dykes are usually ophitic or metophitic epidiorites, 15960, 15961, 6363, 6364, also 7442 Trembraze, 6356 Leggan Point, but some are schistose, 6843, 6844 Manacle Point.

Some of the dykes in this quarter resemble fine-grained, granular gabbros, and may be beerbachites; 6249 Porthoustock, 6703 Dean Point, 6342 Tremenhere.   The dykes which cut the Treleague Quartzite resemble the Porthoustock dykes; 6334, 6336, 6343, metophitic epidiorites, 6344 fine feldspathic gabbro.

The black dykes have often suffered great decomposition and have been changed to a soft, friable, massive rock, easily cut and carved; these are the potstones.   Examples are 5159 Pengersick, 6681b Beagles Point, 6846 Porthoustock.

CHAPTER X

KENNACK GNEISSES

OF all the crystalline rocks of the Lizard the Kennack Gneisses are the ones which have given rise to most controversy. The

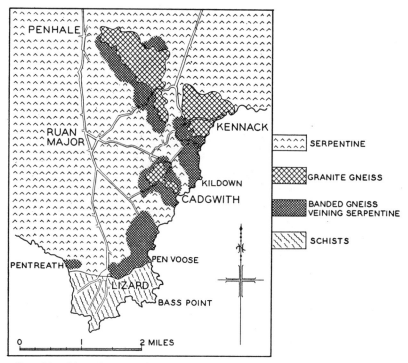

FIG. 14.—*Map showing the principal areas occupied by banded Kennack Gneisses.*

Except at Pen Voose the banded gneisses are found only in the serpentine, forming irregular branching intrusions. They seem to occur as marginal fringes to the principal masses of granite-gneiss.

question whether they were older than, or newer than, the serpentine has been the subject of much discussion. Many observers

who have studied them in the field have remarked their close resemblance to certain parts of the Lewisian Gneiss of the North-
west of Scotland, which were supposed to be the oldest rocks in
Britain. The serpentine, on the other hand, is a deceptive rock,
which, though always metamorphic to a certain degree, looks often
very little different from a normal igneous rock, and at first glance
seems less metamorphic than the banded gneisses. This is

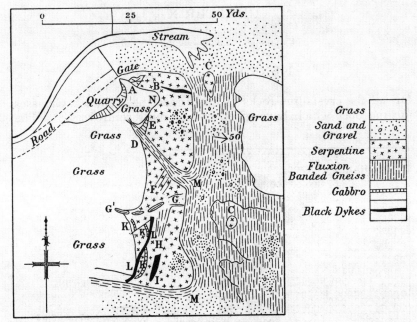

FIG. 15.—*Map showing rocks exposed in the beach at the west side of Kennack
Sands.*

The road leads from Kuggar to the Gate to the north of which is the mouth
of the stream. The cliff is mostly serpentine; below the cliff there is an
intrusive mass of banded gneiss. This contains blocks of serpentine (C.C)
and sends gneiss veins into the serpentine of the cliffs; one of these is a dyke
in good preservation (M.D), another (G.G) has been torn into lenticles. The
banding of the gneiss is roughly parallel to the margin of the serpentine
while at F the fluxion of the serpentine is cut across by the gneiss. A small
gabbro vein occurs at E and a gently sloping gabbro dyke at K.K.K. which
is stepped by small faults and cut across by a black dyke (L). Another black
dyke is seen in the shore at I. The exposures in the beach are often partly
obscured by sand, gravel and boulders.

especially true at Kennack and Pen Voose, the localities at which
these rocks have been most frequently studied. Moreover, certain
facies of the hornblende-schist which have been injected by granite
veins have a great similarity to the banded gneisses, and would
lead to the opinion that these two groups were closely allied. But
on the other hand, certain acid gneisses that belong to the Kennack
Gneiss series have always been regarded as intrusive by geologists
describing the Lizard rocks. Hence there was every possible
occasion for perplexity and confusion.

The best exposures of the banded gneisses are those provided by the cliff sections from Kennack Sands to Pen Voose on the east side of the peninsula. Of these, Pen Voose has been the most frequently described but the rocks there are so jumbled together and intermixed that it is the least easy to interpret. The sections at Kennack and south of Poltesco are much clearer and more convincing. By investigation of these sections it can be established : (a) that the banded gneisses are intrusive into the serpentine, the gabbro and the black dykes; (b) that they contain inclusions of serpentine and gabbro and that the serpentine is contact-altered (pneumatolysed) by the gneisses; (c) that the foliation of the gneisses cuts the foliation of all the older rocks; and (d) that the banded structure of the Kennack Gneisses is essentially due to fluxion in a heterogeneous magma. The facts were first enunciated in a decisive manner by Harford Lowe (1902) though similar conclusions had previously been advanced in a tentative and incomplete manner by Somervail (1888) and Teall (1893).

The Kennack Gneisses consist of a basic and an acid element imperfectly mixed. The basic is black or dark green and is presumably the last portion of the magma from which the black dykes proceeded. In a few places these black dykes contain red, acid, feldspathic streaks which do not seem to be injections from adjacent or contiguous granitic masses. They may be the precursors of the acid portion of the banded gneiss; such dykes may be seen on the west side of Kennack, also at the east corner of Kennack and near Poldowrian. The basic rock is sometimes porphyritic, as at the Cavouga Rock described by Fox (1891), but this is not frequent and the phenocrysts are small and not numerous; it is seldom quite massive but usually shows an imperfect foliation, nearly always less marked than the foliation of the true hornblende-schists: as a rule these basic elements are rather fine-grained, never coarsely crystalline, and they are not epidotic.

The acid portion of the banded gneisses is a white, pinkish or yellowish quartzo-feldspathic rock with abundance of feldspar and obvious quartz. It is less uniform in texture than the basic portion and is sometimes rather coarse, approaching a fine pegmatite, but felsitic varieties also are quite frequent, though never porphyritic. The pure acid constituent seldom carries muscovite and biotite also is scarce. Occasionally it grades into quartz veins, as may be seen at Kennack Corner.

A great part of the banded gneiss may be regarded as having been produced by the reaction of the acid on the basic material. In this way rocks are formed which are neither black nor pale pink. They generally have a grey or brownish colour. The characteristic mineral of this hybrid material is black biotite, and when these rocks are weathered they are often brownish. The pure black material consists mostly of dark green hornblende and feldspar. When biotite appears in it in any quantity there has probably been some interfusion of basic and acid. The typical hybrid material is rich in biotite, which appears in small scales in a quartzo-feldspathic matrix, and the rock is then a fine-grained biotite-gneiss containing also usually a variable proportion of black hornblende.

The acid, intermediate and basic portions of the banded gneiss are very seldom completely blended into a homogeneous mass and never occur in this state to form an outcrop of considerable dimensions. The typical rock has dark and pale stripes contrasting strongly in colour. The breadth of the stripes varies up to several inches but is normally an inch or less. The black bands are less continuous than the pale bands, which often seem to form a matrix enclosing the dark material and dragging it out or stretching it. It is often obvious that the dark material was less fluid or more viscous than the paler material, because the dark bands may be interrupted or discontinuous and the pale bands flow round them and fill the gaps. Possibly also the dark component may have been in some degree softened by the heat of the granitic liquid and by the absorption of acid material.

Fig. 16.—*Fluxion-banded Kennack Gneiss; boulder on shore at Kennack* (*from a photograph*).

The banding of the gneiss may be straight or sinuous. Where the walls that bound the intrusion are visible, the bands are in general parallel to them. If the enclosing rock is serpentine the fluxion of the gneiss is parallel to the junction and as a rule parallel also to the long axis of the gneiss intrusion. The white bands look like the foam streaks on a flooded river which have a direction generally parallel to the course of the stream : but when the gneiss injection bends or where it sends off branches the banding may show undulations and contortions or may locally take a direction that is markedly oblique to the flow of the mixed magma.

Where lumps of serpentine are enclosed in the gneiss the banding always flows around them in a concordant manner, and in the wake of the inclusion the bands gradually draw together to resume their original trend.   All these phenomena are well exemplified in the many intrusions that are exposed in the cliffs between Kennack Gate and Church Cove, and best of all in the sand-scoured boulders on the beach.   As a rule the dark bands are not rod-shaped or linear, but form gently undulating planes; consequently in vertical section the stripes are thin and well defined, but on surfaces that are nearly parallel to the flow-banding or fluxion-foliation the light and dark components may form a flaky irregular pattern with dark patches of indefinite shape enclosed in a reticulate matrix of paler colour.

Fig. 17.—*Venous Kennack Gneiss with granitoid veins penetrating basic hornblendic gneiss, Kennack Sands (from a photograph).*

While the great majority of the gneisses are of the banded type, there are two other varieties that deserve mention.   These are the blocky gneisses and the veined gneisses.   The blocky gneiss contains large blocks of dark material, never angular but always rounded or tapering as if they had been undergoing solution in the acid material.   In Pen Voose two outcrops of this type are well known and have been figured by Teall (1887).   One contains a rounded black lump shaped like a large cannon ball. The other contains an elongated black mass resembling in shape a whale or a porpoise.   These included lumps are generally very basic, showing little biotite.   They were obviously solid when engulfed in the acid magma and may have been derived from the black dykes, though this cannot be proved.

The veined type is produced by the injection of fine, acid veins into a basic or hybrid mass. A good example was figured by Teall from Pen Voose (1887) and typical examples may be seen at Cadgwith. The banded complex in the sands near Kennack Gate is cut by veins of quartz and feldspar, passing into pure quartz veins. In all cases the earliest material is the most basic and the late injections and fine veins are almost pure quartz and feldspar.

Fig. 18.—*Boulder of fluxion-banded Kennack Gneiss, Kennack.*   (A7450)

The intrusions of banded gneiss present a bewildering variety of forms. Some of them are nearly vertical dykes with almost parallel walls. One of this type is seen a few yards south of Kennack Gate (Pl. VIIIB). Others are wedge-shaped or flame-shaped contracting upwards to a point, as, for example, the mass described by Teall and Fox from the cove north of the Lion Rock. In the cliffs between Kennack and Enys Head, however, the commonest form is that of an inclined sill sloping northwards at an angle of about sixty degrees. They often reach the top of the cliff and their original terminations cannot be traced, but their upper and lower surfaces are usually nearly parallel so that they look like steeply inclined sills.   They may be thirty feet or more in thickness, and not infrequently they are accompanied or traversed by faults, which may have the same general direction as the sills or may be gently inclined or nearly horizontal (as seen in the face of the cliff) and shift them laterally.   There are also many gneiss intrusions which are entirely irregular in form.   Below Polbarrow there are some characteristic sills that have a northern dip but there is also much gneissic material that has penetrated the gabbro and serpentine in every direction forming a tangled complex or *mélange* of crystalline rocks in which it is hardly possible to decipher the sequence.   Circular outcrops of gneiss may be seen at the east side of Kennack Sands and between that place and Carrick Luz. They may be bosses or plugs but are more probably arched sills; this is rendered probable by the fact that they sometimes have a central outcrop of serpentine.   In addition there are large masses like the one below the Thorny Cliff at Kennack and the mass on the west of Kennack Sands that may be sills having a breadth of several hundred yards; their boundaries are not sufficiently well seen to define their outlines.   A very thick inclined sill is seen in the north part of Pen Voose Cove.

Not uncommonly the intrusions branch.   This is well seen at Kennack Corner where the large mass in the sands sends numerous thick dyke-like protrusions into the serpentine of the cliffs. The smaller masses also give out branches, or enclose very large masses of serpentine if the branches re-unite.   On Enys Head there is a sill that rises from the sea on the north side and, passing southward, splits into a number of thick branches separated by masses of serpentine.   The fluxion-structure in these branches closely follows the margins of the serpentine or the edge of the intrusions, and there can be no dubiety as to the sequence of the rocks.

Inclusions of serpentine in the banded gneisses are very numerous and may be seen in all good exposures but are commonest in the sills of moderate size.   Their dimensions range from that of an orange to masses of several acres.   One of the largest is the mass at Kennack Corner, just south of the Gate.   Its length is about a hundred and twenty yards and it is riddled with intrusions of gneiss.   Both on the seaward and the landward side the banded gneisses pass around it.   Still larger inclusions of serpentine are found in the granite-gneiss, for example in the fields around Gwendreath.   The smaller inclusions may escape notice because they have been modified by the action of the gneiss, an action which is not purely thermal or contact action, but rather a pneumatolysis or change induced by the operation of the magmatic vapours of the banded gneiss and probably at a comparatively low temperature.   This change consists essentially in the replacement of the original olivine, enstatite, diallage and serpentine of the rock by

hydrous secondary minerals such as talc and chlorite, with tremolite, anthophyllite and haematite or limonite.   There has also been
often an infusion of silica, which yields a certain amount of quartz.
The action is apparently an introduction of water and silica with
probably some alumina and at the same time the removal of
magnesia and iron oxides.   Some of the smaller inclusions have
a dark red colour quite unlike the black or green of the serpentine.
These are rich in tremolite, quartz and haematite.   Enclosed
blocks a yard or two in diameter may be changed to pale green
masses full of chlorite, talc and tremolite, but still showing traces
of the porphyritic enstatite and diallage crystals.   In other cases
the larger blocks of serpentine seem little altered in the interior
but have a fibrous layer adjacent to the gneiss.   The fibres may be
parallel or perpendicular to the mutual boundary and this probably
depends on the amount of relative movement that has taken place.

One of the most interesting features of these serpentine inclusions is their frequent transformation into talc-tremolite-chlorite-
schists.   This is most commonly observed in xenoliths not more
than three or four feet in length.   They have mostly an elongated
or fish-like shape, having been dragged out by the movement of the
viscous surrounding gneiss.   Their pale green surface glistens
with scaly crystals of talc and chlorite and they may be described
as ' ichthyoidal ' masses.   They have usually a schistose structure
throughout and the planes or axes of schistosity are parallel to
those of the enveloping gneiss.   The joint action of pneumatolysis,
metasomatism and directed pressure has changed the massive
igneous serpentine into perfect schists.   Incidentally they prove
that the material of the gneissic sills was being forced along when
it was in a practically solid condition and at a relatively low temperature.

The action of the gneiss upon the serpentine by means of its
magmatic vapour is not confined to the inclusions but appears at
all the junctions of the rocks of these two classes.   It has often
been remarked by writers on Lizard geology that at the meeting
of these two rocks, decomposition appears especially pronounced.
That the change is not normal decomposition due to the action of
percolating surface waters is proved by the fact that it is often
conspicuously absent from the junctions of the serpentine with the
gabbro.   The black dykes apparently have more effect than the
gabbro veins, but their action is quite inconsiderable as compared
with that of the banded gneisses and the granite-gneiss.   Where
the gneiss touches the serpentine there is often a soft, pale, scaly
layer of mingled talc, chlorite and tremolite.   Movement at the
junction has usually arranged the scales and fibres of secondary
minerals parallel to the mutual contact. For several feet the fissures
in the serpentine may be lined with similar material and sometimes
they are occupied with fine tremolitic asbestos.   It has now been
well established that many important deposits of asbestos in serpentine, in Canada, the United States, Rhodesia and elsewhere, have

been produced by the action of vapours exuded from granitic injections into the ultrabasic rock.   In the Lizard there are no deposits of asbestos of commercial value but small specimens may be obtained in many places.   The best known locality is at Kennack, about a hundred yards south of the Gate.   The fibre is short, not over an inch or two, and very hard, as the mineral is usually tremolite and its brittle prisms are seldom flexible.   The fine powdery talc, which also occurs in thin veins, is not sufficiently abundant to be worth exploiting for commercial uses.

There is only one locality in the Lizard where talcose rocks have been extensively quarried.   The ' soap rock ' of Gew-graze on the western coast has long been famous for its peculiar properties. Specimens of this rock can be crushed in the hand like soap; it has also a distinctly soapy feel owing to the abundance of talc. At one time the quarry was worked by Josiah Wedgwood and the rock taken to Staffordshire for the manufacture of pottery. The ' soap rock ' has been produced by the action of a dyke of pink feldspathic granite on the surrounding serpentine.   The dyke is well seen in the cliff above the quarry and the old workings are filled with pieces of the granite which have been thrown away as waste.   Little of the true ' soap rock ' can now be obtained at this locality though in other places in the Lizard such as the north end of Pentreath Beach it is still possible to find some of this material. It is a curious fact that, unlike most deposits of steatite, this one has been formed at the expense of granite not of serpentine.   The ' soap rock ' is a more or less completely steatized granite.   Magmatic vapours from the acid rock have penetrated the serpentine, introducing silica and alumina and dissolving magnesia.   The magnesian solutions in turn have invaded the granite and attacked the feldspar, replacing it to a large extent by scales of talc.   The quartz also has undergone solution and replacement.   When the process is complete the result is a pseudomorph of the granite in steatite.   In most of the specimens that can now be obtained, the replacement is incomplete and the ' soap rock ' contains still a fair amount of alumina.   A large part of the granite dyke has not been steatized or has been altered only slightly, and was thrown on the rubbish heaps during the working of the quarry.

Many of the black dykes that cut the serpentine have also undergone alteration of a similar type.   Their feldspar is changed to a soft aggregate of talcose and sericitic minerals, and the rock, though dark in colour and at first glance not much affected, is so soft that it can be cut with a knife.   As this kind of alteration does not occur in the black dykes that intersect the gabbro there is some reason to believe that it arises from the action of solutions derived from the serpentine.   All the freshest black dykes are found in the gabbro and the dykes in the serpentine are invariably in bad preservation.   The hornblende-schist in contact with the serpentine occasionally seems to have suffered from the same type of alteration.

The distribution of the banded gneisses in the Lizard district is very instructive. None of them is known to occur in the St. Keverne gabbro; on the coast from Carrick Luz by the Black Head and Coverack to Porthallow they have never been observed. West of Carrick Luz they begin to appear and become more numerous as Kennack is approached. From the Green Saddle by Kennack Sands to Kildown there is banded gneiss in practically every little cove. In many places they form one-third to one half of the cliffs. They occupy the south half of Cadgwith Cove and after passing the hornblende-schists of Carn Barrow they reappear as a component of the *mélange* of intrusive rocks between Polbarrow and Pen Voose. On the west coast banded gneisses occur in the serpentine at the north end of Pentreath Beach, in the cove north of the Lion Rock and at Kynance. The picturesque rock scenery of Kynance Cove is in large measure due to the presence of several intrusions of banded gneiss and granite-gneiss in the serpentine. The gneisses are closely jointed and have been eaten out by the sea, forming caves and channels between which the more massive and coarsely jointed serpentine is left standing up as stacks and islets. Very typical banded gneiss and granite-gneiss are seen at Kynance below the hotel and to the west of this near Asparagus Island and The Steeple. They form low rocks almost covered by the sand and boulders of the beach and their true courses and distribution cannot be fully made out; but their presence is sufficiently established and the part they have played in the development of the scenic features is easily realized. West of Kynance there is hardly any banded gneiss though red granite dykes occur here and there; fragments of the gneiss may be picked up on the Kynance and Predannack Downs but none appears in the cliff sections at Ogo Dour or Mullion Cove.

The banded gneisses, like the black dykes, seem to avoid the hornblende-schists. North and south of Cadgwith the serpentine is everywhere permeated by the gneisses, but in the hornblende-schist they are absent. An exception to this rule is possibly provided by the outcrop of schist on the arch leading in to the Devil's Frying Pan; serpentine, schist and gneiss occur there intimately intermixed but this section is one that has puzzled most of the geologists who have described it and different interpretations have been advanced. There may be banded gneiss also in the schist of the Hotel quarry at Cadgwith, but none appears at the Lizard Point, at Predannack, Mullion or Porthallow.

The distribution of the banded gneisses is easily explained if it is understood that they are the marginal intrusions of the principal masses of granite-gneiss. As shown on the one-inch map there are four principal areas of granite-gneiss, Goonhilly, Erisey, Gwendreath and Ruan. Probably also there is a mass of granite-gneiss in Kennack Bay, the continuation seaward of the Gwendreath gneiss, and another may possibly occur off the shore near Polbarrow (Text-fig. 14, p. 99). Between and around these granite masses the serpentine is everywhere permeated by injections of banded gneiss. They were probably the first part of the granite magma and they carried with them the last part of the black dyke magma. The dolerite and the granite refused to blend completely and a banded complex, with many stages of hybridization, was the result. After the composite magma had been intruded, the typical acid magma of the granite-gneiss welled upwards.

The granite-gneiss is the least obtrusive of all the Lizard rocks; its presence was hardly suspected till the ground was mapped on the six-inch scale. On the Lizard coast the granite masses are seen in only one place, Kennack Sands, and even there the outcrop is to a large extent buried beneath ' head ', raised beach and blown sand. The reason why the granite is so inconspicuous is that it weathers more readily than any other rock in the Lizard. Consequently the ground formed by the granite is smooth and grassy with few rocky outcrops. There are no granite tors or crags and nearly all the granite areas are well cultivated. Around the farms are many ' marl ' pits where the decomposed rock has been dug to provide a compost for manuring the fields but quarries in the granite are very scarce because the solid rock is deeply decomposed and concealed beneath a thick layer of subsoil, and the granite, being closely jointed, does not provide large blocks suitable for building houses or stone walls. Only in a few places near Erisey, Gwendreath and Clahar are granite blocks seen in the walls or fields. The mapping of the granite areas, however, is comparatively simple and easy as all the granite masses are intrusive into the serpentine and the latter rock stands out boldly in rocky eminences which surround the level and rather depressed surfaces of the granite outcrops. An exception to this is furnished by the small areas of granite that seem to be quite numerous on Goonhilly and Predannack Downs. There on the surface of the Pliocene platform, fragments of red feldspathic granite can be picked up in many localities, but no boundaries can be laid down for the granite masses which are quite certainly present. These granite outcrops may belong to small intrusions such as are seen in the cliffs at Kynance; as a rule their area is so small that they are not cultivated. The soil on the granite-gneiss differs remarkably from that of the serpentine, being light, friable and rather sandy. It is reddish yellow in colour and full of minute grains of pinkish feldspar and small angular fragments of feldspathic granite, and by these characters there is little difficulty in tracing the extent of the granitic outcrops.

Because of their ready weathering the granitic areas are usually the sites of stream valleys. At Cadgwith, for example, the deep valley of St. Ruan, in which the rectory stands, is certainly to a large extent eroded in rotten granite, which is to be seen in numerous small pits and in the banks of the stream. Similarly the granite of Gwendreath gives rise to the broad valley between Gwendreath and Kuggar. The deep and narrow valley east of Gwendreath probably follows a fault between serpentine and granite. The Erisey granite is crossed by the valleys of two small brooks which unite to form the Polstangey or Poltesco stream. This passes seaward through a narrow valley in serpentine from Poltesco Mill to the sea and the contrast between the rocky slopes in the serpentine and the smooth grassy sides of the valley in the granite is very marked.

The Ruan granite-gneiss is seen in the roadside near Brugan and also at the farm beside St. Ruan. It is pale pink and rather well foliated. Elsewhere it is deeply decomposed. The Gwendreath gneiss is not quarried at present though there are small old pits now overgrown. It is seen on the side of the road from Kennack to Kuggar in several places and in the fields near Gwendreath and to the south of Bray's Cot. All the outcrop of this gneiss is cultivated. This gneiss emerges to the sea at Kennack Sands and the varied exposures of banded gneiss on the west side of Kennack have proceeded from the main mass, part of which is probably concealed beneath the sea. In the ground between Kennack, Kuggar, Ruan Minor and Cadgwith, there is an immense amount of banded gneiss which is seldom seen in solid form, but whose presence is clearly proved by the abundance of fragments in the fields and the character of the soil. Much of this country is really good agricultural land, though the only visible rock outcrops are serpentine and the fertility of the soil must be attributed to the mixed character of the underlying rock.

Similarly there is an area on the east side of Trethevas, between the farm and the shore, where the fields yield fine crops. To the north near Cadgwith and to the west near the Lizard road, the serpentine often shows itself as bare rocky knolls, but east of Trethevas there are few outcrops though in occasional pits in the fields both serpentine and banded gneiss can be seen. The field stones, however, are serpentine and gneiss in about equal proportions with a few specimens of gabbro. Southwards towards Lizard Town and Landewednack Church the same type of rock complex prevails. Two wells sunk near the Lizard village, though only serpentine was visible at the surface, passed through as much banded gneiss as serpentine. On the coast from Church Cove to Polbarrow there is a complex or *mélange* of gneiss, gabbro and serpentine, and there can be no doubt that this extends inland for nearly half a mile.

The Erisey Gneiss has very irregular form and is seen in small pits near Erisey, Trenoon and Trerise. On the south-east and south-west it seems to be margined by a fringe of intrusions of banded gneiss. Only rarely are large blocks of fresh rock to be seen near the farm buildings. The Goonhilly Gneiss is very badly exposed but as it is surrounded everywhere by serpentine its boundaries are easily traced. Near the Lizard road, half a mile north of Penhale, there are two small quarries in this rock which were formerly worked for road-metal. These contain pale pink

PLATE X

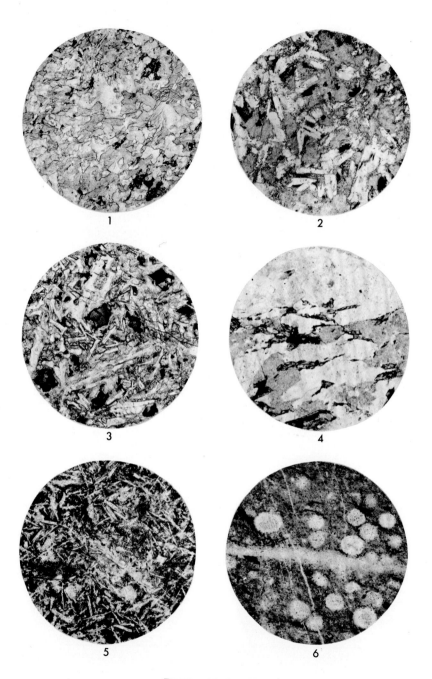

1

2

3

4

5

6

PHOTOMICROGRAPHS

PLATE X

PHOTOMICROGRAPHS.

FIG. 1. Hornblende-schist, N.W. corner of Kennack Cove (E. 5169), magnified 28 diameters, ordinary light. The basic portion of the Kennack gneiss, with green hornblende, feldspar and small granules of sphene. Igneous structures are practically obliterated, and the rock has a fairly good foliation.

FIG. 2. Epidiorite, in gabbro at Kilter (E. 6697), magnified 23 diameters, ordinary light. A modified dolerite or metadolerite, with prismatic plagioclase feldspar enclosed in a matrix of fibrous or mossy hornblende. Evidence of original ophitic structure is present; the rock is metophitic; augite and olivine have disappeared.

FIG. 3. Olivine-dolerite, W. end of Coverack (E. 6849), magnified 23 diameters, ordinary light. The rock contains small crystals of olivine with dark, ferruginous veins; much lath-shaped plagioclase feldspar; ophitic augite, partly fresh and partly changed to fibrous growths of pale green hornblende.

FIG. 4. Biotite-gneiss, N.W. corner of Kennack Cove (E. 17923), magnified 21 diameters, ordinary light. The acid portion of the Kennack gneiss, showing biotite, feldspar and quartz. The rock is thoroughly foliated.

FIG. 5. Spilite, Tregidden (E.5791), magnified 23 diameters, ordinary light. The rock consists of dark reddish-brown pyroxene in shapeless growths enclosing elongated feldspars. The structure is sub-variolitic and there is no metamorphism.

FIG. 6. Radiolarian chert, Mullion Island (E. 1843), magnified 21 diameters, ordinary light. The fine, cherty matrix shows many rounded, pale remains of radiolaria.

CHAPTER XI

THE LIZARD BOUNDARY

EVER since the time of De la Beche the nature and meaning of the Lizard boundary have been an open question. In the first edition of this Memoir (1912) it was discussed from several points of view but left undecided. The reason was that Hill who mapped the ground to the north and Flett who surveyed the area to the south were unable to come to an agreed interpretation. Since then much has been learned regarding the rocks on the north, principally through the researches of Lind Hendriks, and it is now known that the Falmouth and Portscatho beds cannot be Ordovician, as Hill supposed, and the structure of that country has to be reconsidered. This work, however, affects the interpretation of the Lizard boundary only in an indirect manner. The essential problem remains.

Two divergent opinions hold the field. According to one of these, the Lizard boundary is a great dislocation or series of dislocations bringing together two series of rocks differing widely in composition, state of metamorphism and geological age. The crystalline metamorphic rocks of the Lizard are pre-Cambrian or Archaean; the rocks to the north of them are (with few exceptions) Palaeozoic. The boundary line is the site of dislocations which, apart from later complications, belong to the Hercynian (or late-Carboniferous) epoch of earth-movement when the Lizard rocks were driven northwards and crumpled and crushed the Palaeozoic killas against which they were forced. This was the epoch during which the rocks of Devon and Cornwall received their complicated folding and the killas was converted from ordinary shale into slates and phyllites such as it is now.

The alternative view, favoured by Hill, though not definitely asserted as proved, was that the fractures which can be shown to exist along the boundary line were not of cardinal importance and the line as a whole could not be proved to be everywhere the site of faults or thrusts. The rocks on opposite sides of the boundary were of the same age but those of the Lizard had undergone great metamorphism through the agency of igneous intrusions acting during a period of earth-movement. The epoch of injection was post-Veryan (Ordovician) but pre-Devonian. Near Manaccan, far north of the Lizard boundary, mica-schists and hornblende-schists emerged to the surface and were presumably intrusions of Lizard type among Veryan killas, all metamorphosed by pressure and movement while in a heated condition. The Lizard serpentine and gabbro were possibly the plutonic representatives of the Ordovician pillow-lavas and thus furnished a parallel to the serpentine and gabbro of Ballantrae in Ayrshire. Along the boundary line there was a transition from a highly metamorphic to a less metamorphic facies of the country rocks, and fracture and dislocation had taken place there because of the change in the resistance of the rock masses, but this did not conceal the evidence of a transition and it was impossible to establish the existence of a continuous system of fractures.

In such cases it is necessary to consider firstly what are the known and admitted facts on which agreement has been reached, and secondly to discuss what are the fair inferences from the facts. It is clear, for example, that the Lizard boundary is very definite and even when the exposures are not good, can be placed within a hundred yards or so. The geologists mapping the ground from the north and from the south had never any difficulty in coming to an agreement as to its position. In the absence of rock outcrops the debris in the fields is usually sufficient evidence. Allowance must be made for the fact that if the farmyard is on hornblende-schist, fragments of that rock may have been dug for ' marl ' and carted out to the fields. The zone of admixture of different rock types or of possible transition is confined to a breadth of a few yards.

It is also clear that where the boundary line emerges to the coast at Polurrian and at Porthallow it is a fracture or a set of fractures. At Polurrian the hornblende-schists, in a thoroughly crystalline state, are brought against the Devonian killas by a sloping fault-plane which hades south or south-south-east at about forty-five degrees. Between these, as De la Beche noted, there is a ' conglomerate ' in which fragments of both rocks (and of others) can be found, but this conglomerate is clearly a fault-breccia and the interpretation is never in doubt. The fracture runs inland in a straight line for a distance of nearly three miles. At Porthallow the phenomena are less simple. Along the shore for sixty yards east of the Five Pilchards inn there is a jumbled mass of broken rocks which belong both to the Lizard and to the Meneage. In this coarse breccia it is possible to identify great blocks of the garnetiferous granite-gneiss, the silvery mica-schist and the epidotic green schist of the Lizard, mingled with the dark killas and the grey grits of the Meneage country. The garnetiferous granite-gneiss in this breccia appears quite welded with the dark, rather sandy killas. Fragments of greenstone or diabase also appear in the cliffs behind the inn. On the north the rock exposures are lost below the gravel of the beach. To the south there is a fracture which brings in the granite-gneiss, conspicuous as a thick band in the cliff, the mica-schist, the green schist and fine epidotic hornblende-schists, typical Lizard rocks in normal condition. A hundred yards further along the shore another dislocation bounds an outcrop of serpentine which in places is interbanded with hornblende-schist which appears soft, fine-grained and rotten. About two hundred yards east of the corner of the cliff the serpentine and hornblende-schist are closely folded together as has been recorded by Collins (1884a) and several other observers. In the rocky shore a short distance to the south of the place where the little stream flows over the gravel beach into the sea, one of the numerous faults is clearly exposed; on the south is garnetiferous, silvery mica-schist with large plates of chlorite and biotite; on the north, at a distance of three feet or so, dark Devonian killas which has yielded shreds of fossil plants. It is possible to step across the boundary at one step from the highly crystalline schist to the crushed but little altered dark shaly sediment. One of the faults runs for a space close to the foot of the cliff and contains large masses of breccia impregnated with iron and manganese oxides.

In its course from Porthallow across country westwards to Polurrian, the Lizard boundary describes a sinuous and irregular line and passes mostly through cultivated land. As a rule its presence is not expressed by a marked surface feature. It can be traced across fields where there is not even a ridge to indicate its situation, but here and there it follows stream courses for a short distance as near St. Martin's Bridge, Skyburriowe and Gwealeath. At its western end the Polurrian fault gives rise to a deep incised valley. At Chygarkye, where the serpentine reaches the Lizard boundary, there is a sharp distinction between the heather and thorn on the down and the cultivated fields across the dividing line. The Lizard rocks, on the south side, maintain their characters perfectly right up to the boundary. The hornblende-schist, mica-schists, granulites and serpentine show no essential difference as they approach the Palaeozoic killas.   They are not even brecciated, at least not generally, though occasionally, as in the serpentine at Rosemorder, there is slickensiding and polishing such as might be expected in the neighbourhood of a fault. The Palaeozoic rocks, however, on the north are often in a completely brecciated state; the pillow-lava may be in fragments resembling a volcanic ash, and the killas and greywackes are often torn to pieces and embedded in a matrix of crushed debris. The cherty shales are often twisted and contorted and even the quartzite occurs in blocks from a few inches to several yards in length.

It may be stated that, with a few exceptions, the rocks on each side of the boundary maintain the same state of metamorphism as they show at a distance of several miles. The garnetiferous granulites of the Lizard are easily distinguished from the sandy killas and greywacke of the Meneage; the radiolarian cherty shales within a few yards of the Lizard mica-schists, though broken, are quite unmodified in their lithological characters. The pillow-lavas within a stone's throw of the Lizard epidotic horn-blende-schists are still vesicular igneous rocks with perfect igneous structure, and when the serpentine reaches the boundary there is no trace of contact metamorphism in the adjacent killas. Exactly on the junction of the two series in a few places, as at Gwealeath, Skyburriowe and Trethewey, there are occasionally fragments of rocks that do not seem to belong clearly to any of the contiguous formations, but these may be explained as derived from underlying rocks brought up by movement along a great thrust plane.

From Porthallow the boundary follows a stream valley to Treg-lossack and at Pengarrock there is a mass of dark striped phyllite between rocks of Lizard type and rocks of Meneage type. This phyllite is unlike any other rock in the district and was considered by Hill and Reid to be in all probability the Dodman Phyllite, a rock which forms the Dodman Head near Mevagissey and is of uncertain age, but probably older than any of the other Palaeozoic rocks in that part of Cornwall, and possibly of Cambrian age. Thereafter the boundary takes a more westerly direction with horn-blende-schist to the south and brecciated killas and conglomerate on the north. Near Rosemorder it cuts sharply across a small mass of serpentine which stands up prominently in the hornblende-schist and has been quarried for road-stone. Farther west, at Tregidden, there is no good section of the actual junction, but hornblende-schist and very normal pillow-lava can be seen within a few yards of one another: the killas here is much brecciated. At Trethewey, north of St. Martin's Bridge, a powerful fault comes north-west out of the Lizard country and throws the hornblende-schist on the west against pillow-lava and brecciated killas on the east. Some garnetiferous granulite and mica-schists can be found about the fault line and the killas is often cherty and crushed. At Relowas the vesicular pillow-lava may be found within a few yards of perfectly foliated hornblende-schist. West of Relowas sandy killas with quartz veins is seen in the roadside within a few yards of the Lizard hornblende-schists. From Relowas to Chygarkye there are no good exposures, but though the serpentine comes up to the boundary line, there is no sign of metamorphism in the killas. Near Skyburriowe there are a few rock outcrops yielding killas, pillow-lava, garnetiferous and micaceous granulite and hornblende-schist. At this point the boundary suddenly changes its direction and from a western course swings round to the south-west, possibly diverted by a fault as at Bochym Lodge. The best inland exposure of the junction is to be seen at Gwealeath where the Lizard road passes through cuttings in the rock. On the north-west there is radiolarian chert, cherty shale, greywacke and broken pillow-lava; on the south-east mica-schist, garnetiferous granulite and hornblende-schist. Each rock maintains its charac-ters and there is no evidence of a transition. For about thirty yards between the two series there is a mass not well exposed on the roadside and this marks the exact position of the Lizard boundary. At Bochym specimens both of Lizard and of Palaeozoic rocks can be obtained but there are no good exposures of solid rock; the position of the boundary, however, can be fixed with fair exactitude. From there to Polurrian the faulted nature of the junction is quite demonstrable. It is clear that along the whole line from Porthallow to Polurrian the transition zone, if it exists, is only a few yards in breadth, and the differences between the rocks on opposite sides of the boundary are very marked and perfectly consistent. The Lizard rocks and the Meneage rocks preserve their normal characters right up to the boundary zone.

There are also certain distinctions between the rocks of the Old Lizard Head Series and the Palaeozoic rocks of the Meneage that make it very difficult to believe that they are the same, but in a different state of metamorphism. It is possible that there are pillow-lavas among the Lizard hornblende-schists, though this has not been established, but there is nothing to correspond to the massive Veryan quartzite or to the Veryan limestone, and the cherty shales and radiolarian cherts of the Veryan are very different from the feldspathic mica-schists and epidotic green schists of the Lizard.

Even more convincing evidence that the Lizard boundary from Porthallow to Skyburriowe is a line of powerful movement or dislocation, representing a great thrust or series of thrusts, is afforded by the condition of the rocks to the north of that line. For a distance of a mile or more the rocks of the country have been reduced to the condition of a regional breccia, the Meneage crush-breccia. In this breccia many rocks appear that are not found elsewhere in this part of Cornwall. Very powerful forces must have been acting to reduce such rocks as the pillow-lava and the Veryan quartzite to their present condition. As in the breccia there are elements of Upper Silurian and of Devonian age, the period of disturbance is probably Carboniferous and there can be no ambiguity in assigning it to the late-Carboniferous Hercynian orogenic developments which have left so powerful an impress on the rest of Cornwall and Devon.

The balance of evidence is entirely in favour of the pre-Cambrian or Archaean age of the sedimentary rocks of the Old Lizard Head Series, and of the period of their metamorphism and of the intrusion of the Man of War Gneiss. These rocks are part of a vanished land of crystalline schists and gneisses that in all probability had a considerable extension to the south and south-west. The crystalline schists of the Start in Devonshire and the gneiss of the Eddystone are probably members of the same series. The schists and gneisses that occur as pebbles in the Nare Point conglomerate are probably derived from this old metamorphic terrane. The Treleague Quartzite is probably also pre-Cambrian; at least from a comparison with the Gorran Quartzite it seems to be pre-Ordovician and it has also undergone a metamorphism to

which the Dodman Phyllite has not been subjected. The serpentine, gabbro and greenstone dykes of the Lizard are apparently
later than the Treleague Quartzite, and it is not so clear to what
epoch they are to be ascribed, but the absence of any trace of these
intrusions in the Ordovician rocks of the Meneage favours the
hypothesis that these rocks are pre-Ordovician.

To sum up : the Lizard boundary as shown on the one-inch
geological map is a perfectly definite line the position of which
can be easily and sharply located when the exposures are reasonably good.   There is no zone of transition but occasionally
fragments of rocks of unusual character can be found at or near
the boundary. These have probably been brought up along a
thrust-plane. The rocks on opposite sides differ in lithology and
still more in state of metamorphism, and each group maintains
its characters up to the junction. In places this line is a straight
line for some distance and is probably a normal fault, *e.g.* Polurrian, Gwealeath, Trethewey. Elsewhere it is gently curved or
sinuous and is presumably a thrust along which the Lizard rocks
have been driven northwards. There is very extensive brecciation
to the north of the boundary except at the western end where the
breccia has probably been cut out by the Polurrian fault. There is
no evidence of intense regional or thermal metamorphism of the
Ordovician and other Palaeozoic rocks of the Meneage.

CHAPTER XII

THE MENEAGE CRUSH-ZONE

THE district north of the Lizard boundary from Porthallow and Nare Point on the east coast to Garras and Belossack in the west centre of the peninsula is represented in the second edition of the one-inch geological Sheet as occupied by the Crush Breccia. This district has a length from east to west of about seven miles and a breadth from north to south of a mile and a half or rather less. The rocks composing this zone are much fractured and contrast strongly in this respect with the Lizard serpentine and hornblende-schist to the south, and the well bedded, though sheared and folded, slaty killas and grits to the north. The southern boundary is very well defined but on the north the margin is somewhat less definite, though not difficult to locate approximately, and at the western end of the outcrop there is also some uncertainty as to the exact limits of the zone.

The characteristic rock of this country is a dark grey, sometimes almost black, mixture of shale and grit. The shale is black and sometimes cherty; the grits are greyish and usually fine-grained. The harder grits often form lenticles an inch to several inches in length, elongated and tapering at both ends, and arranged in sub-parallel fashion. The shales, unless they are very cherty or siliceous, tend rather to form a matrix enclosing the gritty phakoids. As the fragments are not usually rounded the aggregate can hardly be described as a crush-conglomerate but occasionally where blocks of grit a foot or more in length are embedded in the shattered matrix they have assumed a rounded form and an imperfect resemblance to clastic boulders. Although preserving these general characters, the breccia varies much from point to point. As grits and shales of many different formations may be very much alike it is not an easy matter to identify their source, but some of these are not unlike the Devonian rocks to the north of them; others resemble the radiolarian cherts and cherty shales of the east coast near Porthallow, but in their crushed state they are not always recognizable. In certain parts of the district there are abundant fragments of vesicular pillow-lava, giving the rock a resemblance to a sheared volcanic ash or schalstein. Mica-schist, hornblende-schist, granophyre and occasionally gneiss are also found as ingredients of the crushed rock but can rarely be diagnosed without microscopic examination, and there are often diabases and spilitic rocks of various types, but the Lizard serpentine and gabbro are rather conspicuously absent. The Treleague Quartzite has never been proved to enter into the breccia and the Gorran Quartzite, though it is present as large floating masses, is seldom broken up into small fragments; vein-quartz is not uncommon in some places. No trace has been discovered of the Cornish post-Carboniferous granites, elvans and lamprophyres. In most places the breccia is a rather soft rock that crumbles under the hammer and rarely yields strong blocks suitable for building into stone walls but occasionally, as in the large road-stone quarry at Carn, half a mile east of Manaccan, the rock is very tough and hard and makes good road-metal. On the east coast most of the breccia is easily eroded by the sea but at the Turwell, a little projection on the shore below Penare, the breccia is often much iron-stained and is thoroughly indurated.

In this breccia there are larger masses of lenticular form that have sufficient extension to be represented on the one-inch geological map. These masses are surrounded on all sides by breccia of varied composition, and are in some places penetrated by it, but, as the exposures are never good and continuous, their boundaries cannot be laid down with precision, and only their general relationship to the enveloping breccia can be indicated on the maps. They are interpreted as floating masses derived from geological formations that can in some cases be identified, while in other cases their age and source are not evident, and such inferences as can be drawn from their composition and position are based on conjectures that may prove to be more or less justifiable. Many of the larger isolated or insular outcrops consist of rock masses that are themselves intensely brecciated and veined in all directions by an intricate network of secondary products, though the fragments have not been torn apart but retain in considerable measure their original relations. This is especially common in the pillow-lava and other rocks of spilitic type, in the hornblende-schist and the granophyre. The quartzite on the other hand is more resistant and forms strong blocks of intense hardness that are used for all kinds of building, gate-posts and even lintels. The cherty radiolarian shales, from their rapid variations in character, are reduced to an agglomeration of fragments unless they are protected by masses of pillow-lava. Exceptions to the above rule, however, are not seldom encountered. Locally the pillow-lavas are present in masses that have preserved not only the original blocky or pillow structure in great perfection but also the minute igneous characters as revealed by the microscope. In a few places the quartzite has yielded fossils sufficiently well preserved to enable us to form an opinion regarding its geological horizon. Speaking generally we may say that most of the insular masses enclosed in the breccia have been shattered rather than sheared; they have been broken up but the pressure has not been sufficient to cause much interstitial movement; their original structures igneous or clastic have been well preserved and they have not been reduced to a schistose condition; if new minerals have been produced in them they are secondary rather than metamorphic.

Of the rocks that occur in these insular masses the following are most important : hornblende-schist, mica-schist, granophyre, quartzite, pillow-lava, soda-granite, conglomerate, while there are also considerable areas of radiolarian chert and cherty shale, killas and grits of various types and ages, and limestones of more than one date.

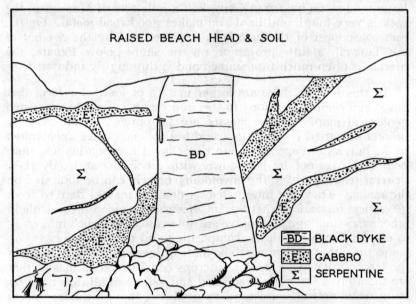

FIG. 19.—*Dykes in cliff at Coverack.* (*Explanation of Plate XI A*).
A well-defined black dyke of olivine-basalt (B D) (somewhat metamorphic) cuts across several irregular veins of schistose or flaser-gabbro (E) in the serpentine rock which forms a low cliff overlain by debris, soil, head and raised beach.

The hornblende-schists have their principal outcrops in the northern part of the crush-zone along a tract extending from Gillan Creek eastwards to St. Martin's Green. The largest mass lies to the south and east of Choon but the best and most accessible exposures are on Gillan Creek half a mile east of Manaccan. For several hundred yards in the low bank at the west side of the Creek the schists are seen on the roadside and on the wooded slopes above. They are not again found on the south side of the valley, though specimens are present in the fields near Tregithey about half a mile further east. No outcrop of hornblende-schist is known on the east coast near Penare, but schists are present in the breccia. At Gillan

(A 7496)

A. Coverack Shore. Black dyke and gabbro
    veins in serpentine

PLATE XI

B. Nelly's Cove, north of Porthallow.
    Crush breccia

(A 659)

Creek the rock is in a state of very thorough brecciation and is mostly a fine, silky dark green schist, with yellow epidotic veins. It is so much broken up that the direction of the foliation is by no means evident and the junctions with the adjacent rocks also are obscure. Hill notes that in addition to fine, silky well-laminated schist there are also two narrow bands of more coarsely crystalline rock in which there are traces of ophitic structure though the rock is thoroughly uralitized. The western extension of this area of hornblende-schist cannot be definitely located but it is interesting to note that it seems to be associated with the mica-schists that outcrop to the east of Manaccan Church.

The large outcrop to the south of Manaccan and to the south-east of Choon, as shown on the map, appears to cover several hundred acres but the exposures are so few and so widely separated that this may really consist of a number of separated masses surrounded by killas-breccia. Fragments in the soil are very numerous but pits and quarries are few. The rock crosses the valley rather less than half a mile south of Manaccan and specimens may be obtained in the road and in a small quarry. The rock is very fine-grained, dark green, and very shattery; most specimens fall to pieces under the hammer, but under the microscope it is a true hornblende-schist with very fine laminar foliation, acicular or finely crystalline hornblende and a good deal of epidote (5317, 5318). In its westward extension the hornblende-schist can be traced by the debris in the fields and by occasional marl pits, but is mostly in an advanced state of decomposition. At Choon and at Tregonwell (the farm a quarter of a mile north-east of Choon) there are old pits near the farmyards where the rotten schist has been dug for marl, and small kernels of less decomposed rock may be obtained : there are also several small quarries in the little valley south of the old chapel marked on the map.

Several hundred yards west of Choon the hornblende-schist is again seen in a narrow valley leading north to Landrivick. The rock here is of mixed character, rich in hornblende and epidote and often well foliated. A short distance farther north, in the banks of the same stream, much decomposed hornblendic rocks are found which have some resemblance to uralitic diabases. One of the best exposures of the rocks of this group is near Carplight (5248, 5249) about a quarter of a mile south of Choon where there is a small quarry on the banks of a streamlet. In this locality the schist is much brecciated and in parts rather coarsely crystalline. It is full of epidote and chlorite, with hornblende crystals lying in a crushed or flaser matrix. The fine, laminated, silky hornblende-schists rich in epidote are also present at this locality.

The Mica-schist of Manaccan. For a distance of about a quarter of a mile east of Manaccan churchyard fragments of mica-schist are abundant in the cultivated fields and larger blocks may be seen in the adjacent stone walls, but there are no quarries in this rock and no positive outcrops are visible in the fields. The mica-schist, however, persists to Roscaddon, the farm east of Manaccan, where it seems to alternate with hornblende-schist and slaty breccia. No definite outlines can be laid down for the mica-schist outcrop but it is so distinctive in appearance and so much more highly crystalline than the common slates and phyllites of the region that its peculiarities have attracted attention since the early years of last century. The rock is silvery grey in colour with large plates of chloritized mica and usually very little quartz or feldspar; many specimens are so soft as to be easily crushed in the hand (probably owing to decomposition) and its softness combined with its pale greenish colour give it a strong resemblance to talc-schist. Two points about it merit attention—its marked difference from the prevailing killas of the Meneage and its close association with the silky hornblende-schist of Gillan Creek.

The hornblende-schist and mica-schist of the Meneage crush-zone are far more highly metamorphic than any other rocks that appear as important constituents of the breccia, yet in some respects they are different from the typical Lizard schists. Apart from their intense brecciation, which may be regarded as accidental and not an original characteristic, the hornblende-schists are very rich in epidote and in chlorite. These minerals often occur in fine quartzose veins that cut across the foliation and in such cases they may be regarded as presumably secondary and as having been formed during or after the brecciation. When epidote, however, occurs in parallel, laminar foliation it recalls a prominent feature of the Lizard epidotic hornblende-schists and may then be of earlier genesis. The Meneage hornblende-schists are in many cases exceedingly fine-grained and silky with plane or flat foliation; sometimes they have a very fine-grained ' augen ' structure with larger crystals enveloped in a matted fibrous matrix. Coarsely crystalline hornblende-schists are absent or rare. Now in the Lizard the coarse hornblende-schists seem to cling to the margins of the serpentine and as the serpentine does not occur in the Meneage crush-zone their absence might be expected. Very fine silky hornblende-schists occur in the Lizard, principally near Porthallow and Old Lizard Head. They are not at all unlike the Meneage schists and resemble them also in being associated with mica-schists. Furthermore, it is quite probable that the finely crystalline state of the Meneage hornblende-schists is the consequence of a metamorphism superinduced by crushing and movement, a kind of mylonization, or a change of the type which has been described as degenerative, retrogressive or diaphthoritic.

The Manaccan Granophyre.—In the lane which leads south from Manaccan, half way down the slope to the bridge, there is a pink or bright red rock exposed at the roadside—the Manaccan Granophyre. Its outcrop is small, not more than a few acres, and it seems to be enclosed on all sides in the usual dark grey Meneage Breccia. The rock is veined with many small strings of quartz and carbonates and is so thoroughly brecciated that it shatters under the hammer and pieces as large as a cricket ball are not easily obtained. In microscopic section (6302) it proves to consist entirely of micropegmatite, which, though fine in places, is usually rather coarse and forms divergent aggregates that give rise to a rude spherulitic structure. The feldspar is rather cloudy but polarizes well, and there seems to be no biotite or muscovite. Porphyritic crystals of feldspar are absent or scarce in the sections and have imperfect crystalline outlines. This rock is unique, as nothing like it has been encountered in the Lizard or in the rest of Cornwall: that it is not restricted, however, to the outcrop near Manaccan is shown by the presence of fragments, identical in character, in the breccia on the east coast at the Turwell, below Penare. Although intensely brecciated it has never been found in a sheared or metamorphic condition.

The Meneage Quartzite.—The quartzite may be said to be the characteristic rock of the Meneage Breccia, because where it is present it is easily recognized and its fragments, being very hard and durable, are abundant in the fields. On the east coast the quartzite is exposed in a conspicuous lenticle below Penare. This mass is boat-shaped, pointed at both ends, about thirty yards long and ten in breadth. It forms a notable object in the grassy slope above the cliff of bare rock. From that point south to the north side of Nelly's Cove the quartzite occurs in blocks often of great size, embedded in a brecciform matrix of killas, chert, cherty shale and many other rocks. The shore below the cliff is strewn with great blocks of quartzite, mostly sub-angular, as the waves have not been sufficiently powerful to roll them about. These blocks have evidently been washed out of the soft shales and breccia during the recession of the coast by the attack of the sea. Inland the quartzite is present in a broad strip of ground extending westwards for about seven miles to the neighbourhood of Bochym. The typical area of its occurrence may be said to be south of the hornblende-schist and north of the pillow-lava. It is absent or rare about Gillan Creek and Manaccan and does not occur, at any rate in quantity, near the Lizard boundary. South of Manaccan, however, and around St. Martin pieces of it are seen in every field.

The quartzite has been broken up, in immense quantities, for use as road-stone and for building stone walls, but for these purposes recourse has been had principally to the numerous blocks that at one time cumbered the fields and were cleared away in progress of cultivation. Occasionally a few piles of stone or larger individual blocks are still left but the clearance has been so general and complete that except for the stones in the walls and small fragments in the soil there may be little evidence of the former abundance of quartzite blocks. Small pits in the fields are not uncommon and are usually overgrown but there is no large quarry in which the quartzite is now worked. The small areas which are marked on the one-inch map only serve to indicate in a general way

the places where it is specially abundant or where the most
continuous masses have been observed.   Taken as a whole the rock
consists of lenticles of varying size embedded in a breccia which
contains a large proportion of killas or, shale.

West of St. Martin the quartzite is often seen in fields and
walls : blocks of it are common north and west of Trelowarren and
around Garras.   West of Chygarkye it was quarried for a time.
From Belossack to Bochym it appears not uncommonly in the stone
walls but there is evidence that it has been sometimes transported
for building purposes.   There is a large lump of quartzite in front
of the Wheel Inn at Cury Cross Lanes.   It seems to stop about
two miles from the west coast as it is not seen around Mullion and
there is no trace of it on the cliffs at Poldhu and Gunwalloe.

Although a very hard rock, the quartzite is often much
brecciated.   It is traversed by narrow veins which have been
occupied by secondary deposits of quartz that have firmly
recemented the mass.   There is little trace of bedding and as a
whole the rock is extraordinarily pure, consisting of quartz with a
little feldspar and hardly any mica.   Shaly bands are practically
absent.   Though sometimes slightly yellow where broken with a
hammer the rock is almost snow-white on weathered surfaces.   It
is sharply distinguished from the Treleague Quartzite by the
absence of the fine hornblende needles and garnet in the interstitial
cementing material that characterize the latter rock : consequently
also it weathers with a much lighter colour and seldom shows rusty
stains.   In its petrographical characters it bears a very close
resemblance to the Gorran Quartzite as is agreed by all geologists
who have described the Meneage rock.   The Treleague Quartzite
has never been found in the Meneage Breccia, at any rate in such
a condition that it could be positively identified.

Collins (1879b) was the first to find fossils in the Meneage
Quartzite; he obtained a specimen of *Orthis* in broken rock near
St. Martin.   There seems to be no room for doubt that the Meneage Quartzite and the Gorran Quartzite are on the same horizon,
which is generally conceded by palaeontologists to be Ordovician
(Caradoc or Llandeilo).   It is the only rock in Cornwall which
can be definitely proved by fossil evidence to belong to that geological period.   During his survey of the district, Hill found a
quarry a quarter of a mile south of Mudgeon which yielded fairly
well preserved casts of brachiopods which were identified by Ivor
Thomas as "*Orthis calligramma* Dalm; cf. var. *Carausi* Salt;
Rafinesquina?".   These were pronounced by Clement Reid to be
species found in the Gorran Quartzite at Perhaver.   The locality
is about half a mile north of St. Martin's Church and is marked
by an asterisk on the one-inch map.   Further specimens were
collected from the Mudgeon quarry in 1938 by Mr. Dewar and
have been examined and reported on by Dr. Stubblefield (1939)
who finds that the supposed *Orthis* is really *Chonetes* (*Plico-*

chonetes) *plebejus* Schnur and the *Rafinesquina*? is *Douvillina elegans* Drevermann, both of which are Lower Devonian fossils. This is the first record of Lower Devonian in the Meneage Breccia. The Mudgeon rock is a grey-green silt and Hill and Reid were probably in error in identifying it with the Meneage Quartzite.

In a shale between tide-levels at Carn on Gillan Creek Mr. Dewar has collected fossils which Dr. Stubblefield has assigned also to Lower Devonian (*op. cit.*).

The pillow-lava.—Like the Meneage Quartzite the pillow-lava is confined to the region of the Meneage Breccia. Some of its outcrops were known in the early years of the nineteenth century and were shown on De la Beche's map but attention was first drawn to its special characters and associations by Fox and Teall's descriptions of Mullion Island (1893). They showed that the ' greenstone ' of the island had perfect pillow structure and was covered by layers of cherty shale and radiolarian chert alternating with one another in thin beds a few inches thick. The pillows are globoids from six inches to three feet in diameter and are very often vesicular, with concentric bands of steam cavities nearly parallel to their surfaces. The vesicles may be empty or filled with calcite and chlorite, and not infrequently they are elongated in a direction tangential to the surface of the pillow. Many of the pillows have a fine-grained skin that may have been originally glassy and is often cracked and fissured. Pillows also occur that have a large central cavity which may be filled with calcite or with yellow masses of epidosite. The angular interspaces between the pillows are occupied by shale, with or without chert, or by rotten debris that may have been ash or volcanic fragments, or rarely by an impure, grey or greenish limestone. The perfect preservation of the pillow structure and of the bedding of the shales and cherts shows that the rocks have escaped pressure and deformation in a marvellous manner. In appearance they are about the most normal-looking igneous rocks in the whole of Cornwall. As might be expected, the igneous structure revealed by microscopic examination is also completely conserved. The minerals of the rock are not badly weathered and are principally feldspar, reddish brown augite and iron ores. Porphyritic feldspars are uncommon and the rock as a whole is fine-grained. Its most marked character is the sub-radiate disposition of the long, narrow and lath-shaped feldspar crystals. The augite forms an interstitial mass without definite outlines, enclosing the feldspar : the structure resembles a pin-cushion and is an approach to the variolitic. This is quite common in the pillow-lavas or spilites and is still more perfect in some of the spilitic fragments in the Menaver Conglomerate. Olivine is absent and porphyritic crystals of augite are rare. The feldspar is near oligoclase, and, like the augite, may be to some extent replaced by secondary minerals, such as calcite, sericite, chlorite and epidote.

Mullion Island is separated from the Lizard shores by half a mile of sea and the pillow-lava does not occur in the opposite cliffs. Hence it is not possible to state positively why the pillow-lavas emerge to form the island; probably the cause is a complex of faults, but the presence of the lavas is sufficient to show that the displacements that accompany and produced the Meneage Breccia have an extension under sea to the south west of Mullion.

Along the Lizard boundary from Polurrian to Bochym the pillow-lavas do not show at the surface, probably thrown out by the powerful Polurrian fault, but from Gwealeath east to Porthallow as was first shown by Prior (1904) there are many outcrops of them and sometimes they occupy a considerable space. In many places they occur within a few yards of the Lizard hornblende-schists to which they present a complete contrast, as though both series are originally igneous rocks the lavas retain their primary igneous structures and characters in great perfection, while the Lizard rocks are typical metamorphic schists.

Interesting sections of the pillow-lavas, cherts and cherty shales are to be seen in the neighbourhood of Gwealeath both in the farmyards of Gwealeath and of Boscawen, and in the road-cuttings in the sides of the Helston road. They are in close proximity to or in actual contact with the mica-schists, garnetiferous granulites and hornblende-schists of the Lizard. The pillow-lava is in some places a compact rock, not much weathered, but as a rule it is brecciated and breaks up into fragments. The cherty shales are also in a state of disintegration and the exposures are not sufficiently clear to show their real relationships. In microscopic section the pillow-lavas show good igneous structure but the minerals are seldom in a fresh state (Pl. X, 5). East of Belossack the pillow-lava is seen in several places and appears to occupy a considerable area, and for a distance of about half a mile fragments of the igneous rocks are numerous along the Lizard boundary. A narrow belt of killas-breccia seems to intervene between the rocks of Meneage and those of Lizard types. The next outcrop of the pillow-lava is more than a mile farther east; it occurs in the roadside west of Relowas, with brecciated cherty killas, within a few yards of the Lizard hornblende-schists. At Relowas farmyard there is typical Lizard hornblende-schist and a few yards farther north the fields contain many fragments of breccia in which spongy pieces of lava are very common. The lava fragments are flattened and their cavities are mostly empty; the rocks are much decomposed and no solid outcrop of lava shows itself. A deep narrow valley lies between Relowas and Trethewey, occasioned by a powerful fault that comes from the south-east and has been excavated by the action of the stream. On the east bank of this valley the pillow-lava is again encountered. At this locality the rock is often much brecciated and impregnated with epidote. Killas and chert are also found in the banks and in the stream. In the fields between

Trethewey and St. Martin's Church there is much debris of pillow-lava and probably there is a fairly extensive area of lava hereabouts, as is indicated on the one-inch map.

The largest outcrop of the pillow-lava begins a little east of Newtown and extends for about three miles to a point half-a-mile east of Higher Boden. It follows the outline of the Lizard boundary very closely and the hornblende-schist and pillow-lava are often separated only by a strip of killas-breccia a few yards in breadth. To the north there is conglomerate which is sometimes apparently mixed with the pillow-lava or resting on it and containing fragments of it; and when lava and conglomerate are both brecciated and sheared it is difficult to define the exact nature or origin of the mixture. The exposures as a rule are bad but in several places the lava forms a strong, prominent outcrop and may be quarried for road-stone, as at Tregidden and Higher Boden. At Tregidden there are several small quarries and one of considerable size. The rock is compact, fine-grained, and hard. It is not markedly vesicular and shows the pillow structure imperfectly. Around Treworgie also there are bare outcrops of the igneous rocks and the fields are full of pillow-lava fragments.

At Higher Boden there is a quarry which shows the characters of the pillow-lava better than at Tregidden and is the best inland exposure of this rock in the Meneage. The dark fine-grained spilite is only sparingly vesicular but the pillow structure is very well displayed. The rounded, sack-like masses are one or two feet in diameter and have a thin, smooth, external crust. Pockets of dark shale occur between the pillows but there is little chert. The lava must have a considerable thickness though in this respect the section in Higher Boden quarry does not equal that of the south-west side of Mullion Island. Brecciation is not conspicuous and the shape of the pillows is so well preserved that it is impossible to believe that the rock mass has been much deformed by shearing. In this neighbourhood, and especially in a small isolated mass near Roskruge, porphyritic structure is a rather common feature of the lava, the phenocrysts being plagioclase feldspars which may attain the length of half an inch and are conspicuous on broken surfaces of the rock. In microscopic section they prove to be often much decomposed and replaced by sericite, calcite, prehnite and epidote.

On the eastern shore, at Nelly's Cove, a short distance north of Porthallow, the pillow-lavas occur both in the beach and in the cliffs. The characteristic pillow structure is very pronounced throughout this outcrop and thick seams of radiolarian chert and black siliceous shale accompany the igneous rock. At this place there has been a considerable amount of movement, crumpling the shales and disturbing the pillow-lava. Pale bands, often brecciated, cross the lava outcrop. The relations to the adjacent rock masses are not clear, being probably faults. In places there are more coarsely crystalline streaks but as a whole the lava is very fine-grained and its minerals are seldom in good preservation. The assemblage of lava, radiolarian chert and shale are so similar to those of Mullion Island as to leave no room to doubt that the rocks of these two localities are of identical age and origin.

In the killas-breccia that accompanies the pillow-lavas, fragments of highly vesicular spilite are quite common. Some of them are globular and resemble volcanic bombs but usually they are flattened or cake-shaped. It is not certain, however, that they are volcanic tuffs, as where all the rocks are so shattered the lavas also must have suffered. There are, nevertheless, in a few places thin layers, among the lava outcrops, that consist of sub-angular or concavo-convex fragments of volcanic glass mostly decomposed to a sort of brown palagonite. A specimen from near Bojorrow (5205) consists of this material and, in the palagonite, spherulites, steam cavities and occasional feldspar crystals may be detected. Similar rocks have been found associated with pillow-lavas in the Mevagissey area.

The Gallentreath Soda-granite.—On the north side of Porthallow Cove a mass of grey igneous rock rises above the gravel of the beach and reaches the top of the cliff. Its outcrop has a breadth of thirty or forty yards and on the north it abuts against the pillow-lava and shale while to the south it adjoins the stratified grey shale and grits; its relations to adjacent rocks are obscure and probably it is faulted on both sides. This grey granitic rock is unique in the Meneage and fragments of it have not been identified in the breccia. It is a hard, tough rock though obviously brecciated and veined in many places with quartz and carbonates. On microscopic examination it proves to consist mainly of albite in fairly well-formed crystals : there is also a less amount of untwinned orthoclase but there is no biotite or dark minerals though they may be represented by chlorite. Some specimens have a porphyritic structure with a fine-grained matrix which carries quartz and many small rectangular crystals of clear albite. The rock is in a good state of preservation ; it has been locally much brecciated, especially towards its margins, but is much more coherent than the Manaccan Granophyre. From its petrographical characters its affinities with the spilite magma are clearly recognizable and it seems to be an intrusive or hypabyssal rock of the pillow-lava series. Chemical analyses show a strong affinity with the soda-granite of Tayvallich, Argyllshire, and the keratophyre of Gorran, Cornwall, both of which are members of the spilitic suite of rocks.

The radiolarian rocks.—After Fox and Teall had discovered the radiolarian cherts of Mullion Island it was found that these rocks had a very wide distribution in the Meneage. Wherever the pillow-lavas occur the cherts are also found though they seem to vary considerably in abundance from place to place; at some outcrops of the lavas as at Tregidden and Higher Boden there is comparatively little chert while at Mullion Island and Porthallow

cherts are present in great quantity.   With the chert there is
always shale, which is usually black or dark grey, and in the best
sections these rocks alternate in thin beds usually only a few inches
in thickness. The cherts vary much in colour. On Mullion
Island the purest specimens are pale grey but dark grey and black
varieties are equally frequent, especially when the chert is somewhat argillaceous, and bright red colours are occasionally seen
when the iron ores in the chert are thoroughly oxidized.   A
green colour indicates the presence of chlorite, probably derived
from weathered volcanic material.   In most localities the chert has
undergone brecciation and is crossed by numerous very thin white
veins that consist of secondary quartz, but in microscopic sections
the presence of radiolaria often in fairly good preservation is easily
recognized and the rocks are never granulitic or extensively
recrystallized.

In the inland districts the cherty beds are seldom well exposed
but cherts are seen with the pillow-lavas in several places near
Tregidden, also in the valley west of Trethewey and at Belossack
and Skyburriowe.   In the side of the Lizard road at Gwealeath
there are beds of chert and dark shale.   Fox has reported chert
bands at Chypons a mile north-east of Mullion.   Chert and cherty
shale also occur in many places where there is no trace of
pillow-lava.   On the east coast north of Nelly's Cove for nearly
half a mile there are many little recesses in the cliff where the sea
has eroded a breccia of dark shale with varying abundance of thin
chert bands; the pebbles on the beach are mostly hard chert.
Beds of grit of varying thickness also occur in the brecciated and
distorted masses that form the cliffs but no pillow-lava is seen north
of Nelly's Cove.   There are large fallen masses of the white
quartzite all along the shore.   From this place across the peninsula
to Gilly and Garras on the Coverack road chert fragments are often
visible in the debris in the fields, and as the quartzite also is
plentiful it is probable that this country is underlain by a similar
breccia to that seen on the east coast.   Apparently this zone dies
out as, though in a south-westerly direction the cherts can be found
along the Lizard boundary, they do not appear on the west coast.
The exact nature of the western termination of the Meneage crush-
zone is by no means clear, and though several explanations might
be offered there is not sufficient evidence to remove the obscurity;
its approximate position, however, can be easily fixed.

To George Jennings Hinde we are indebted for a careful study
of the radiolaria in the chert of Mullion Island (1893). He figured
and described a number of forms, most of which are known as low
as the Devonian, and he does not arrive at any definite conclusion
as to the geological horizon of the deposit. No subsequent
palaeontological work has been done on these interesting rocks.
The Mullion Island cherts are probably the best yet discovered in
the Meneage district for purposes of microscopic study (Pl. X, 6)
as they have undergone very little recrystallization, but radiolaria

have been preserved in the chert of many other outcrops and may deserve a more thorough-going study than they have yet received.

Limestones.—In the Meneage Breccia there is very little limestone and that rock is not quarried now in any part of the district. On Mullion Island a little limestone occurs among the cherts and shales, in small pockets and between the pillows but not in regular beds. It is a rough, grey, impure, crystalline limestone and unfortunately, so far as is yet known, it contains no decipherable fossils. Among the cherty beds at Porthallow and in one or two coves north of Nelly's Cove a few irregular scraps of limestone have also been encountered; presumably they belong to the same series as those of Mullion Island and they have yielded no fossils except possibly traces of crinoids. There is no means of determining their exact geological age.

Very much more important, however, are the limestones of Fletching's Cove. Although of inconsiderable extent they have been known for a long time and in fact were indicated on the original geological maps of De la Beche. In these limestones Sherborn (1904, 1906) discovered fossils, which, though imperfect, seemed to indicate a Silurian age, probably either Wenlock or Ludlow, and, in the Veryan district, Lind Hendriks has found limestone masses of similar character and provenance that also contain fossils apparently belonging to the Wenlock or Ludlow. They occur always as detached masses in a shear-belt or crush-breccia and consequently they furnish little evidence regarding the geological age of the surrounding rocks. But they are of great interest as suggesting that the Meneage Breccia contains not only Ordovician quartzite but also Silurian limestone. On the other hand Stubblefield and Spath (1939) have re-examined Sherborn's fossils and consider that they are indeterminable. Hence the identification of this limestone must depend entirely on its lithology.

In the inland districts occupied by the Meneage Breccia, Hill found occasionally small, shallow, old pits which according to tradition had at one time been worked for limestone. They are now grassed over or used as ponds for cattle and it is only with great difficulty that fragments of calcareous rock can be obtained in or around them. Probably they mark the sites of calcareous lenticles in the breccia and it is clear that they were of very small dimensions and have been completely worked out.

Devonian.—On the one-inch geological map published in 1912 two belts of rocks in the Meneage have received the Devonian colour and symbol. One of them lies on the north side of the pillow-lavas west of St. Martin, the other occupies a similar position relatively to the pillow-lava band that stretches from Newtown to Trewothack. The latter was continued to the east coast at the Turwell below Penare but in the 1934 map this outcrop was cut short a mile from the coast. The rock exposed in the cliff at the Turwell is very complex and difficult to understand but a large series of micro-sections has been cut from it and they seem to be all an authiclastic breccia among which it was not possible to identify any normal conglomerate : it is of course quite possible that in this breccia fragments of conglomerate may be present and if so it is of no great significance in the geology of the area. The ' Devonian ' beds are only seen in the inland districts and there is an almost complete absence of good sections. The best are those seen in the valley between St. Martin and Trelowarren and in the banks and roadside in the valley between Tregidden and Trezebal. They consist of grits and shales, in which the bedding is often well preserved and they have very much the same character as the rocks seen on the west coast about Gunwalloe, where there are fossils that are presumably Devonian. As a whole they are less sheared and broken up than the cherty shales and radiolarian cherts and this may be due to protection from the pressures coming from the south by the main outcrops of the pillow-lava group.

More definite evidence is afforded by certain outcrops at Porthallow Cove where both on the south and the north side there are beds of shale and grit which are lithologically very similar to the Devonian rocks of the west coast and have yielded plant fragments to Professor Lang. They seem accordingly to belong to the Hendriksi horizon discussed in Chapter XIV.

Conglomerate.—A feature of the Devonian rocks in the localities above mentioned is the occasional presence of beds of coarse grit and rather fine conglomerate containing pebbles that are sometimes three or four inches in diameter. The matrix is sandy and spotted with decomposed grains of feldspar. In such a district as the Meneage where crush-breccias are so abundant it is necessary to be cautious in accepting any rock as a clastic conglomerate but especially to the north of Tregidden and to the west of St. Martin there are rocks which from the shape and variety of their pebbles and from the absence of evidence of interstitial movement seem to be undoubtedly true conglomerates. The pebbles are grit, shale, quartzite, chert, lava and various crystalline rocks such as granite and schist, and most of them, though not all, seem to be of local derivation. Hill arrived at the conclusion that these beds rested unconformably on the pillow-lava and overlapped it. It is to be noted that this conglomerate does not appear on the shore at Porthallow or on the west coast; that is to say it is absent from those localities where the Devonian beds have proved to contain fossils. Its relations to the Menaver Conglomerate are also somewhat doubtful, but in the 1934 map it has been accepted as a band in the Devonian.

Interpretation.—The zone of broken rocks which has been described as the Meneage crush-belt can be explained on the hypothesis that the crystalline schists, gneisses and serpentine of the Lizard have been shoved northwards by powerful earth-stresses and have broken up the Palaeozoic strata on the north of them and reduced them to their present condition.

About a mile south-south-west of Mullion village and rather more than a quarter of a mile to the south of the farm of Trenance the Predannack road crosses the junction of the hornblende-schist and the serpentine. The actual junction is a plane of fault or dislocation which runs south-westward and emerges on the coast in the middle of Mullion Cove behind the harbour wall. The fault-plane dips east-south-east at about forty degrees. In all probability this is not a normal fault but a thrust, by which the serpentine on the south has been forced northward, over-riding the hornblende-schist which there is reason to believe, in the northern part of the Lizard, forms a roof to the serpentine intrusion. Where the fault crosses the Predannack road there is an old quarry or pit mostly overgrown with thorn and in this pit between schist and serpentine there is a thin band of dark, shaly killas of very normal appearance, though soft and crumbling, and by no means resembling the coarsely crystalline Lizard mica-schists. This killas has presumably been brought up along the thrust-plane, having been torn from a subjacent mass. If so we are at liberty to assume that the hornblende-schist about Mullion Cove and Polurrian has been driven northwards over the Palaeozoic rocks for a distance which in this locality is approximately a mile, and there is no difficulty in believing that the killas and other rocks, thus over-ridden, have been broken up and torn apart, with the production of a regional breccia.

The curious fact that this breccia does not emerge to the surface at the northern boundary of the Lizard from Polurrian to Bochym may be explained on the hypothesis that the zone of breccia has been cut out by the Polurrian fault, which would then be a down-throw to the south, bringing the over-riding schist against the killas. Alternatively of course we may suppose that at this locality there is a clean fracture and the underlying Palaeozoic rocks gave way along a definite plane, escaping brecciation owing to the freedom of movement along the fracture. On that hypothesis the Polurrian fault would be a thrust from the south.

These movements have generally been ascribed to the Hercynian orogeny, the late-Carboniferous mountain-building which has folded and crushed all the Palaeozoic rocks of Cornwall, and this is in accordance with the evidence that has been accumulated in the Meneage and the Lizard. It cannot be denied that at other epochs folding and movement may have taken place in these rocks, but no positive evidence of this has been obtained, and the assumption seems unnecessary to explain the recorded facts. It is possible, however that some of the faulting may be post-Carboniferous or even Tertiary but the main folding is clearly post-Devonian.

On this hypothesis the Meneage crush-zone might contain any rocks that had existed in this part of Cornwall up to the close of Carboniferous time when the Hercynian movements took place.

It is true that nothing has been identified in the breccia that is newer than mid-Devonian but later rocks may be present though not yet recognized. On the other hand the late-Devonian and Carboniferous rocks may never have been deposited in this quarter, or if deposited may have been removed by erosion before the movements supervened, or, again, they may be absent because the breccia contains only a slice of the geological sequence of strata and is bounded below and above by planes of disruption.

An analysis of the Meneage Breccia shows that it contains certain elements of which the age is determinable and others of doubtful horizons. The hornblende-schist and mica-schist of the neighbourhood of Manaccan have many of the distinctive characters of the Lizard schists. Hill regarded them as part of his 'Veryan' but the mica-schist has little resemblance to the Llandeilo shales which accompany the Meneage Quartzite. It is not certain that the Treleague Quartzite occurs in the Meneage Breccia, and Cambrian rocks also appear to be absent unless the Pengarrock phyllite, which resembles the Dodman Rock, belongs to that formation. The Meneage Quartzite is definitely Ordovician (Llandeilo or Caradoc); with it Hill placed certain shales, grits, cherts and cherty shales, limestones, pillow-lavas and tuffs to constitute his Veryan formation. Unfortunately, for all these rocks except the Quartzite palaeontological evidence is lacking. The cherts and cherty shales may or may not be Ordovician; probably some of them are. Undoubtedly certain cherts are very closely connected with the pillow-lava, at Mullion Island for instance, but the fossils they contain are not sufficient to establish their geological age. Lind Hendriks has tentatively placed these pillow-lavas somewhere in the Middle Devonian, but that also lacks definite proof. Much might be said on both sides of this question but it must be left open as there is no firm basis for discussion. The presence of Silurian rocks (Wenlock or Ludlow) in Fletching's Cove has been asserted but there is nothing to indicate whether the breccia contains other strata belonging to that epoch. Finally, Lang has recorded the presence at Porthallow of grits and shales containing traces of fossils presumably not older than Middle Devonian. No trace of Carboniferous rocks has yet been found.

It would be unwise to assume that the strata which have been identified by fossil remains represent the complete sequence of strata originally deposited in the Meneage. The great majority of the rocks in the breccia have been so crushed that any fossils they may have contained have probably been obliterated. The gaps in the recorded sequence are certainly extraordinary but a discussion of them would lead to consideration of the Palaeozoic history of Cornwall which is beyond the scope of this memoir, though reference to it must be made in the description of the Menaver Conglomerate which is to follow.

The constituents of the Meneage Breccia are not without traces of an orderly distribution which may have a structural significance. In the north we have the belt of schists—the hornblende-schist and mica-schist and next these the granophyre. Then follows the belt characterized by the Meneage Quartzite with grits and cherty shales. Farther south come the lenticles of Silurian limestone : thereafter a broad belt of pillow-lavas, and radiolarian cherts, accompanied by conglomerates; and finally Devonian grits and shales. The sequence is apparently ascending from north to south, the newest rocks being near the Lizard boundary, a sort of regional southward dip in the constituents of the breccia-zone, which may reflect the original arrangement of strata in a great block resting on a thrust or series of thrusts and topped by another great thrust which brings on the Lizard rocks to the south.

CHAPTER XIII

MYLOR BEDS

ALONG the northern edge of this geological Sheet there is a long strip of sedimentary rocks belonging to the group that has been called the Mylor Beds. This name was given by Hill to certain strata that occur at Mylor in the neighbourhood of Falmouth, and were traced from there to the east side of the district now under description. In the present Sheet they extend from Mawnan Smith in the east, past Constantine and Boskenwyn Downs to Helston, Breage and Porthleven. On the north, for six miles, they are penetrated by the Carnmenellis Granite which has produced a considerable amount of thermal metamorphism in the Mylor slates. This metamorphic aureole has an average breadth of a mile and fades away gradually on its southern borders into the region of unaltered sediments. The granite itself enters the area of this Sheet for a distance of six miles from east to west but for less than half a mile southwards. It has a great extension in the country to the north and reaches the vicinity of Camborne, a distance of ten miles. The Mylor country in this Sheet has the shape of an elongated wedge; in the west near Helston and Breage it has a width, from north to south, of about four miles. At Boskenwyn Downs it is less than two miles wide and farther east, near Porth Navas, less than a mile, which is also its breadth where it passes out of the Sheet in a north-east direction near Mawnan Smith. These rocks, however, are believed to cover a wide area, encircling the Carnmenellis Granite and extending north-west to the country around Hayle and south-west to Marazion and Penzance. They are considered to be the principal sedimentary group of the south-west of Cornwall.

The group characters of the Mylor Beds are lithological and their distinctive constituents are dark shales with thin bands of pale sandy sediment. The shaly material is dark grey or sometimes blue-black, but occasionally lilac or purple. The sandy bands are thin, mostly a fraction of an inch in thickness, and are repeated in great numbers an inch or so apart. The result is a striped rock, dark grey and pale yellow, of which a considerable thickness may be often seen made up of alternating stripes, very characteristic in the field exposures. As the rocks are intensely folded and sometimes much brecciated the stripes are often crinkled, corrugated, bent back or undulating, folded into anticlines and synclines, or torn apart and recemented to form a many-patterned mosaic.

This sedimentary banding is not universally present, but fairly thick masses of shale, dark grey, pale blue, purple or sometimes buff in colour, occur also in the Mylor Series. There is generally a distinct cleavage, which has a different angle in the shales and in the arenaceous bands, but the shales are never sufficiently homogeneous, fine-grained and well cleaved to yield good roofing slates. Moreover in the great majority of the exposures the Mylor Beds are permeated by quartz veins in vast numbers. These seem to have no constant direction except that they are more common perpendicular to the bedding than along it. They vary in thickness from several feet down to mere threads. They branch, unite, interosculate, ramifying in all directions. As a rule they consist of pure, white, highly crystalline quartz, but may include slips of shale, seams of chlorite or thin deposits of carbonates, iron oxides or pyrites. They are not the same as the metalliferous veins which also occur in the Mylor Beds and have been worked for ores, but they are less regular, less persistent, thinner as a rule, and belong to a much earlier period. The quartz veins are sometimes folded like the arenaceous bands, but as a whole they seem to be of somewhat later origin than the main folding and the brecciation of the shales. In all probability, however, they are to be ascribed to the intense pressures and mechanical movements induced in the Mylor Series during the period of folding, shearing, fracture and displacement. They belong to the last stages of that process, when interstitial movement was dying down and the dissolved silica in the rock masses was being excreted, segregated and deposited in joints and fissures.

Although these shales are the characteristic Mylor rocks they are never alone. With them are always grits in beds from an inch or two up to two or three feet in thickness. These grits are seldom coarse and rarely conglomeratic. They are mostly grey in colour where scoured by the sand of the beaches, but their weathered surfaces are yellowish or brown. Current bedding is not a marked feature and they are often fairly pure with small admixture of shale. They seem to be neither carbonaceous nor calcareous. Ripple marking and concretions are occasionally visible on their bedding planes. They are never sufficiently abundant and well bedded to yield good building stone, and in most exposures their bedding, which is always conspicuous, is much broken and interrupted by movement during folding; the beds are distorted and torn apart while the plastic shale flows in between them, and often blocks of grit have been separated and rolled till they resemble clastic boulders. By brecciation and fluxion of this type crush-conglomerates may be produced, but these are never extensive, though very frequent in places where the movements have been strong and irregular.

Of the other components of the Mylor group there is little to be said. Though igneous greenstones are frequent there are no beds of ash and there seems to be no volcanic material in the shales. Very thin seams of dark argillaceous chert or lydian stone are not uncommon though very inconspicuous. They have never been found to contain fossils and their origin is obscure. Occasionally also there are thin impersistent seams of ferruginous dolomite, which may show cone-in-cone structure. It is a remarkable fact that nowhere have the Mylor Beds been proved to contain beds of limestone.

The Mylor rocks are everywhere much broken and folded. In the country under description they have always a dip between south and east, mostly south-south-east, with an east-north-east strike. The angle of dip is variable but is usually about forty-five degrees, though higher and lower inclinations are by no means uncommon, but they are seldom nearly horizontal. The bedding is usually very well preserved and is obvious even in the thin striped shales. It is best seen and most regular where the grit beds are of fair thickness as these seem to have obstructed folding on a small scale. In the coast sections there is also an immense number of faults or thrust planes which also have a general dip to south-south-east like that of the strata though at a higher angle : these thrusts occur every twenty to fifty yards and are easily detected where there is a distinctive bed of grit or a thin sill of greenstone. As a rule they have not a great throw and the displaced segments of a recognizable bed can often be picked up at a distance of a few yards. They seem to counteract the steady south-east dip and to repeat the same beds at short intervals. Hence they produce the impression of an immense thickness of fairly uniform rocks, dipping in a constant direction, while really the same beds are recurring and the apparent thickness is deceptive. Evidence of folding also is constantly present; the folding is apparently nearly isoclinal (hypisoclinal). The axial planes of all the folds have the same south-east dip and the folds are mostly narrow, less than a hundred yards across, but they are seldom complete as the thrust planes cut through them, often on the north-west sides of the anticlines. The thrust planes then act like the folds by bringing up again beds that would have been carried downwards by the prevalent steep dips. There are many variations of this type of structure displayed in the coastal cliffs and it is impossible to read a definite stratigraphical sequence in the rocks as the combined effects of folding and thrusting are so complex, but the general impression, which may be entirely deceptive, is that there is an ascending sequence to the south ; this is a consequence of the steady south-east dips, but there is other evidence to support it.

Although the stratification is well preserved in the Mylor rocks, and the cleavage though omnipresent is seldom so highly developed as to obliterate the original structures, no fossils have yet been found in them. In many places cleavage is rudimentary and in others it is parallel to the bedding. The bedding planes of the grits are often well exposed but no trace of fossils has been observed. Nor do the Mylor rocks contain fragments of older rocks which would give a clue to their relative age. Hence their geological position is uncertain, and opinions must be founded on evidence that may prove delusive if fossils are ever discovered.

No base is known for the Mylor rocks in this or any other part of Cornwall; on the other hand they seem to pass up conformably into the rocks that lie on the south-east of them—the Falmouth Beds of the Gramscatho. For this reason they may be provisionally placed either in the Lower Devonian or somewhere near that horizon. Hill believed that they were early Ordovician or pre-Ordovician but Upfield Green maintained that they were Gedinnian (Lower Devonian) and this view may be nearly correct. On account of the intense folding and faulting it is probable that there are infolds of Falmouth rocks in the area represented on the maps as belonging to the Mylor Beds, especially near the junction of the two groups, but there is little evidence of this in the coast sections, and in the inland country the exposures are often so inconclusive that the boundary lines can be regarded only as approximations.

The best section of the Mylor Beds in this Sheet is afforded by the cliffs that extend for three miles from Tregear Point past Porthleven harbour to the north end of the Loe Bar. For most of the way there is either a tide-washed rocky platform or a gravel beach below the cliff and the rocks can be examined without difficulty at low tide. Every characteristic of the Mylor Series is displayed in this section. Mylor striping is seen in many places between Porthleven and the Loe in very perfect development, and the bedding of grits and shales is invariably well preserved. In addition to the numerous thrusts there are locally belts of breccia in which the rocks may resemble a crush-conglomerate. About half a mile north-west of Porthleven, greenstone sills begin to appear, and from there to a point a mile south-east of Porthleven they occur in considerable numbers. Quartz-veining is everywhere conspicuous though irregular in its intensity, being much more pronounced in some places than in others; the quartz veins also ramify through the greenstone sills. At the north end of the section the killas shows occasional spotting probably induced by the Tregonning Granite, but in the rest of the section evidence of contact alteration is never impressive, and in fact is confined to a few beds that seem to have been specially susceptible.

Around Helston, although the land is mostly cultivated, there are numerous exposures of Mylor Beds in small quarries and in the roadside cuttings. There is an interesting section in the roadside near St. John's, where the beds are much broken and contorted.

Near Castle Wary typical Mylor striped beds are seen in a

small quarry, and there are some good sections in the grounds of
Penrose near the Loe Pool.   Further east, on Boskenwyn Downs,
there are numerous outcrops and the fields are strewn with
fragments of quartz from the quartz veins.   The south-east dip is
maintained, often at comparatively low angles.   At Pollard the
dark grey slates show traces of spotting due to the proximity of the
Carnmenellis Granite.

Between Boskenwyn and Polwheveral there are comparatively
few exposures but there is abundant quartz and shale debris in the
fields.   At Polwheveral and Porth Navas the rocks often display
the characteristic Mylor banding and the abundance of quartz
veins, though there are many signs of thermal alteration.   At the
mouth of Polpenwith Creek the blue slates and fine grit beds show
little of the Mylor fine banding, but this appears again in the rocks
on the opposite side of the creek north of Calamansack.   Further
to the north-east, at Roskillen, the dark slates with bands of grit
have been much brecciated and sheared.

Contact metamorphism.—The aureoles of thermal alteration
surrounding the Godolphin and Carnmenellis granites lie within the
area of Mylor rocks, and where these strata are highly argillaceous
they often show a considerable amount of recrystallization; the grit
bands are seldom affected to any great degree.   These aureoles
have been depicted on the geological map by a reddish overprint
on the Mylor colour and the intensity has been made to diminish
as the distance from the granite margin increases.   The outer
boundary of the aureole is always difficult to define as the mineral
changes in the rocks gradually die away and become imperceptible.
Moreover, in any group of beds having variable petrological
characters, there are some which more readily show contact
metamorphism than others.   Some beds may be spotted while
others appear quite normal; there are also cases where in a limited
area the beds show spots, while around them other beds apparently
of similar composition are free from spotting.

The aureole of the Godolphin Granite, in the north-west corner
of the map, extends from Breage to Tregear and has a breadth
varying from half a mile to over two miles.   A small strip of
country on the coast between Porthleven and the Loe is shown
also as consisting of contact-altered beds, but the changes in this
district are very slight and there is no adjacent granite unless one
is concealed beneath the sea.   The Carnmenellis Granite has altered
the Mylor Beds along its southern margin for a distance of a mile
to more than a mile and a half.   A slight degree of metamorphism
has been noticed in the rocks as far south as Gweek and
Mellangoose, but around Helston it is by no means conspicuous
or widespread.   The variation of the breadth of the aureole,
where the sedimentary rocks are so uniform along the strike as is the
case in the Mylors, may be due to the variation in the depth of the
granite below the surface.   Hence it is possible that the Godolphin
Granite plunges steeply in the Breage district and has a much

more gentle underground slope near Tregear Point. The
Carnmenellis Granite shows less difference in this respect, and if
there is an underground junction between these two granite masses
it must lie at a considerable depth, as their visible aureoles are not
confluent. The vertical thickness of the zone of perceptible
contact alteration is probably about two thousand feet.
Theoretically, if the beds are uniform along the aureole, and if
the surface of the ground is horizontal, the boundaries of the zones
of the aureole should correspond to depth contours of the underground surface of the granite. If the exposures were sufficiently
good, it might be possible to divide the aureole into zones of
increasing metamorphism each with its characteristic mineral
associations in the altered beds. The outermost zone would
contain slates with faint and sporadic spotting, and the external
margin of this zone would be very difficult to define owing to the
fact that certain beds are more susceptible than others. In this
zone we might place the districts around Porthleven, Sithney,
Helston, Mellangoose, and Gweek. The next zone would contain
the bulk of the aureole, having a breadth of about a mile.
Throughout this zone the slates are generally spotted but the grits
show little induration or mineral change. The spots are mostly
small, about the size of a pin's head, and darker in colour than the
matrix of the slate; they may be elongated and also flattened along
the bedding planes. In the inner parts of this zone the spots are
often larger and may be a quarter of an inch in diameter; sometimes they have very irregular sheaf-like outlines. Spotted slates
are found in the aureole of the Godolphin Granite about Methleigh
and Penbro: also in many places near the south edge of the
Carnmenellis Granite. A very good section across the aureole is
afforded by the Porth Navas creek south of Constantine, and at
Roskillen and Penpoll farther to the east. In microscopic sections
many of the smaller spots seem to be made up of scales of
muscovite and chlorite with indefinite, nearly isotropic material.
They seem to be due to a process of aggregation with a tendency to
crystallization, and if new minerals, such as cordierite or
andalusite, have been formed in them, they are either too imperfect
or too decomposed to be determinable. Nearer the granite there
is a zone, sometimes having a breadth of two or three hundred
yards, in which the slates tend to become crystalline. Muscovite
and biotite, in small well defined scales, are abundantly present
and the slates assume the aspect of a fine micaceous schist. In this
zone andalusite is by no means uncommon, but chiastolite and
cordierite seldom make their appearance. The andalusite crystals
may develop in the spots or independent of them : as the alterations
progress the spotting tends to disappear and also the schistosity
and the rock becomes a compact hornfels with biotite, muscovite,
andalusite, quartz and feldspar. Tourmaline is often present in
these hornfelses, but tourmalinization on a large scale is not
prevalent in this part of the aureole of the Carnmenellis Granite.

This is probably connected with the limited development of mineral veins, greisen and tourmaline, in the adjacent granite.

Microscopic sections of specimens taken from the innermost contact zone at Polwheveral and Treviades show that these rocks contain much deep brown biotite and muscovite with quartz, feldspar and andalusite. The bedding is not obliterated but is still apparent owing to thin bands rich in quartz. The andalusite may be colourless or may in certain crystals show areas intensely pleochroic with a rose-pink to purple colour, and is irregularly scattered through the rock. The spots are faint in some specimens but in others they are large, irregular and leafy, and consist mainly of muscovite and biotite and sometimes contain crystals of andalusite either in their interiors or projecting through their edges.

The most intense stages of contact alteration are to be observed in the pieces of slate which have been caught up in the granite. These are numerous and may be conspicuous as dark patches in the pale feldspathic granite, usually less than a foot in diameter. They are mostly very rich in black mica and sometimes have a distinctly schistose structure, resembling specimens of biotite-schist. In his account of the Carnmenellis Granite, Ghosh (1934) has given an interesting description of the petrography of these inclusions with many chemical analyses. The changes produced in these inclusions are not only thermal, due to the heat of the granite, but also in part chemical, owing to the tendency of the hot granitic liquid to assimilate or digest the foreign material. Minerals tend to be formed similar to those which are in solution in the granite or crystallizing out of it. The most important of these are biotite, muscovite and feldspar. The slate differs from the granite in containing more alumina, magnesia and iron oxides and less silica and alkalis, but the latter are to some extent borrowed from the granite which has abundant quartz and feldspar. The assimilation is never complete, however, and the residual alumina and magnesia (along with silica and some iron oxide) form cordierite, andalusite and tourmaline. In the Land's End Granite these inclusions sometimes contain corundum and sillimanite, and garnet appears rarely in the slates of the aureole, but these have not been reported from the Carnmenellis Granite. The last stage in the digestion of these inclusions of slate is shown by dispersed crystals of cordierite (often altered to pinite) and andalusite in the granite, often accompanied by wisps of biotite and muscovite. These are common in all Cornish granites and indicate that they are to be regarded as ' contaminated,' that is to say, their mineral composition has been modified by the incorporation of fragments of the country rock.

CHAPTER XIV

GRAMSCATHO BEDS

THE occurrence of plant-remains of indeterminable character at the Baulk Head, near Gunwalloe, and at Polnare Cove, near Nare Point, had been known for a considerable time (Fox, 1901), but they were so ill preserved and so fragmentary that their affinities were extremely doubtful. It was recognized, however, that they were of sufficient importance to render it extremely probable that the beds containing them belonged to the Devonian, and small areas having the Devonian colour were shown on the 1912 edition of the one-inch map in these neighbourhoods. To find satisfactory boundaries separating these from the adjacent beds, assumed to be Ordovician, was no easy matter, as the rocks of these areas were very similar.

The other beds south-east of the Mylors along the Loe Pool and thence to Gweek and the mouth of the Helford River were named Falmouth and Portscatho Beds from localities to the east of Falmouth where they had previously been encountered in course of the mapping. Subsequently much light was thrown upon the problem by the researches of Miss E. M. Lind Hendriks, who made a very careful and assiduous search of the outcrops both in the Lizard and the Mevagissey Sheets. She found, in a limited number of places in the Meneage, thin seams of coaly matter in the bedding planes of the grits and shales. These plant fragments appear as dark impressions and must be carefully distinguished from the thin patches of black shale in the grits, and dark concretions, which also are frequently seen; the best of the plants show organic structure in microscopic sections, and in a few cases the outlines of simple or branching leaf-forms may be recognized. No other fossils that can be identified have been found in these rocks though traces of brachiopods and of corals (*Pachypora*?) have been occasionally seen.

The plant-bearing beds occur in rocks formerly mapped as Devonian, at Baulk Head, Jangye Ryn, Castle Hill (Gunwalloe) and Polnare Cove; as Veryan, at Polurrian Cove, Poldhu Cove, Gunwalloe Church Cove and Porthallow; as Falmouth Beds at Gunwalloe Fishing Cove and in the cliffs below Chyvarloe at the south end of Loe Bar. They occur also in Portscatho Beds at several places in the Mevagissey Sheet. There is no reason to doubt that these fossiliferous beds are all on or about the same horizon, at any rate there is nothing in the nature of the plants to discredit that supposition, and consequently the Portscatho, Falmouth and Manaccan strata in which they occur were grouped together and called Gramscatho Beds by Hendriks (1931) and Flett (1933).

The plant-remains have been exhaustively studied and described by Professor Lang (1929) and from his account we take the following summary of his conclusions :

" Most of the remains are of larger or smaller fragments of what is probably in most cases secondary wood. A few branched specimens are described and compared with larger branched specimens from the Manaccan beds.

" By adopting suitable methods the detailed structure of the secondary wood has been fully ascertained in one specimen from the Portscatho Beds at Pendower. This is named *Dadoxylon hendriksi*. Traces of definite structure corresponding to that shown by this specimen have been found in other specimens from the Portscatho Beds, in a specimen from the Falmouth Beds, and in a specimen from the Veryan Beds. These various specimens link on the bulk of the ill-preserved remains to *Dadoxylon*.

" Small fragments with altered structure, but in one case with indications of spirally thickened elements, are described from the Portscatho Beds.

" A single specimen of a slender axis that bore spirally arranged appendages, is described, from Veryan Beds.

" The interest of these plant-remains in relation to the possible age of the beds is discussed. If the beds are shown by geologists to be older than the Upper Devonian and of Middle Devonian age, these plant-remains would afford one of the earliest satisfactory records of such highly organized secondary wood. The interest would be proportionately greater should the beds prove to be Lower Devonian or pre-Devonian.

" It can be said that wood of this organization is at present known from the Upper Devonian and probably from the Middle Devonian; it is not known from Lower Devonian or Lower Old Red Sandstone rocks. It would, however, be unsafe to decide on the ground of the plant-remains alone that the Cornish beds under consideration must be younger than the Lower Devonian, though, taking into consideration all the plant-remains, a Middle Devonian age seems to be indicated."

As a consequence of these investigations the Falmouth, Portscatho and Manaccan beds of the 1912 map were swept into the Gramscatho Beds of the 1934 Sheet. The plant-bearing Veryan Beds at Porthallow are incorporated in the Meneage Breccia : the Veryan Beds of Gunwalloe, Poldhu and Polurrian are shown as Gramscatho. The probable age of the Gramscatho is Middle Devonian.

These discoveries by Lind Hendriks and Lang revolutionized the geology of the Meneage; beds which had been supposed to be of Ordovician age were now known to be Devonian, and when a new edition of Sheet 359 of the one-inch geological map was prepared in 1933 the stratigraphy was revised in accordance with the latest information and an explanatory notice was published in the Summary of Progress of the Geological Survey (Flett, 1933). Since then Hendriks has published her full results and her interpretation of the Meneage, Veryan and Mevagissey districts (Hendriks, 1937). This marks a very notable advance in our knowledge of the geology of Cornwall and has cleared up some problems that hitherto were very obscure.

The strata containing *Dadoxylon hendriksi* and the affiliated flora (the Hendriksi Beds) have been identified at so many points in the Meneage that they clearly cover a large area. The plants are best preserved where the bedding is well marked and where cleavage is rudimentary, absent or strictly parallel to the bedding planes, and it seems probable that if the conditions were favourable, many other localities might have been added to the list of those in which the fossils have been detected.

The stratigraphical relations between the Gramscatho Beds and the Mylors will probably not be definitely settled till fossils are found in the Mylors; the balance of evidence, however, is in favour of an upward succession from Mylors to Gramscathos. The steady prevalence of a south-easterly dip in the coast sections from Porthleven to Gunwalloe probably means nothing; it is quite likely that there is a general inversion of the beds. But the Mylors have some features that indicate that they may be the underlying rocks. They are slightly more metamorphic and more phyllitic in the shaly beds. Quartz-veining is more intense and more widespread, and the distortion of the strata with production of crush-breccias and crush-conglomerates is more pronounced. Probably for these reasons both Hill and Hendriks have thought it probable that the Mylors are older than the Gramscathos. They may be Lower Devonian or even Gedinnian as was suggested by Upfield Green (1904b).

The Falmouth Beds appear to be a natural group differing lithologically from the Mylors to the north of them, and their characteristics and distribution were recognized by De la Beche (1839). They are a group of grits and shales which have mostly brownish, buff or yellow colours and are often pinkish and sometimes pale green. Hence they are paler and more variegated than the Mylors, which are usually dark grey to black though never carbonaceous. The Falmouth Beds are also softer than the Mylors and decompose more readily and this no doubt tends to accentuate their brownish and yellowish tints, though these are essentially original and not superinduced. Quartz-veining is on the whole less frequent and less pronounced than in the Mylors, but owing to the softness of the shales, quartz fragments are very numerous in the fields as the shales have broken down and released them. Among the Falmouth Beds there are occasional areas of darker rocks that have resemblance to the Mylors, though usually without the characteristic striping, and these may be upfolds or blocks of Mylor strata inserted by faulting. In the beds mapped by Hill as Falmouths the Hendriksi flora has been found in two

places, at the south end of Loe Bar and at Gunwalloe Fishing
Cove, and in both these cases the fossiliferous strata have little of
the Falmouth character, but are strong, hard grits with dark shales;
still it is not possible to prove that they have been inserted among
Falmouth Beds by a process of faulting.

The type exposure of Falmouth Beds is on the south shore at
Falmouth where all their characters are well exhibited, but this is
beyond the boundaries of the present Sheet.   On both the west
and the east coasts of the Meneage there are cliffs and shores
composed of Falmouth Beds that have all the characters of those of
the type locality.   On the west coast they start about a quarter of
a mile south of the Loe Bar and continue to a short distance north
of Gunwalloe Fishing Cove.   They have a very steady and regular
dip to the south-south-east at varying angles but usually about
forty degrees.   Evidence of isoclinal folding is often noticeable
and there are very numerous faults or thrusts that have a steep
south-easterly dip.   Most of these faults seem to have a small
throw but in places there is a considerable amount of brecciation.
Quartz veins occur but are rather local and distinctly less common
than in the Mylors, north of the Loe Bar.   In addition to the usual
buff and yellowish colours of the group, there are beds of sandy
shale which are pinkish, grey or pale green.   The plant fossils
which occur in this coast line are not found in the typical sandy
brownish Falmouth Beds but in dark, little cleaved shales and
thickish grey grits near the Baulk Head and at the south end of
Loe Bar.   On some of the bedding planes they are quite numerous
but always fragmentary and usually undecipherable; woody or
coaly layers are scarce.

From the west coast a band of rocks of Falmouth type can be
traced across country to Mawnan Smith on the east coast.   The
pinkish shales and yellow grits can be seen along Carminow Creek,
a branch of the Loe Pool, and thence across the Lizard road to the
south of Helston Downs there are many fragments in the fields but
few exposures.   At Gweek, the road cutting on the west of the
valley near the Methodist Chapel shows laminated, soft, pale,
sandy shales and brown or reddish grit bands and there are several
outcrops in the neighbourhood of the stream.   Further east, at
Calamansack and Polwheveral Creek there are buff sandy beds
with blue slates which extend along the shores of the Helford
River, and similar beds are seen in the creek near Porth Navas.
Although little reliance can be placed on lithological characters as
a guide to geological horizon in country like southern Cornwall,
there seems reason to believe that both the Mylors and the Falmouth
Beds of this district are stratigraphical groups deserving
recognition.

At Portscatho, Hill's Portscatho Beds have yielded the
Hendriksi flora, but in the Meneage none of the beds that Hill
assigned to this group have been proved to contain the zonal
plants.   It is clear, however, that the distinction he made between

Portscatho and Manaccan beds at Gunwalloe is fallacious and his boundary line between these two formations is impossible. The Portscatho Beds are not a natural group and must be discarded; they are merely the Manaccan Beds where they were not suspected to be fossiliferous. With them the Falmouth Beds were incorporated into the Gramscathos because the Hendriksi flora had been found in them. The Falmouths may be the lower subdivision of the Gramscathos.

There are very excellent sections of the Hendriksi Beds along the western coast line of the Meneage, both in the coves and in the cliffs and even the latter are often accessible for considerable distances at low tide. At the Baulk Head, south of Gunwalloe Fishing Cove, the strong grey grits and thin dark shales have preserved their bedding in extraordinary perfection and the cleavage is often faint and evanescent. Further south in Halzaphron Cove, there is much faulting and brecciation, but from Pedngwinian south to Poldhu there are magnificent exposures of the folded Gramscathos. They have steep dips mostly to south-east and the folding is especially well seen at Jangye Ryn, where an anticlinal arch has its summit indented by a minor syncline. Although the beds on this coast are often contorted and disrupted the bedding is everywhere obvious and there is much dark grey grit in bands up to two feet in thickness. Quartz-veining varies much in abundance and intensity, being mostly rather scanty but in some places is almost as intense as in the Mylors. At every few yards there is a fault or thrust, often marked by a thin line of crush-breccia, and usually eroded by the sea, giving rise to a little cove. These faults or thrusts are steeper than the bedding and seem to keep repeating the strata again and again. There are no limestones in this section, though thin layers of dark dolomite, often with cone-in-cone structure, occur occasionally, and not infrequently in the dark shales there are thin seams of argillaceous cherty material, or carious, interbedded quartz secretions.

The distance from the south end of Loe Bar to Polurrian Cove, where the coast line consists wholly of Gramscatho Beds, is about six miles and if the average dip is about forty degrees the thickness of the group would be about three miles, which is preposterous. On the other hand the frequent occurrence of the plant-bearing horizon along this shore indicates that the same beds are being constantly repeated by isoclinal folding and by thrusting counteracting the dips. Probably the whole thickness of the Gramscatho Beds in this section is not more than a few hundred feet, and the appearance of great thickness is deceptive.

Although the coast section has been carefully searched there is no evidence of volcanic tuffs, and there are no pillow-lavas or intrusive greenstones. The Cury diabases do not come within a mile of the west coast. Equally striking is the absence of conglomerate anywhere in the cliffs from Porthleven to Polurrian. The Menaver Conglomerate must either be very local or must belong to the uppermost part of the Hendriksi Beds. The absence of radiolarian cherts also is very noticeable, and there is nothing to recall the Meneage Breccia of the east coast north of Porthallow. The radiolarian cherts, the pillow-lavas and the regional breccias appear to be restricted to the Meneage crush-zone.

Strata of the Portscatho type were mapped by Hill on the east coast as extending from the north edge of the Sheet to Gillan Harbour, on both sides of the entrance to the Helford River and across country westwards along the estuary to Mawgan, and thence to Gunwalloe.

About Rosemullion Head there is much sandstone, with dark slate and sandy killas. The dips are irregular but mostly to the south-east. At Mawnan there are fine cherty-looking siliceous beds among the slates, and the rocks are often brecciated or torn into lenticles. Isoclinal folding is frequently conspicuous and occasionally the breccias resemble crush-conglomerates. At Parson's Beach there are beds of sandstone four or five feet in thickness. On the south side of the Helford River from The Gew to Dennis Head and thence westwards to St. Anthony the strata are mostly brownish grits and sandstones with grey or yellowish sandy shales. Vein-quartz is not specially abundant though locally well developed. Traces of fossils have been found along this shore but nothing decipherable. The dips are mostly south-east at an angle of thirty to forty degrees, but vary both in direction and in amount. Faulting or thrusting is constantly present and increases in frequency as the section is traced southwards : many of the smaller faults are occupied by quartz veins. Probably the same beds are being constantly repeated and the thickness of the strata is really quite moderate. From St. Anthony along the Helford River the beds maintain their character. There is abundance of grit and sandstone, usually in thin beds, with grey or dark shale and sandy shales of brownish colour, everywhere broken and displaced by small faults which run parallel to the strike. Although folding is not conspicuous there can be no doubt that there is constant repetition of the beds, and though there is great local variation and individual beds can never be traced for any considerable distance, the general character is well maintained. Occasionally dark shales may be intercalated that have a resemblance to the Mylor Beds and more frequently greenish or reddish strata appear for a space, recalling the Falmouths. There is no certainty that these are not upfolds or infolds of rocks belonging to these groups, but the great prevalence of rocks having the Portscatho facies along the stretch of country from Helford, through Mawgan to Berepper makes it probable that this is a stratigraphical group. The fact that plant-bearing beds have not been found along this outcrop, except on the west coast, no doubt involves some degree of uncertainty, but so far as information is at present available that seems to be no reason to believe that they do not form a definite stratigraphical unit.

CHAPTER XV

MENAVER CONGLOMERATE

ON the south side of the entrance to the Helford River and Gillan Harbour there are certain beds of conglomerate, grit and shale that have attracted much attention from geologists since the beginning of last century. The principal masses of conglomerate are found in three localities: Nare Head, Menaver Beach and Flushing, while the shales and grits occupy the rest of the coast section.

At Nare Head the massive conglomerate forms a cliff over a hundred feet high and must have a thickness of more than two

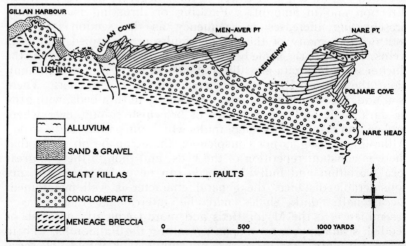

Fig. 20.—*Sketch-map of the shore from Nare Point to Gillan Harbour (after J. B. Hill).*

hundred feet. It is almost free from interbedded sandstone and shale and contains blocks more than a foot in diameter, but as the cliff is vertical and its base is submerged, it is not easily inspected. It seems to differ, however, in no important respect from the conglomerate of the other outcrops. The conglomerate is bounded on the south by a fault which brings it against the hard, compacted

Meneage Breccia well seen at the Turwell, but the conglomerate itself and the shales and grits to the north of it are never much brecciated and consequently have not been ascribed to the Meneage Breccia, of which the northern boundary is taken at the south side of Nare Head.

Nare Point is about a third of a mile north of Nare Head, and between these headlands is Polnare Cove. The conglomerate stops at the south of the cove, apparently cut off by a fault, and in the cove are clay-slates with sandy and calcareous beds well stratified and not severely brecciated. In the slates there are frequent traces of fossil plants and also obscure remains of corals and brachiopods. The plants have been tentatively ascribed by Lang to the Hendriksi flora and the strata in which they occur show no important

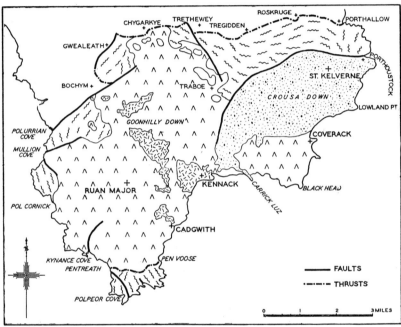

FIG. 21.—*Major faults and thrusts of the Lizard Area.*
(St. Kelverne should be St. Keverne).

difference from the Gramscatho Beds which are well developed on the west coast. Some of the grits are slightly conglomeratic. Nare Point also consists of killas and grits, without distinctive characters, along with a band of breccia that may be due to crushing or faulting. From Nare Point in a south-west direction the slates and grits persist for several hundred yards and are then succeeded by the Menaver Conglomerate which forms Menaver Beach, followed by blue-black slates, lilac shales and grits. As we approach Gillan Cove there are conglomeratic bands and farther west, at Flushing, there is a considerable mass of conglomerate that forms a projecting headland.

In the grits and slates along this shore there are obscure traces of fossils, which may be brachiopods or corals, but the plant beds of Polnare Cove are apparently not repeated. As usual in this part of Cornwall there is evidence of faulting every here and there, but it does not seem to be important, and though the rocks are occasionally brecciated, they do not approach the Meneage Breccia in this respect. The remarkable conglomerate of these three outcrops presents so many unusual characters in common that they must be regarded as belonging to the same bed and the general character of the associated strata indicates that they may well be placed in the Hendriksi Beds.

The Menaver Conglomerate (to give the group a general name) is a true conglomerate and not a crush-conglomerate, though undoubtedly it has been crushed in places. It contains too great a variety of rocks and there are too many of them that are not derived from adjacent strata, to have been formed by mechanical crushing from the rocks with which it occurs. Yet as an erosional conglomerate it presents many features that are perplexing. Among its ingredients the following rocks have been identified :—

Metamorphic :—phyllite, mica-schist, granulite, mylonite, sheared quartzite, hornblende-schists (rare, rotten), ferruginous schists, sheared granites, garnet, epidosite, vein-quartz.

Igneous :—granophyre, albite-diabase, hornblendic and epidotic diabase, spilite, keratophyre, quartz-keratophyre, palagonite (?). The keratophyres are often sub-variolitic and belong to types not known in western Cornwall. The spilites are seldom vesicular.

Sedimentary :—grit and greywacke, slate and shale, cherty slate, chert (no limestone).

The majority of these rocks are such as might reasonably be expected to occur in the Lizard province though no identically similar rocks may be at present exposed at the surface. But the general facies of the Gramscatho strata as exemplified in the excellent outcrops on the western shores of the Meneage and along the banks of the Helford River does not produce the impression that they were deposited in close proximity to a land surface. They seem to have been laid down in moderate depths of water; conglomerates and coarse grits are absent and there is much fine shale indicating sub-littoral conditions. The drifted plant-remains and the general absence of limestone make it improbable that the land was far away, but as the plants are reduced to mere shreds and fragments they were presumably transported from a moderate distance.

Even more impressive than the variety of materials in this conglomerate is its tumultuous character. The matrix is sandy rather than shaly. Blocks of several inches, up to a foot in diameter, are very common. There are also lumps of quartzose grit that may be three feet or more across.   De la Beche remarked that some of them must weigh nearly a quarter of a ton.   They are slightly rounded at their corners (or barrel-shaped) so that they must have been rolled about, but it is inconceivable that they had been carried from some distance by waves or currents.   And mixed with the conglomerate there is fine dark shale, indicating conditions of quiet water.   It is extraordinary also that in the conglomerate there are numerous lumps of black shale imperfectly rounded. The accumulation in fact has a resemblance to a quarry dump or scree that had been modified to some extent by the action of the waves.

Another point about this conglomerate that deserves to be considered is its very local distribution.   The three outcrops occur within a distance of rather over a mile.   There is no trace of this rock in the Gramscatho Beds along the Helford River or on the west coast or elsewhere.   It thins out very rapidly westwards and though about two hundred feet at least at Nare Head, it is about twenty feet thick at Flushing.   This gives it a resemblance to a cone of detritus.

It has generally been considered as the local representative of the conglomeratic beds at Grampound and Ladock and has been placed at the base of the local Devonian, but the latest researches show that it probably belongs to the Hendriksi Beds of the Gramscatho, and as these presumably pass down into the Mylors it cannot be a local base.   As a matter of fact it seems to be more probably the highest Devonian bed in the Meneage succession or at least one of the highest.

In 1885 Somervail and Fox described certain rocks of the Meneage as volcanic breccias and tuffs and suggested a volcanic origin for the Menaver Conglomerate.   Strange as it may seem, this is the only hypothesis that appears to offer a firm basis for the explanation of its remarkable features.   We know that volcanic activity was rife in eastern Cornwall and in Devonshire during mid-Devonian, late-Devonian and early-Carboniferous times.   If we suppose that a volcanic orifice burst out on the Devonian sea bottom in the vicinity of the present Nare Head it is easy to imagine that a low cone would be built up consisting of the rocks through which the opening had burst.   These blocks, torn from the subjacent rocks, would be of all sizes and would comprise representatives of all the strata down to the vicinity of the volcanic focus.   The resulting cone would be slowly washed down by waves and currents and its materials strewn about over a limited area while the sands and muds of the period were accumulating around and among them.   Many of the blocks in the conglomerate resemble the grits, shales, cherts and spilites of the adjacent country.   The presence of schists and gneisses indicates that these rest on a foundation of metamorphic rocks.   The great variety of lithological types found in the Menaver Conglomerate would arise from the fact that it contains representatives of all the underground strata of this district and possibly also of some rocks now removed by denudation.

An obvious objection to this hypothesis is the fact that material of volcanic origin does not predominate in the conglomerate. The spilitic rocks are not highly vesicular and do not look like volcanic bombs, but if highly vesicular they might have been ground to powder by the blocks of quartzite and grit. There is, however, a noteworthy abundance of keratophyres belonging to types not elsewhere found in Cornwall. The keratophyric and quartz-keratophyric magmas are highly explosive, and the lavas of this type are often shattered to fragments by their own vapours. The explosion might have been due to a keratophyric magma. Alternatively we may suppose that the volcano resembled those of the Maars of the Eifel or the cauldrons of the Ries which have blown out great apertures from which large quantities of meta-morphic and sedimentary rocks have been cast out, but have ejected igneous material only in small quantities.

The relation of the Menaver Conglomerate to the conglomeratic beds that occur with the pillow-lavas about Tregidden and Treworgie is by no means clear. The Tregidden beds are much finer-grained and do not contain large blocks of quartzite: the pebbles are small, mostly not over two or three inches in diameter, but they include schists, granitoid rocks, diabases and other lithological types that imply transport of material. One peculiar feature, however, may be significant—the presence in the matrix of the conglomerates of fine yellowish grains of weathered feldspar. A similar matrix is seen in certain beds associated with the Menaver Conglomerate. Unfortunately the southern belt of conglomerate does not emerge to the east coast, or, if it does, is so sheared and brecciated as to be unrecognizable, and it is not known to accompany beds that contain the Hendriksi flora. Hence its position is doubtful, but there is no difficulty in believing that it may be the thinned edge of the conglomerate of Menaver Beach.

The absence of pebbles of Lizard serpentine and gabbro from the Menaver Conglomerate seems to be well established and has occasioned comment. If this were an erosional conglomerate it might be explained either by supposing that the Lizard intrusives were not forced up to the surface before the Hercynian movements or that they were not injected into the Lizard schists before the Middle Devonian. But if the Menaver Conglomerate is the product of a volcanic explosion the simplest explanation of the absence of these rocks is by supposing that the Lizard serpentine and gabbro do not extend northwards beneath the Palaeozoic rocks so far as the south shore of Gillan Creek. This is rendered more probable if we consider that the break between the killas and the Lizard schists would naturally take place at the margin of the deep-seated intrusive plutonics which would act as solid and resistant masses, driving the schists northwards.

The Menaver Conglomerate, if admitted to be of volcanic origin, does not, unfortunately, throw much light on the problem of the age of the Meneage pillow-lavas. From their association with radiolarian cherts they were at first thought to be presumably Ordovician like the similar assemblage in the Southern Uplands of Scotland. It is now known, however, that pillow-lavas and cherts occur in all the Palaeozoic formations and also in the pre-Cambrian. Hill was of opinion that they formed part of his Veryan (Ordovician) Series but had doubts whether they might not be Devonian as along the Lizard boundary they are accompanied by a conglomerate which he placed in the Devonian. Lind Hendriks considers that in the Meneage and Veryan areas there may be two sets of pillow-lavas, one of which is Lower and the other Upper Devonian. So far as the Meneage is concerned it is difficult to believe that the pillow-lavas are not one series as they are so similar in their microscopic characters. Their peculiar sub-radiate or semi-variolitic structure is very characteristic and is not found in equal development in any Devonian pillow-lavas of the south-west of England.

The Menaver Conglomerate lies among rocks which have the fossils of the Gramscatho Beds. But among the admirable exposures of the west coast where the Gramscatho Beds extend for several miles there is no conglomerate and no pillow-lava. Similarly there is an absence of these types of rock in the Mylors, and though some of the Penzance greenstones may be lavas, they are not accompanied by cherts. For these reasons it is probable that the Meneage pillow-lavas are either pre-Mylor or post-Gramscatho. Unless fossils are found in the cherts or in the patches of limestone that occur among the lavas this question will not be definitely settled.

CHAPTER XVI

GREENSTONES AND DOLERITES

IN the Helston and Porthleven districts that are numerous masses
of greenstone, all of which seem to be intrusive into the Mylor Beds.
The rocks are dark green, massive, rarely schistose and usually
rather fine-grained.   As a rule they are not badly sheared and
do not form hornblendic or chloritic schists though locally they
may assume a schistose habit where they have been traversed by
planes of movement.   At their edges they are firmly welded to the
adjacent killas, of which they often contain small fragments and
sometimes larger blocks, or even masses which appear to separate
the greenstone into distinct minor sills.   Contemporaneous
segregations may be present, usually more feldspathic and of
lighter colour than the main rock, and occasionally the sills have a
banded character, the bands varying in composition, colour or
coarseness of grain.

In their petrographical characters the rocks are epidiorites or
uralitic diabases, sometimes retaining traces of ophitic structure.
Not infrequently they contain scattered phenocrysts of feldspar,
which may preserve remains of their original crystalline outlines,
or may have been drawn out into lenticles.   There is no trace of
porphyritic augite or olivine.   The greenstones weather to dark
brown, friable, ferruginous earths, and many of them show
spheroidal weathering with concentric rotten crusts.   The original
columnar jointing is seldom retained, but some sills have a platy
structure parallel to their extension, which seems to be primary.

The great majority of them are in a state of advanced alteration
and consist of hornblende in fibrous or ragged crystals, with
chlorite and carbonates.   The feldspar when fresh seems to be
mostly albite, but it is often represented by calcite, prehnite,
sericite, epidote and other secondary minerals.   Chlorite is
exceedingly common and in many of the rocks it is more abundant
than hornblende.   The hornblende has sometimes a tendency to
imitate ophitic structure as it forms aggregates of highly irregular
outline penetrated by the pseudomorphs of elongated rectangular
feldspars, but often a general parallel orientation can be noted in
the hornblende fibres and chloritic flakes which gives the rocks an

incipient schistosity. Epidote and zoisite are less abundant than calcite and other carbonates.

There are many quarries in the greenstones as formerly these rocks were much used for building and as road-stones, but now these quarries are mostly neglected and overgrown or obscured by rubbish. The best exposures of this group of rocks are on the coast both north and south of Porthleven Harbour. They begin to appear at the west edge of the Sheet near Methleigh Beacon where there is a thin sill a few feet thick severed by small faults. Forty yards farther south there is a six-foot band and another which can be traced inland for a short distance and has been worked for walling-stone. These outcrops are often dislocated by small faults but they follow the general trend of the killas in this neighbourhood, which is north-east, and their dip is in accordance with that of the contiguous Mylor slates. As we approach Porthleven Harbour the greenstones increase in number and in the quarter of a mile north of the west pier there are at least eight sills varying in thickness from a few feet up to about forty feet. They all dip south-east like the killas surrounding them and appear to be concordant with the slates, but when their edges are closely examined, they may be transgressive and inclusions of the slate are not uncommon. The sills, however, do not send out veins into the slates. The rocks have been very much disturbed by faults and planes of shearing and the outcrops of the sills are often shifted for several yards. Only the thickest sills can be traced for more than a short distance, and even these may taper out and die away rapidly in a manner that suggests that they have been intersected by planes of movement. The smaller sills may wriggle or jump from place to place and their separated parts can be traced in the rocky foreshore. The greenstones participate in the distortions of the killas in such a way as to show that they were injected before the folding, but, on account of their massive character, they are less twisted and contorted than the slates and grits, which seem to have yielded and flowed around them. Quartz veins are almost as numerous in the greenstones as in the killas. They are often a foot or two in breadth and branch freely; many of them may be seen to pass from the greenstones into the killas, but they show few signs of folding and are probably somewhat later in origin than the flexures and contortions in the sedimentary rocks.

On both sides of the entrance to Porthleven Harbour there are strong masses of killas and on these the piers and breakwater are partly founded. The channel of the harbour is probably the site of a killas mass which has been eroded by the sea and the stream between two ridges of greenstone.

On the south side of Porthleven Harbour the greenstones are even better displayed than on the north-west. In a distance of a mile there are eleven outcrops, some having a breadth of only a few feet while the largest near Parc-an-als is not less than seventy feet thick. Few of them can be traced down the beach, which is covered with fine gravel, but near the pier there are several which are shifted about by small faults in the rocky foreshore. The greenstone sills all follow the strike of the killas and have the south-east dip which marks all the rocks along the shore. In the fields above the cliff there are no outcrops and the ground is all under cultivation. The sills are cut by numerous faults which are mostly parallel to the general strike and more nearly vertical than the prevalent dip, so that on one side the outcrop of the sill is very frequently delimited by a movement-plane. None of these sills is really schistose and they seem to have suffered less distortion than the killas around them, but it is quite clear that they were in place before the folding and crushing of the sediments.

There is little contact alteration of the shales by the igneous rocks, but usually at the junction the killas is bleached and hardened; it has less micaceous sheen and sometimes there are traces of spotting. Transgressive junctions, which are not due to relative movement, may frequently be observed, and inclusions of killas in the greenstone, though usually small, may sometimes have a length of several yards. The greenstones are compact, not vesicular, rather fine-grained, sometimes carrying porphyritic feldspars, but much decomposed. There are no traces of slaggy tops, but the margins of the sills are usually finer-grained than the centres, and seem to have been chilled. In the adjacent killas there are no signs of ashes or bombs such as would be expected to be present if the igneous rocks were lavas, and the whole aspect and behaviour of the greenstones are in harmony with the theory that they are intrusions which have followed the bedding planes of the original shales and sandstones with remarkable consistency.

The Porthleven greenstones strike across country in a north-east direction with the Mylor Beds in which they occur. Between Porthleven and Helston they must be present in considerable numbers though owing to the cultivated nature of the ground they are seldom seen. On the roadside, however, near Penrose Hill, two outcrops of greenstone have been quarried and another small band is seen in a quarry at Ventonvedna. At Lanner Vean a small band, about six feet wide, is exposed in the farmyard. In the deep valley of the Cober and on the roadsides in the lower part of Helston there are numerous exposures of greenstone. At Castle Wary there is an old greenstone quarry, and another mass occurs between that point and Helston. At Parkventon, north-east of Weeth, there is a quarry in greenstone adjoining the high road and several narrow sills of greenstone are seen near St. John's Hospital. In the higher ground to the south-east of Helston there are several important greenstone sills. One of these has been extensively quarried for building stone near the Union Workhouse; it is from sixty to seventy yards in width but is divided into three or more bands by intercalations of knotted slate and probably the breadth of the outcrop is increased by folding or faulting. About a quarter of a mile to the north-east a small pit by the roadside probably marks the continuation of this sill and on the south-west at a similar distance there is a quarry which may mark the extension of the greenstone in that direction. It is evident that the outcrops, as at Porthleven, have a lenticular shape and the thickest sills die out in a short distance.

North-east of Helston greenstones occur on both sides of the Falmouth road though the known outcrops are probably only a small proportion of the sills actually present in this well-cultivated country. The most interesting are those in the railway cutting a short distance north of Helston Station. At least eight greenstones are seen in a distance of a quarter of a mile. Most of them are thin, having a breadth of only a few feet, but some of them are twenty yards across as seen in the cutting. They are all fine-grained and free from marked schistosity. Many of them are much decomposed at the surface but large blocks of hard rock were also obtained when the cutting was made and may still be seen in the adjacent walls. The killas is often faintly spotted, perhaps by the contact action of the granite.

Two miles farther to the north-east a greenstone is seen at Trewennack within a short distance of the Carnmenellis Granite. This is a compact rock with paler bands which give it a laminated appearance. The outcrop has a breadth of about sixty yards. Owing probably to the contact action of the granite, this rock proves, under the microscope, to contain pale green augite and yellow epidote, with sphene and grains of zinc blende.

Dolerite.—In the neighbourhood of Cury there are several outcrops of dolerite which have been given a dark red colour on the geological map because they are in a much better state of preservation than the epidiorites of Porthleven and Helston. They are small masses of irregular shape and mostly ill exposed in cultivated ground, but there are several small pits in the largest mass near Cury. The rock is unlike the pillow-lavas, because it is not vesicular and is devoid of pillow structure. The adjacent shales show some evidence of contact alteration. Under the microscope the rock from White Cross (5634) is an ophitic diabase with much fresh, brownish purple augite and traces of decomposed olivine. Other specimens from near Cury Church (5640) are porphyritic with fresh augite. There is little evidence of shearing in any of the specimens. The feldspar is often decomposed with production of albite, prehnite, calcite and epidote, but when fresh is zoned plagioclase ranging in composition from labradorite to oligoclase. In some characters, such as their state of preservation, these dolerites resemble the pillow-lavas, but their microscopic characters indicate that they are intrusive, and they may be hypabyssal members of the spilite group. That they retain their original igneous structures so much more perfectly than the Porthleven greenstones may be due to their being on a higher geological horizon and consequently having been subjected to less intense pressure during the epoch of folding and movement.

CHAPTER XVII

GRANITE, ELVAN AND LAMPROPHYRE

THE Carnmenellis Granite occupies only a very small part of the area represented on this Sheet, extending for about five miles along its northern border from east to west and for less than half a mile from north to south. Similarly the Godolphin Granite, in the vicinity of Breage, projects for about a quarter of a square mile into the north-west corner of the map. Their principal extension is in the adjacent Sheets, to which they properly belong, and their general characters are described in the memoirs on these Sheets.

Both of these granites are of the well known Cornish type, with large white porphyritic crystals of orthoclase or perthite feldspar, often fluidally arranged, muscovite, biotite, tourmaline, and occasional crystals of andalusite and cordierite (or pinite). The Godolphin Granite differs from the Carnmenellis Granite in being much finer-grained. In the Carnmenellis Granite the conspicuous feldspar crystals are usually an inch and sometimes three or four inches in diameter. As that granite has been very extensively quarried, especially near Falmouth, for many years, its external characters are familiar to all who take an interest in British granites. The margin of the granite forms rising ground, mostly under cultivation, and the junction with the killas to the south is not well exposed in sections, but there are many small quarries within the area covered by this Sheet, and some abandoned mines, so that it is easy to obtain specimens of the granite at no great distance from the edge of the intrusive mass. An exhaustive study of this granite has been made by Ghosh (1934). He finds that there has been a succession of intrusions of slightly different type and that the western side of the outcrop in this Sheet consists of a coarse granite with large and abundant porphyritic crystals of orthoclase in a coarsely crystalline groundmass of quartz, feldspars, muscovite and biotite; tourmaline and andalusite are seldom absent. Some varieties contain abundance of biotite; in others muscovite is present in fair quantity. There are acid and basic variations which may appear as segregations or as veins, and the basic types in addition to much biotite contain abundant andalusite. This is the kind of rock that has been much quarried in the neighbourhood of Constantine. A second type of granite is present in the vicinity of Brill and is believed to be intrusive into the coarser granite. It is finer in texture and more rich in biotite than the coarse granite but contains also many porphyritic feldspars with much biotite and some muscovite (which is partly secondary and developed by crushing or by pneumatolytic action from the feldspars). It is intersected by many pegmatitic veins usually more feldspathic than the surrounding rock and coarsely crystallized. These veins may be rich in albite and sometimes contain fluor, apatite and topaz. There are also dark bands which carry much biotite and seem to be segregations; sometimes the rock has a gneissic banding, apparently due to fluxion, with alternating dark and light streaks of slightly different composition.

The Carnmenellis Granite in the neighbourhood of Penryn is famous for the enormous blocks that can be quarried from it. Monoliths weighing a thousand or even three thousand tons can be obtained; in this respect it resembles the granites of Egypt. This property arises from the scarcity of open joint fissures, while the granite at the same time possesses the property of splitting readily in certain definite directions when it is attacked with wedges. The granite in fact has a grain, like a piece of wood, arising no doubt from the orientation of its principal minerals. In the sound rock of the quarries the joints are latent, but may be developed by the quarrymen. The quarries are worked according to the grain of the rock, and when joints appear as fissures they also follow the grain.

The direction of easiest cleavability is about north-north-west and is known as the ' cleaving-way.' At right angles to these and also vertical is the ' tough-way ', pointing about east-north-east. In addition to these two vertical planes there is a third nearly horizontal and cutting the others at right angles. Consequently the large quarried blocks have faces perpendicular to one another, and great rectangular columns can be cleaved out of the rock.

Parallel to these three main structural directions there are systems of joints, which may form open cracks. When the rock is weathered decomposition follows these joints, and when the granite varies in hardness and resistance to weathering from place to place, the well known granite 'tors' may be produced, showing blocks piled on one another like ruined masonry. The horizontal joints or ' floors ' are most conspicuous in the superficial parts of the rock and though their origin is apparently structural they seem to be emphasized or elicited by the changes of temperature and of moisture occasioned by proximity to the surface.

This cleavage and joint system, so well known to the quarrymen from very early times, has been described by Collins (1912) and Hill (1906) and the distribution and orientation of the joint systems has more recently been studied and described by Ghosh.

He has also pointed out the existence of diagonal joints; these may be vertical following directions intersecting the principal vertical joints above described, at angles of forty to fifty degrees, or they may be slanting with a dip of fifty degrees or more while their strike is parallel to either of the two principal series of vertical joints. Similar phenomena have been described by Osman in the granite of the Scilly Isles and by numerous investigators from granites on the Continent and in America, but no fully satisfactory explanation of the the method of their origin has yet been propounded. They seem to depend on tensions in the granite occasioned by regional stresses after or during crystallization and cooling but they also depend in some measure on the structure and orientation of the crystals of the rock. Thus the horizontal joints or floors seem to correspond to the arrangement of the biotite plates in the granite, while the cleaving-way is probably connected with the flow structure as demonstrated by the long axes of the large feldspar crystals.

The cleaving-way or north-north-west joints have a similar direction to many of the ' cross-courses ' which intersect and often shift the tin-bearing lodes, while the lodes themselves have generally a parallelism to the tough-way or east-north-east joints. The elvans also have been injected into fissures that have usually an east-north-east or eastern direction. Some of the tough-way joints are parallel to the most frequent faults and thrusts as exposed on the sea coasts and it is notable also that many of the tin lodes have been the scene of movement at different periods with intense brecciation of the veinstones. Hence the two dominant joint systems, north-north-west and east-north-east are not confined to the granites but have a complicated history and seem to pervade all the strata of the country. They may be latent (in the granite) or open fissures, or planes of movement, or the seat of dyke injections or mineral veins and their distribution and causation are not local but regional.

Elvans.—The elvans of this Sheet exhibit the usual characters of this group of rocks in western Cornwall. They form dykes varying in breadth from a few feet up to twenty or thirty yards and have mostly an east-north-east or north-east direction which corresponds in general to the strike of the strata in which they occur. Their age in relation to the granite is not clearly defined; none of those under description cuts the granites of the Sheet, so far as is known, but in the district farther north there are several elvans intersecting the granite. Hence some Cornish elvans are later than the granite masses but others may possibly be older. In composition the elvans do not differ much from the granites, and they consist of the same minerals, feldspar (mainly orthoclase), quartz, biotite and usually muscovite. In many of them tourmaline is developed locally and some contain cordierite in the form of pinite. They are never so coarsely crystalline as the granites but mostly have a fine-grained groundmass in which lie larger

crystals of feldspar and quartz with sometimes pinite and cordierite. At the margins they have usually a chilled edge. A faint
and indefinite fluxion-banding is not infrequent, but they are never
schistose though sometimes brecciated by faulting. Tourmalinization occurs, though usually on a limited scale, and is most evident
along margins and fissures, though sometimes tourmaline is
disseminated through the rock; this mineral is mostly found replacing the feldspar. The elvans are not vesicular. They may
show kaolinization in some degree, and they also may contain other
minerals like tourmaline, topaz, fluor and tinstone, indicating the
operation of pneumatolytic processes.

A group of elvan dykes stretches across country in a south-west
direction from Mawnan Smith and Constantine towards Cury and
Gunwalloe. Their outcrops can be seen on the sides of roads and
valleys but cannot be traced for more than a few yards except in
the case of the elvan of Mawgan. Two elvans are seen on
Porth Navas Creek on the shore half a mile south of Roskillen and
another in a small inlet facing Porth Navas. Another is exposed
on the east shore of Polwheveral Creek, and at the head of the same
creek there are two more elvans. These dykes are mostly two or
three yards in breadth, but the one in Polwheveral Creek farthest
south may have a breadth of six yards. They contain porphyritic
crystals of quartz and feldspar with some muscovite, and the matrix
is felsitic.

Another group of elvans occurs in the Mawgan district and has
been quarried for many years. The principal dyke of this set
crosses the head of the Helford River near Bonallack and passes
about half a mile north of Mawgan Church. It was shown on the
map of De la Beche (1839). Another elvan a little south of
Mawgan has been quarried; it was described by Thomas (1843).
Near Rosevear there are two dykes which have been quarried and
two miles farther to the south-west, along the same line, there
is a dyke at Nantirret; traces of elvan have also been seen at
Sowanna (half a mile north of Cury). Of this group the most
important is the Bonallack elvan which in the quarries has an
apparent breadth of twelve to fifteen yards. Another important
quarry has been opened in it near the Mawgan road. It is rather
coarse-grained, containing biotite crystals in addition to porphyritic quartz and feldspar; the matrix is in places graphic and
elsewhere micro-poikilitic.

In the district about Breage and Sithney in the north-west
corner of the Sheet there are several elvans. Four dykes occur
about half a mile east of Breage and may be seen in the slopes above
the stream that flows down to Porthleven. The most important
elvan of this district, however, is the one that is quarried near
Sithney and is probably the same as the elvan, which, more than
a mile to the south-west, can be traced for many yards across
country near Penbro. This dyke is fine-grained, non-porphyritic and impregnated with pyrites in its northern outcrops, but

farther south it is rather coarsely crystalline with porphyritic feldspars up to an inch in length and many large grains of quartz. In the undergound workings of the mines east of Breage, elvans have been encountered in several places.

Lamprophyres.—The lamprophyres of this Sheet are few in number and are restricted to the east coast about the Helford River. Their presence was known to De la Beche but their nature was first recognized by Collins (1884). The best known is the one exposed in the cliffs near Mawnan half a mile north-east of Toll Point. It has a north-east course which is in accordance with the strike of the killas and also with the trend of the shore. Hence it has been exposed by erosion in more than one place, which is apt to give the impression that it occurs in lenticles (De la Beche, 1839, p. 94, fig. 11). What is probably the same dyke is seen about a quarter of a mile south of Mawnan. The average course of the dyke is about south-west; it is from four to six feet in width and dips to the south-east at forty or fifty degrees. In the killas it runs somewhat irregularly but it is clearly posterior to the folding, though in places it is intersected by small faults. Like many other lamprophyres it contains numerous enclosures of slate and of quartz detached from the quartz veins in the surrounding killas.

There are traces of a lamprophyre in the churchyard at Mawnan and another dyke outcrops on the north shore of the Helford River about a quarter of a mile west of the coastguard station; this is much decomposed and has a breadth of twenty feet. Probably the same dyke is seen on the south shore near Kestle where it is ten feet wide. Its continuation can be traced on both sides of the creek above Frenchman's Pill. This chain of outcrops has the characteristic south-west trend. Another lamprophyre dyke is seen at The Gew on the south side of the entrance of the Helford River; it is eight feet wide and gives off several branches. Traces of a dyke are also visible on Menaver Beach.

These lamprophyres present the usual characters of this group of rocks in Cornwall. In the hand specimen they are of brown colour with numerous shining dark flakes of biotite that may have a sub-parallel arrangement. They decompose readily to spheroidal lumps, and yield a brown earth with glistening scales of mica (often altered to chlorite). Under the microscope they are seldom fresh, but the mica may be strongly pleochroic with angular outlines and dark borders. The feldspar is often much decomposed but seems to be mostly orthoclase. Hence the rocks are minettes as a rule, though there may also be some kersantites. Augite is present in some specimens and there is hornblende in the dyke north-west of Helford. A common feature is the abundance of crystals of apatite.

CHAPTER XVIII

PLIOCENE

THE patch of quartzose gravel which lies on the top of Crousa Down and is crossed by the high road to St. Keverne and Coverack has been known to observers for more than a century. De la Beche (1839) remarks that ' it resembles no other accumulation of superficial debris within considerable distances.' Its unusual character led Budge (1843) to suggest that it was of ' diluvial ' origin. These gravels cover about a third of a square mile, and are situated at an elevation of 360 feet, almost on the summit of the down. They lie, in fact, on the present water-shed and obviously cannot be ascribed to the action of any of the streams that are now existent, but belong to a period anterior to the development of the present surface features. They contain no fossils and their geological age can only be inferred from indirect evidence. From their position on the surface of the platform, in a locality where the platform is well preserved, there is no difficulty in believing that their origin is associated with the development of that surface feature, and dates back to the time when the Lizard platform was a dominant factor in the physiography. A similar deposit of gravel occurs at Polcrebo, near Nancegollan, on the west side of the Carnmenellis Granite; it occupies an area of about half a square mile at an elevation of 500 feet and though resting on granite consists largely of quartz pebbles from the quartz veins in the killas, in which respect it closely resembles the gravel of Crousa Down. Still more significant is the presence at St. Erth, between Penzance and St. Ives, of extensive deposits of sand and clay that contain many fossils; from their palaeontology they have been ascribed to the lower part of the Pliocene. They lie in a valley that was probably a strait occupied by the sea and their fossils are all marine. Reid has described this deposit in his ' Pliocene Deposits of Britain ' (1890) and came to the conclusion that it was laid down in a channel or strait at the depth of about 50 fathoms. As the sand pits are 100 feet above sea level this indicates a depression of the land of about 400 feet. Reid's latest views on the subject are given in the Geological Survey Memoir on ' The Land's End District ' (1907). Pliocene sands are also known at

St. Agnes Beacon at an elevation of 375 feet but they are unfossiliferous. Reid (*loc. cit.*) points out that these deposits indicate that in early Pliocene time the south-west of Cornwall was an archipelago of granite islands, resembling the Scilly Islands at the present day, surrounded by a shallow sea in which lived mollusca, belonging to species many of which are now extinct, and the general facies of the fauna indicates climatic conditions distinctly warmer than those now prevailing in Cornwall. These facts give a clue to the age of the platform which is so characteristic of the Lizard and Meneage and leave little room for doubt that it belongs to the early part of the Pliocene period. Further evidence of this submergence has been found in the London district and in Kent where Pliocene deposits are known at an elevation of 700 feet above the sea.

The surface of the gravels of Crousa Down is markedly different from that of the surrounding gabbro. The gabbro ground is covered with large blocks that have weathered out of the underlying rock mass; the Pliocene gravel on the other hand forms smooth level country with a scanty growth of heather and thorn and is partly occupied by a plantation of trees. The boundaries of the gravel are consequently fairly easily determined though there is no marked surface feature. But traces of the gravel are to be found in many parts of the downs though there is in no other place a deposit of sufficient thickness to be worth working. On Goonhilly Down near the Dry Tree and near Traboe cross-roads, rounded pebbles of white quartz from an inch to six inches or more in diameter may be found here and there, and even on Kynance Down similar pebbles are not exactly uncommon and there is no evidence that they have been transported by human agency. They are most common on the banks of the small streamlets that cross the downs and many of them may have been carried down from higher levels. On Kynance Down flint pebbles are not rare, but at Crousa Down they are seldom seen. On the Scilly Islands Barrow found flint pebbles at an elevation of 200 feet and considered that they were transported by floating ice during the Glacial Period, but there is no sign of glacial deposits on the Lizard platform.

The Crousa Down gravels have been extensively worked for materials for road-mending and for paths. There are many old pits in the gravel area, mostly overgrown with thorn ; and there is one large pit still in operation. The thickness of the deposit seems to vary from ten to sixteen feet ; its base is seldom seen as the deeper parts of the pits tend to be filled with water and there is no drainage. Occasionally however the underlying gabbro is exposed ; it is much weathered and covered with rounded boulders of comparatively sound rock. The gravel in the deeper layers is stratified and contains thin, interrupted intercalations of yellow sand and of white clay, resembling pipe-clay. Towards the upper surface the gravels are disturbed and the bedding planes are often curved and twisted ; this is probably due to alternate deep freezing and thawing of the soil during a time when the climate was much more rigorous than at present. In these contorted layers many of the pebbles have their longest axes vertical as if they had been sinking down in a soft matrix. The vast majority of the pebbles are vein-quartz and only the smaller ones are well rounded; the larger pebbles have a surface marked by many small irregularities. The source of the quartz is probably the veins that traverse the killas that lies to the north of the Lizard boundary. Quartz veins are very rare in the Lizard rocks, though sometimes occurring in the mica-schists and more rarely in the hornblende-schists, but they are frequent in the Gramscatho and Mylor slates. They must have been transported for several miles to their present situation. There are no pebbles of serpentine, gabbro or greenstone; only the hardest and most durable rocks are represented in the gravel; granite pebbles are rare and deeply decomposed, but small, dark grey or blue, much rounded fragments of quartz-tourmaline rock occur in some numbers and prove the derivation of material from the margins of the granite north of the Helford River. Apparently the Helford River valley was completely filled up with detritus at the time when the Crousa Down gravel was accumulated, but there are no traces of Pliocene deposits in that valley similar to those that occur at St. Erth. There are also pebbles of dark chert but it is doubtful whether flint pebbles are present; if so they are rare at Crousa Down. Milner (1922) and Boswell (1923) have investigated the heavy minerals of the Crousa Down gravel and there has been some discussion as to the meaning of the results; but all the minerals known to occur in the gravel are present in the rocks of the Lizard peninsula and the country immediately to the north, and there is no indication that any materials have been transported from a greater distance.

The persistence of the gravel deposit on Crousa Down may be ascribed to several causes. In the first place it was on the whole a coarse-grained deposit full of pebbles, and may have been a gravel bank deposited on a shoal or ridge on the Pliocene sea bottom. Furthermore, it is on the water-shed where stream action is at a minimum. Fine sands and clays would have been washed away by rains and rivulets and would gradually disappear. It is quite possible that a large part of the Pliocene sea bottom in this neighbourhood was bare rock, or only thinly covered by fine sand. The depth of water was apparently about ten fathoms, which would expose fine sediment to the action of waves and currents and leave only the coarser material. Probably gravel ridges were only local. The fine debris moreover would be readily washed away by the waves as the platform slowly rose above sea level. The absence of fossils may be due to the action of percolating water, for the matrix as a whole is sandy and porous though there are occasional seams of clay that locally obstruct the passage of water.

CHAPTER XIX

PLEISTOCENE AND RECENT DEPOSITS

DURING the Glacial Period the sheets of ice that covered the north of Britain did not invade the Cornish peninsula though there may have been local and temporary accumulations of snow on some of the higher ground.   Consequently there is no boulder-clay or transported drift on the country under description though by the inclemency of the climate there was much disintegration of the superficial rocks and occasionally floods were caused by the melting of the snow.   The most striking evidence of the former prevalence of glacial conditions is the presence of numerous erratics on the beaches; the commonest rock represented is flint, which can be found in nearly every cove.   There are also boulders of granite, gneiss, quartzite and other rocks, but caution must be observed as frequently Falmouth granite, Plymouth limestone and Newlyn greenstone may be found on the shores in conditions which imply that they were brought as ballast in fishing-boats. Some unusual rocks may also have been derived from the ballast of the numerous ships that have been wrecked on this coast.

The best known erratic in this area is the Giant's Rock which lies on the shore about a mile west of Porthleven Harbour.   It is a huge block, estimated to weigh fifty tons, and is so large that even the heavy storms that break on the coast of Mount's Bay have been unable to shift it or roll it about, and it lies where it was stranded by the ice floes of the Glacial Period.   The rock is a microcline-gneiss, pinkish in colour, and contains a few garnets as large as cherries.   It is not a British rock and its source has never been ascertained.   At no great distance there are other large erratics, several feet in diameter, of quartzite, granite, gabbro, etc. that may have arrived at the same time as the Giant's Rock. They seem to have been washed out of the sands of the Raised Beach, of which deposit there are patches resting on the old rock platform. This would indicate that the Raised Beach in this neigh-bourhood belongs to one of the Glacial stages of the Pleistocene. Erratics of gabbro and other rocks also occur in the Raised Beach at Gunwalloe, and De la Beche has remarked the presence of flints in the Raised Beach deposits at several places (1839, p. 429) but flints occur in the modern shore deposits and may in some places have been washed ashore from Eocene or other strata on the sea bottom. The great accumulation of rolled flint gravel that forms the Loe Bar and is spread northwards along the foot of the cliffs to Porthleven is one of the most wonderful features of the Cornish coast; Reid (1904) has suggested that it is derived from Eocene beds occupying the floor of Mount's Bay and some such explanation seems necessary to explain its origin.

Head.—Further evidence of glacial conditions is provided by the deposits of Head that occur in some valleys and in sheltered situations on the coast. The Head is a rubble of angular stones, sometimes of considerable size, embedded in a fine stony loam. It is always purely local in its origin and consists only of materials derived from adjacent outcrops of rock. Usually unstratified, it may occasionally show a rough bedding, but for the most part the larger angular blocks are scattered irregularly through the mass. No fossils have been found in it, but it is undoubtedly of Glacial origin and belongs to a time when the rocks were split by severe frosts, and during periodical thaws the mass moved slowly down the slopes. It forms a mantle or fringe to some of the valleys and resembles a river terrace but is distinguished by its irregular upper surface and the unrolled state of its component blocks. In this district it is wasting away, partly under the attack of streams and of the sea and partly by the washing action of rain where it is not covered by a dense coat of vegetation. The cliffs on the east side of the peninsula are generally capped by a deposit of Head which ranges in thickness from a few feet up to thirty or forty feet. It is especially well seen around Coverack and between that village and the Black Head. The cliffs of gabbro near Lowland Point and Manacle Point also are frequently surmounted by a coating of Head, especially in the little coves. A well known deposit of Head is seen at Nelly's Cove a short distance north of Porthallow, and has been figured by De la Beche (1839, p. 431) and in the first edition of this Memoir : it rests upon deposits of the Raised Beach : other accumulations of Head are seen at The Gew and Dennis Head. At Rosemullion a Raised Beach is covered by Head, closely resembling the conditions at Nelly's Cove and also figured by De la Beche (1839, p. 432). At Coverack there is a well marked Raised Beach platform with a thin deposit of gravel and boulders, covered by a thick accumulation of Head, both in Coverack Cove and in Perprean Cove.

The most striking deposits of Head in this district, however, are those of Lowland Point and of Polnare Cove between Nare Head and Nare Point. At Lowland Point the rocky platform of the Raised Beach forms a low, flat plain on which lies a deposit of fine, sandy material which has a thickness of twenty feet in several places. This material differs from the gravels of the Raised Beach and the present shore in containing few rounded pebbles or boulders except at its base. It consists mainly of fine, angular fragments of weathered feldspar and other minerals from the gabbro which forms the cliff at some distance behind the shore. Under the action of frost the rocks have been swept forwards to cover the rocky platform which must have been nearly bare of gravel and sand at the time when it was elevated. Under the Head there are large boulders of gabbro, and rocky ridges sometimes project above the surface.

On the west coast Head is comparatively rare, probably because the cliffs are receding more rapidly before the attack of the waves but small patches can be seen at Caerthillian Cove, Kynance, Polurrian, and between Gunwalloe and the Loe Bar. About a mile south of Porthleven there are two small areas of Head occupying shallow valleys which form notches in the face of the cliff.

Raised Beaches occur along the coasts represented on this Sheet but they are nowhere continuous or conspicuous. They are best preserved on the eastern shores; on the west they are found only in a few places widely scattered. The principal beach is one that is from five to fifteen feet above present high-water mark; it seems to belong to the same period of depression and though there is no evidence of its exact age it is probably of no great antiquity. It is very often overlapped by the Head, which is apparently more recent, and possibly it belongs to the earlier stages of the Glacial Period. This beach is most frequently seen on the sheltered east coast and is characterized by a thin deposit of sand, gravel and rounded boulders, resting on a rock platform which in some places has a breadth of fifty yards or more but mostly is a mere shelf at the base of an old cliff.

South of Falmouth, in the north-east corner of the Sheet, the Raised Beach is present at Sowans Hole and for half a mile south of Rosemullion Head, as far as Mawnan. Traces of it are found in the Helford River and at The Gew and Dennis Head. South of Nare Point there is a wide flat expanse of Head resting on Raised Beach gravels and a rock platform. At Nelly's Cove, Porthallow, and Sowans Hole, Raised Beach and Head are well exposed in section in a prominent rocky cliff. In this quarter the beach deposits are in places consolidated to a firm conglomerate and form the roof of caves eroded by the sea. This is also seen in some localities south of Coverack.

The Raised Beach platform of Lowland Point, covered by a layer of Head, is a marked feature of the coastal scenery and is the broadest expanse of this nature in the district. Around Coverack there are many sections showing Raised Beach covered by Head. The beach deposits are thin, only a few feet in thickness, and the platform is much eroded. From Coverack to the Black Head remains of Raised Beach deposits are visible in several coves. Around Carrick Luz, Kennack and Cadgwith there are few traces of Raised Beach though a patch of fine gravel with rounded stones may be seen on the serpentine in the middle of Kennack Cove. About the Lizard Point, Kynance and Ogo Dour only careful search will reveal traces of Raised Beach deposits or platform. There is a small mass of sandy gravel on the south side of Old Lizard Head. At Caerthillian and Kynance the bare rock platform is locally preserved but mere scraps of sandy beach deposits are all that remains. At Gunwalloe Fishing Cove, and between there and the Loe Bar, the Raised Beach can be followed for many yards. It is only six to ten feet above high-water mark, and the gravels are firmly cemented by black oxides of iron and manganese. Between the Loe Pool and Porthleven scraps of Raised Beach gravels can be seen in several places and at Pargodonnel Rocks, about a mile north of Porthleven, there are interesting remains of Raised Beach gravels, firmly cemented, in crannies in the cliff. At this locality there are numerous large erratics probably transported by floating ice (p. 168).

A remarkable Raised Beach, discovered by Teall, is seen in the cliffs of hornblende-schist facing the Bumble Rock on the west side of Housel Bay. It is about twenty-five feet above sea-level and occupies a small recess in the cliff. From its elevation and the indurated character of the gravel it is probable that this is the oldest Raised Beach in the Lizard District. A still higher Raised Beach was observed at Penlee, south of Penzance, by Reid. It is sixty-five feet above Ordance Datum and was described and figured in the Land's End Memoir (1907, Plate IV). It is the highest Raised Beach in Cornwall.

Buried Forests.—The Raised Beaches are not the only signs of changes in the relative levels of land and sea in Recent times. It is well known that in the Falmouth estuary and in Mount's Bay after heavy storms, branches and roots of trees and traces of other vegetation that apparently grew and flourished *in situ* are sometimes exposed beneath the present sea level. Remains of man have been found in some of these deposits, a proof of human occupation of Cornwall during the period of forest growth. From the evidence of the old tin-works near Falmouth the land stood at least forty feet higher than at present and the climate was also somewhat milder. Within the boundaries of this Sheet there is little evidence directly bearing on this question but Rogers (1859) has recorded that at Wheal Cober, a quarter of a mile south of Helston, a shaft was sunk through thirty-three feet of alluvium (or fourteen feet below high-water mark). The Loe Bar has been bored to a depth of sixty-eight feet (or thirty feet below low-water level) without touching rock. The Helford River and the Loe Pool are submerged valleys which were eroded at a period when the land stood at a relatively higher level, and, though their origin may date from a considerably earlier time than that of the Buried Forests they were, no doubt, in some degree deepened during that epoch. In Porthleven Harbour stumps of oak and willow were observed by Rogers (1818b) below low-water mark.

Alluvium.—Marine alluvium is forming at Gweek and the head of the Helford River and also in the Loe Pool below Helston; its accumulation may be accelerated in the latter locality by debris from the tin-mines. There is little fresh-water alluvium in this district as the streams are small and have mostly a fairly rapid course to the sea. River terraces are nowhere well displayed. The largest extent of river alluvium is that of the Loe Valley near Helston and of the stream which flows down to Porthleven. On the Crousa Downs gabbro there are stretches of ground occupied by marshy clays with occasional pools owing to the retentive nature of the sub-soil, but in the Lizard and Meneage peninsula as a whole the deposits of alluvium that fringe the streams have only an insignificant extent.

CHAPTER XX

―――――

ECONOMIC GEOLOGY

MOST of the ground represented on this Sheet is under cultivation. The only extensive area of waste land is on Goonhilly Down and Kynance Down but parts of the gabbro on Crousa Down are rough pasture. Mixed farming preponderates, mostly dairy farming, but there are considerable areas of oats, wheat, mixed corn, and roots, though pasture and hay occupy the widest area. Flower growing is practised in favourable situations, as around Helston, Porthoustock, Ruan and Cadgwith; and early vegetables such as broccoli and cabbage are extensively cultivated, but there is little fruit growing and the old cider orchards are often neglected.

The soils vary enormously and their nature is closely dependent on the underlying rock. In the granite country there is a loose, sandy soil, rather coarse-grained with weathered feldspar and quartz. The higher granite ground is partly uncultivated, probably owing to the exposed position. Paris (1818a) has noted that where the granite joins the killas the mixed soil is much more productive than the pure granite soil or ' growan.' There is very little peat on the granite moors except in occasional hollows and marshy places. The soil on the killas is generally a stiffish grey clay with many angular pieces of quartz derived from the quartz veins in the underlying rock. This soil when well drained is fertile, though often cold and late. Where greenstone occurs among the killas the soil is much improved and there is very good land around Helston and Porthleven on areas having rocks of this type. The weathered outcrops of greenstone in some of the sheltered valleys are exceedingly fertile and produce abundant crops and the rotted greenstone soil has in former years been often carted out by the farmers and spread on the killas soils as a natural fertilizer. Probably the best land of the district is upon the hornblende-schist that stretches from Mullion to Porthallow. This soil is dark red in colour when dry; it is deep, rich, freely drained and easily worked; every kind of crop grows on it in profusion. Some of the hornblende-schists are rotted to a depth of twenty feet, as may be

observed when wells are being sunk in it.   An exception to the
excellence of hornblende-schist soils is provided by certain areas of
coarse Traboe hornblende-schist on the north side of Goonhilly.
On these the soils are shallow and relatively infertile and consequently a good deal of this ground is left in pasture and seldom or
never ploughed.   At the Lizard the hornblende-schist is all
cultivated and presents a marked contrast to the serpentine, most of
which is barren down.   The mica-schists of the Lizard area and at
Porthallow have much fine hornblende-schist mixed with them and
make soils of the highest quality, as may be seen around
Porthoustock and Porthallow.   Both fruit and flowers grow well
on these soils.   The Meneage Breccia also is covered with fields of
the highest fertility as might be expected from the great variety of
rocks which it contains.

The serpentine soils are poor and seem to be about the least
valuable in Cornwall.   The unmodified serpentine of the downs
yields a yellow or buff clay full of weathered blocks; this soil is
shallow and the bare rock projects or is everywhere near the
surface.   The ferruginous clay is almost impermeable to water
and after heavy rains the surface of the downs is covered with
water which slowly drains away.   In a few places the serpentine is
decomposed or disintegrated to a depth of several feet but the soil
is sterile.   There is evidence that a considerable area of the downs
has been enclosed and under cultivation at some former time but
most of it has been allowed to relapse to its original state.
Apparent exception to this statement is provided by certain areas
that seem to be serpentine but consist of farming land of quite good
quality.   This kind of ground occurs between Lizard Town and
Cadgwith, around Ruan Minor and Kuggar.   The only rocks seen
in situ are projecting knobs of serpentine, but examination of the
stones in the soil shows that there is much banded gneiss and
granite-gneiss which have weathered down and make no appearance
as prominent outcrops.   Some of this mixed land, or modified
serpentine, is of considerable fertility.   The pure serpentine soils
also have in some places been much improved by shell sand,
hornblende-schist or granite-gneiss debris, and, though still
inferior, yield moderate crops.

The soil on the gabbro is famous for its fertility.   It is a deep,
rich, yellow loam, and the blocks of weathered rock are often
prominent in the fields though most of them have been broken
up to build field walls, or to mend the roads.   Around St. Keverne,
Lanarth and Rosenithon the crops are very fine in most seasons,
and Paris (1818) said that ' in point of luxuriant fruitfulness this
country may be denominated the Garden of Cornwall.'   It is
especially good wheat land.   Some of the fertility may be
attributed to the greenstones which break down more readily than
the gabbro and also provide drainage channels.   The granite-
gneiss of the Lizard district yields a lighter soil than the
hornblende-schist, and is more apt to be parched in dry seasons,

but it is excellent for most crops and may be specially adaptable to flower growing. Its quality is improved by the presence of banded gneisses as the hornblende furnishes lime, iron and magnesia. The only areas of granite-gneiss that are uncultivated are near the highest part of Goonhilly Down and are of no great extent.

Water Supply.—Helston has a good supply, taken from the granite downs near Porkellis; it furnishes water also to Porthleven and some adjacent districts. Most of the villages have a supply, *e.g.*, Mullion, Cadgwith and Coverack though not always superabundant in a dry summer when there are many visitors. Lizard Town is at present seeking an enlarged supply from wells. The farms and scattered dwelling houses have good wells, and small supplies can generally be obtained at no great depth, though in the hornblende-schist country the wells may be forty feet deep and in the killas there is some uncertainty, as the water is principally in joints and fault-planes while the rock itself is rather impervious.

Building Stone.—For these purposes in former times the local rocks were principally used. Around Helston the weathered greenstones furnished a soft rock, easily trimmed and very durable. Blocks of killas were much used at Porthleven, and granite at Constantine. The hornblende-schists rarely furnished stone suitable for building houses but a constant supply was obtained from the serpentine of the downs, which might be quarried but was often simply collected from the loose rock on the surface. It is generally believed that the serpentine is liable to split and is not waterproof. Many of the older farm houses are built wholly or partly of cob, a mixture of clay, straw, and small stones. Some of these houses have stood for two or three hundred years and are said to be both warm in winter and dry, but they are rapidly disappearing. Around Constantine the granite was the great building stone, and throughout the district dressed granite was taken from Constantine to form sills, lintels, steps and gate-posts.

At present many buildings are being erected with concrete blocks and this is a rapidly growing industry. The favourite gravel is the fine flint pebble-gravel of the Loe Bar, Porthleven and Gunwalloe, but crushed killas, greenstone, hornblende-schist and tremolite-serpentine are also employed as material for concrete blocks and are apparently suitable for the purpose.

In the neighbourhood of Constantine, Brill, Mabe and Budock there are many quarries in which the Carnmenellis Granite is worked for building stone but they are mostly north of the boundary of this Sheet. They furnish dressed granite for the whole of this district.

Road-stone.—There are abundant supplies of good road-stone in the area represented in this map and there is a considerable export. At Porthoustock the St. Keverne Stone Company and the West of England Road Metal Company have extensive quarries, with modern stone-crushing apparatus, and together employ more than 200 men.   On the south side of Porthoustock Cove the stone quarried is gabbro intersected by many greenstone dykes : on the north side of the cove the quarries are working in hornblende-schist.   At both places jetties have been built for shipping the crushed stone and the industry has expanded considerably of recent years.   For the local roads a few quarries continue to produce road-metal, the principal being Mullion Cove (hornblende-schist), Countybridge (tremolite-serpentine), Crousa Down (gabbro, mostly loose blocks from the downs), Relowas (hornblende-schist), Mawgan (elvan), Tregidden (pillow-lava).

Mines.—Mining for metalliferous ores has not been carried on on a large scale in this district for many years and is at present abandoned.   Perhaps the most important mine was Wheal Rose on the cliffs east of Porthleven.   Collins (1912) states that this mine was once very extensive and profitable and was active for over 200 years.   It closed down after 1872 and at present only the old ' burrows ' remain.   Adits of this mine are seen below the cliffs a mile east of Porthleven.   The adjacent mine, Wheal Penrose, according to the same authority, was also at one time an important source of argentiferous lead ore but closed down about 1850.   The lodes in these mines are ' cross-courses ' striking north-north-west, and it has been suggested that they are the same as Wolf's Cross-course in Wheal Vor.   Another old and abandoned mine is Wheal Pool which was situated on the east side of the Loe Pool ; Carne (1818) says that this mine had been worked for lead for two hundred and fifty years.   It was closed down about 1830.   There are old shafts in the vicinity of Helston which probably also belong to abandoned lead mines. Near Constantine there are several deserted mines, the 'burrows' of which are visible on the side of the road from Helston to Falmouth.   Noble (1871) states that the Brogden Iron Mine in 1868 was producing brown haematite from a lode bearing E. 5° S. and there was an adjacent lode bearing E. 25° S.   Wheal Anna Maria in this neighbourhood was at work in 1908, in search of tin and copper ores, but did not continue. There is no mining in that district at present.   The district around Breage in the north-west corner of this Sheet has been an important source of tin and copper ores up to recent times but their lodes hardly enter into the country under description and are considered in the Memoir on Falmouth and Camborne to which they properly belong.

Collectors of minerals have known for more than two hundred years that native copper was found in the Lizard serpentine, particularly in the neighbourhood of Mullion, and there are traces of former mines in several parts of the district, though none of them seems to have had a long life or a successful career.   Copper seems to be generally disseminated through the serpentine and is found in small quantities in the native state at Lizard Town,

Pentreath, Coverack, Goonhilly and Ruan Major. In the serpentine quarries at present working at Countybridge and Meaver, copper, malachite and grey copper ore (probably chalcocite) may be observed in thin veinlets. The copper is not associated with any other rock than the serpentine, and has not been found in the schists, gabbro or gneiss. Locally it has been concentrated in veins by some kind of pneumatolytic or hydrolytic action probably due to the vapours in the serpentine and not to later injections of granite, as the debris left in the old mines shows the association of the copper ores with minerals such as talc, chlorite and tremolite which may be due to pneumatolysis or to crushing.

The principal copper mine in the Lizard district and the only one that has been working during the last hundred years is situated about a mile south-west of Mullion and is variously designated Wheal Unity, Ghostcroft or Goosecroft, and Wheal Trenance. From this mine a large block of native copper was obtained in 1847. It measured 7 ft. 6 in. in length, 2 feet in breadth and from 4 to 12 inches in thickness. It is now in the Museum of Practical Geology, London. Capital was raised and mining was actively pursued for some time but without commercial success. The site of the mine is indicated by several shafts which follow a line extending nearly due north for a distance of four or five hundred yards. The mine buildings have disappeared and the 'burrows' of waste are small but they have been reduced by carting away for mending footpaths and roads and little trace of copper ores can now be found in the debris.

In Mullion Cove there are several adits or workings of small size but it is not known whether they communicate with the mine which is situated half a mile inland. Apparently this mine was abandoned about the year 1860.

There is an old mine shaft near Polurrian Cove, apparently sunk to the fault rock between hornblende-schist and killas. In Predannack the six-inch map shows a mine shaft, Wheal Foss, which is said to have been in search of china clay (probably steatite). On Goonhilly Down there are the remains of old mines, probably for copper, at a place known as Mine Waters. On the south coast near Beagles Point, a mile east of Carrick Luz, there are three small shafts and in the stream valley to the north are traces of an old working. Sedgwick (1822) states that these mines were in search of copper ore and had been discontinued before his visit. A small working was started a few years ago in the valley south of Mullion but is now closed down. At several places such as Porthoustock, Church Cove and Pen Olver there are signs of old trials in the cliffs, but none of them seems to be of importance.

The Soap Rock of Gew-graze has been extensively quarried and seems to be now exhausted. It was used in the manufacture of pottery and Josiah Wedgwood was at one time interested in it. Paris (1818) states that it was " worked by Mr. Dulwyn of

Swansea, for which he pays Lord Falmouth, the proprietor, £75 per annum. About 12 tons are annually exported," but when Sedgwick visited Gew-graze in 1819 he found that mining operations had ceased. There is no record of subsequent activity.

Among other minerals present in the district mention may be made of gold, which has frequently been obtained in small flakes in the bed of the stream near Manaccan, and platinum which Davison (1925) reports from alluvia on the north side of the serpentine. Chromite occurs in all the Lizard serpentines but never in workable amount.

Serpentine.—The industry of cutting and polishing serpentine is centred in the Lizard district where there are workshops at Lizard Town, Kynance, Church Cove, Mullion, Ruan Minor, Cadgwith and Coverack. It is mostly carried on in small workshops employing only a few men and it is many years since the factory at Poltesco was closed and dismantled. Owing to the large number of visitors who come to the district in motor cars and char-à-bancs in the summer months there has been a considerable increase in the sale of polished serpentine goods. Ornamental stone suitable for the purpose is obtained in many parts of the serpentine district; it is principally the bastite-serpentine though the chromite-serpentine is also used and the dunite-serpentine from the neighbourhood of Traboe. The stone must not only show a rich variety of colours but must also be very thoroughly decomposed, as if there are hard crystals of enstatite or diallage they are difficult to polish and if they break up on turning they are apt to scratch the surface of the ornaments. Each of the recognized districts contains stone of distinct appearance though several varieties may be found in one locality. Small pits are opened by the workers in search of stone and a royalty is paid to the proprietor of the ground. Among the places now frequented the principal are Tor Balk, Kynance Down, Holestrow, Yellow Carn, Trethevas, Cadgwith, Ruan Major, Goonhilly, Bray's Cot, Traboe, Carn Kennack and the Eastern Cliffs between Kennack and the Black Head. The stone is very carefully chosen by the workers, special regard being paid to beauty of colour and absence of flaws. Most of the ornaments are of small size, less than a foot in diameter, and brooches, buttons, beads and small articles for personal wear are usually also on sale. Each worker has generally certain sources to which he habitually resorts so that the goods have often an individual character. There is also an export trade as serpentine ornaments are sold in Penzance, Falmouth and many other towns but the manufacture is almost wholly restricted to the Lizard peninsula.

BIBLIOGRAPHY

1602. CAREW, R. The Survey of Cornwall. Reprinted in 1723?, 1769 and 1811 (London).

1758. BORLASE, W. The Natural History of Cornwall. Oxon.

1778. PRYCE, W. Mineralogia Cornubiensis, a Treatise on Minerals, Mines and Mining. London.

1791. GREGOR, W. Sur le Menakanite. *Journal de Physique* (Paris), vol. xxxix, pp. 152-160.

1794. KIRWAN, R. Elements of Mineralogy. 2nd edit. Vol. i, p. 153 (Steatites); vol. ii (1796), p. 326 (Menachanite).

1811. BERGER, J. F. Observations on the Physical Structure of Devonshire and Cornwall. *Trans. Geol. Soc.*, vol. i, pp. 93-184.

1811. DE LUC, J. A. Geological Travels. Vol. iii, Travels in England.

1818. CARNE, J. (a) On Elvan Courses. *Trans. Roy. Geol. Soc. Corn.*, vol. i, pp. 97-106, 241.
    (b) On the Discovery of Silver in the Mines of Cornwall. *Trans. Roy. Geol. Soc. Corn.*, vol. i, pp. 118-126.

1818. DAVY, (SIR) H. Hints on the Geology of Cornwall. *Trans. Roy. Geol. Soc. Corn.*, vol. i, pp. 38-50.

1818. MAJENDIE, A. A Sketch of the Geology of the Lizard District. *Trans. Roy. Geol. Soc. Corn.*, vol. i, pp. 32-37.

1818. PARIS, J. A. (a) Observations on the Geological structure of Cornwall, with a view to trace its connexion with, and influence upon its Agricultural Œconomy, and to establish a rational system of Improvement by the scientific application of Mineral Manure. *Trans. Roy. Geol. Soc. Corn.*, vol. i, pp. 168-200.
    (b) On Stones and Clays annually Exported from Cornwall, for the purposes of Architecture, Manufactures, and the Arts. *Trans. Roy. Geol. Soc. Corn.*, vol. i, pp. 231-234.

1818. ROGERS, J. (a) Observations on the Limestone of Veryan and the neighbouring parishes. *Trans. Roy. Geol. Soc. Corn.*, vol. i, pp. 114-117.
    (b) Vegetable Remains in the Basin at Porthleven. *Trans. Roy. Geol. Soc. Corn.*, vol. i, pp. 236-237.

1819. GREENOUGH, G. B. A Geological Map of England and Wales.

1821. SEDGWICK, A. On the Physical Structure of those Formations which are immediately associated with the Primitive Ridge of Devonshire and Cornwall. *Trans. Camb. Phil. Soc.*, vol. i, pp. 89-146.

1822. CARNE, J. On the relative Age of the Veins of Cornwall. *Trans. Roy. Geol. Soc. Corn.*, vol. ii, pp. 49-128.

1822. ROGERS, J. On the Serpentine District of Cornwall. *Trans. Roy. Geol. Soc. Corn.*, vol. ii, pp. 416-423.

1822. SEDGWICK, A. On the Physical Structure of the Lizard District in the County of Cornwall. *Trans. Camb. Phil. Soc.*, vol. i, pp. 291-330.

1827. CARNE, J. On the Granite of the Western part of Cornwall. *Trans. Roy. Geol. Soc. Corn.*, vol. iii, pp. 208-246.

1827.   HAWKINS, J.   On the Changes which appear to have taken place in
         the primitive form of the Cornish Peninsula.   *Trans. Roy.
         Geol. Soc. Corn.*, vol. iii, pp. 1-16.

1828.   —————————.   Some general Observations on the Structure and Com-
         position of the Cornish Peninsula.   *Trans. Roy. Geol. Soc.
         Corn.*, vol. iv (1832), pp. 1-20.

1829.   —————————.   Some Observations made in Cornwall, in the summer
         of 1829.   *Trans. Roy. Geol. Soc. Corn.*, vol. iv (1832), pp. 40-46.

1829.   OEYNHAUSEN, C. VON, and H. VON DECHEN.   On the Junction of the
         Granite and Killas Rocks in Cornwall.   *Phil. Mag.*, ser. 2, vol.
         v, pp. 161-170, 241-247.

1831.   BOASE, H. S.   Contributions towards a knowledge of the Geology of
         Cornwall.   *Trans. Roy. Geol. Soc. Corn.*, vol. iv (1832), pp.
         166-474.

1834.   —————————.   A Treatise on Primary Geology.   London.

1838.   SEDGWICK, A.   A Synopsis of the English Series of Stratified Rocks
         inferior to the Old Red Sandstone, with an attempt to determine
         the successive natural groups and formations.   *Proc. Geol. Soc.*
         vol. ii, pp. 675-685.

1839.   DE LA BECHE, H. T.   (a) One-inch geological map 32 (Old Series),
         Lizard Head.
              (b) Report on the Geology of Cornwall, Devon, and West
         Somerset.   *Mem. Geol. Surv.*   Index by Clement Reid (1903).

1839.   GREENOUGH, G. B.   A Geological Map of England and Wales.   2nd
         edit.

1839.   SEDGWICK, A., and R. I. MURCHISON.   Classification of the older
         rocks of Devonshire and Cornwall.   *Proc. Geol. Soc.*, vol. iii,
         pp. 121-123; also *Phil. Mag.*, ser. 3, vol. xiv, pp. 241-260, 317.

1839.   WILLIAMS, D.   On as much of the Transition or Grauwacke system
         as is exposed in the counties of Somerset, Devon, and Cornwall.
         Proc. Geol. Soc., vol. iii, pp. 115-117, 158-162.

1840.   SEDGWICK, A., and R. I. MURCHISON.   On the Physical Structure of
         Devonshire, and on the Subdivisions and Geological Relations
         of its older stratified Deposits, etc.   *Trans. Geol. Soc.*, ser. 2,
         vol. v, pp. 633-703.   (Slates of Cornwall, pp. 664-669).

1841.   BUDGE, E.   On the Conglomerates and Raised Beaches of the Lizard
         District.   *Trans. Roy. Geol. Soc. Corn.*, vol. vi (1846), pp. 1-11.

1841.   PEACH, C. W.   An Account of the Fossil Organic Remains found on
         the South-east Coast of Cornwall and in other parts of that
         County.   *Trans. Roy. Geol. Soc. Corn.*, vol. vi (1846), pp.
         12-23; also *Rep. Brit. Assoc.* for 1841 (1842), p. 61.

1841.   ROGERS, J.   Notice of the Serpentine of Pennare.   *Trans. Roy. Geol.
         Soc. Corn.*, vol. vi (1846), pp. 41-42.

1842.   BUDGE, E.   On the tract of Land called the Lowlands, in the Parish
         of St. Keverne.   *Trans. Roy. Geol. Soc. Corn.*, vol. vi (1846),
         pp. 59-63.

1842.   PEACH, C. W.   On the Geology of part of the Parish of Gorran, in
         Cornwall.   *Trans. Roy. Geol. Soc. Corn.*, vol. vi (1846), pp.
         51-58.

1843.   BUDGE. E.   On Diluvial action, as exemplified in the Gravel-beds
         and Sienitic formation of Crousa-Down, in the parish of St.
         Keverne.   *Trans. Roy. Geol. Soc. Corn.*, vol. vi (1846), pp. 91-98.

1843.   THOMAS, R.   Contributions towards a Description of the district of
         Meneage.   *Trans. Roy. Geol. Soc. Corn.*, vol. vi (1846), pp.
         108-110.

1843.   WHITLEY, N.   Remarks on the minor Fractures of Rocks, illustrated
         by specimens.   *Trans Roy. Geol. Soc. Corn.*, vol. vi (1846),
         pp. 104-105.

1844. BUDGE, E. On the Hornblende Slate and other associated Rocks of the Meneage District. *Trans. Roy. Geol. Soc. Corn.*, vol. vi (1846), pp. 173-180.

1844. PEACH, C. W. (a) On the Fossil Geology of Cornwall. *Trans. Roy. Geol. Soc. Corn.*, vol vi (1846), pp. 181-185.
    (b) On the Organic Fossils of Cornwall. *12th Ann. Rep. Roy. Corn. Poly. Soc.*, pp. 65-69.

1846. BUDGE, E. On the Granitic and other associated Rocks of Cornwall and Devon. *Trans. Roy. Geol. Soc. Corn.*, vol. vi, pp. 288-293.

1846. MURCHISON, R. I. A brief review of the Classification of the Sedimentary Rocks of Cornwall. *Trans. Roy. Geol. Soc. Corn.*, vol. vi, pp. 317-326; also *Edin. New Phil. Journ.*, vol. xliii (1847), pp. 33-41.

1847. SHARPE, D. On Slaty Cleavage. *Quart. Journ. Geol. Soc.*, vol. iii, pp. 74-105. (Devon and Cornwall, pp. 94-97).

1847. ANON. *Mining Journ.*, vol. xvii, pp. 262, 285. (Copper-mining at Mullion).

1848. EDMONDS, R. Notice of Land Shells found beneath the surface of Sand-hillocks on the Coasts of Cornwall. *Trans. Roy. Geol. Soc. Corn.*, vol. vii (1865), pp. 70-71; also *Edin. New Phil. Journ.*, vol. xlvii (1849), pp. 263-264.

1848. GARBY, J. A Catalogue of Minerals found in Cornwall, with their Localities. *Trans. Roy. Geol. Soc. Corn.* vol. vii (1865), pp. 72-92.

1848. JOHNS, C. A. (a) On the Land-Slip at the Lizard. *Quart. Journ. Geol. Soc.*, vol. iv, pp. 193-194.
    (b) A Week at the Lizard. Subsequently a 2nd and 3rd edit. London.

1848. ANON. *Mining Journ.*, vol. xviii, p. 377. (Copper-mining at Mullion).

1849. ANON. *Mining Journ.*, vol. xix, p 502. (Copper-mining at Mullion).

1851. AUSTEN, R. A. C. On the Superficial Accumulations of the Coasts of the English Channel, and the Changes they indicate. *Quart. Journ. Geol. Soc.*, vol. vii, pp. 118-136.

1852. SEDGWICK, A. On the Slate Rocks of Devon and Cornwall. *Quart. Journ. Geol. Soc.*, vol. viii, pp. 1-19.

1853. DE LA BECHE, H. T. The Geological Observer. 2nd edit. London. (pp. 455-458, and chapter xxx).

1853. HAUGHTON, S. Notes on the Serpentines of Cornwall and Connemara. *Journ. Geol. Soc. Dublin*, vol. v, pp. 136-139.

1858. GREG, R. P., and W. G. LETTSOM. Manual of the Mineralogy of Great Britain and Ireland. London.

1859. PHILLIPS, J. Presidential Address to the Geological Society. *Quart. Journ. Geol. Soc.*, vol. xv, Proceedings, p. lvii.

1859. ROGERS, J. J. Strata of the Cober Valley, Loe-pool, near Helston. *Trans. Roy. Geol. Soc. Corn.*, vol. vii (1865), pp. 352-354.

1863. ENYS, J. S. On Specimens of Hornblende and Serpentine from the junction at Porthalla. *31st Ann. Rep. Roy. Corn. Poly. Soc.*, pp. 42-46.

1865. GREENOUGH, G. B. A Geological Map of England and Wales. Revised edit.

1866. BATE, C. S. An Attempt to Approximate the Date of the Flint Flakes of Devon and Cornwall. *Trans. Devon. Assoc.*, vol. i, part 5, pp. 128-136; see also *Pop. Sci. Rev.*, vol. vi (1867), pp. 169-184.

1866. WHITLEY, N. On recent Flint Finds in the South-West of England. *Journ. Roy. Inst. Corn.*, vol. ii, pp. 121-124.

1867. FOX, C. Presidential Address to the Royal Geological Society of Cornwall. *54th Ann. Rep. Roy. Geol. Soc. Corn.*, pp. 16-17 (contained in vol. ix of the *Transactions*).

1867.   SMYTH, W. W.   Presidential Address to the Geological Society.   *Quart. Journ. Geol. Soc.*, vol. xxiii, Proceedings, p. lxiii.

1869.   PEACH, C. W.   On the discovery of Organic Remains in the Rocks of Nelly's Cove, near Porthalla; and of some Curious Organic-like Masses in a quarry near Hayle.   *Trans. Roy. Geol. Soc. Corn.*, vol. ix (1878), pp. 55-58.

1870.   CHURCH, A. H.   Cornish Serpentine.   *The Student*, vol. iv, pp. 81-83.

1870.   PEARCE, R.   Note on Chrome Iron in the Serpentine of the Lizard.   *Trans. Roy. Geol. Soc. Corn.*, vol. ix (1878), pp. 99-100.

1870.   WHITLEY, N.   Indications of Glacial Action in Cornwall.   *Journ. Roy. Inst. Corn.*, vol. iii, pp. 184-186.

1871.   COLLINS, J. H.   A Handbook to the Mineralogy of Cornwall and Devon.   Truro and London.

1871.   PHILLIPS, J. A.   On the Chemical Composition and Microscopic Constitution of Certain Cornish Rocks.   *Phil. Mag.*, ser. 4, vol. xli, pp. 87-107.

1872.   COLLINS, J. H.   The Iron Ores of Cornwall.   *Mining Mag. and Review*, vol. i, pp. 177-182.

1872.   NOBLE, G.   Remarks on Mineral Veins in the Parish of Constantine.   *Rep. Miners' Assoc. Corn. and Devon*, pp. 45-46; and *39th Ann. Rep. Roy. Corn. Poly. Soc.* (1871), pp. 74-76.

1872·   STEPHENS, H.   Remarks on the Mineral· Phenomena of Huel Rose, in the parish of Sithney.   *Rep. Miners' Assoc. Corn. and Devon*, pp. 47-49; and *39th Ann. Rep. Roy. Corn. Poly. Soc.* (1871), pp. 77-80.

1873.   BARNETT, A. K.   Observations on the Elvan Courses, Greenstones, and Sandstones, of Cornwall, with Remarks on their Associated Minerals.   *41st Ann. Rep. Roy. Corn. Poly. Soc.*, pp. 143-181.

1875.   TYACK, W.   On a Deposit of Quartz Gravel at Blue Pool, in Crowan.   *Trans. Roy. Geol. Soc. Corn.*, vol. ix (1878), pp. 177-181.

1875.   WHITAKER, W.   List of Works on the Geology, Mineralogy, and Palaeontology of Cornwall.   *Journ. Roy. Inst. Corn.*, vol. v (1878), pp. 61-110.

1875.   WORTH, R. N.   The Building and Ornamental Stones of Cornwall, with notes on their Archaeology.   *Journ. Roy. Inst. Corn.*, vol. v (1878), pp. 215-219.

1876.   ALLPORT, S.   On the Metamorphic Rocks surrounding the Land's-End Mass of Granite.   *Quart. Journ. Geol. Soc.*, vol. xxxii, pp. 407-427.

1876.   ARGALL, W. H.   On the Elvan Courses of Cornwall.   *Rep. Miners' Assoc. Corn. and Devon*, pp. 37-64.

1876.   BELT, T.   The Drift of Devon and Cornwall, its Origin, Correlation with that of the South-east of England, and Place in the Glacial Series.   *Quart. Journ. Geol. Soc.*, vol. xxxii, pp. 80-90.

1876.   KING, W., and T. H. ROWNEY.   On the Serpentinite of the Lizard— its Original Rock-condition, Methylotic Phenomena and Structural Simulations of Organisms.   *Phil. Mag.*, ser. 5, vol. i, pp. 280-293.

1876.   PHILLIPS, J. A.   On the so-called " Greenstones " of Western Cornwall.   *Quart. Journ. Geol. Soc.*, vol. xxxii, pp. 155-179.

1877.   BONNEY, T. G.   (a) On the Serpentine and associated Rocks of the Lizard District; with Notes on the Chemical Composition of some of the Rocks of the Lizard District, by W. H. Hudleston.   *Quart. Journ. Geol. Soc,.* vol. xxxiii, pp. 884-928; see also *Phil. Mag.*, ser. 5, vol. iv, pp. 74-75.

            (b) The Lherzolite of Ariège.   *Geol. Mag.*, N.S., dec. 2, vol. iv, pp. 59-64.

1877. COLLINS, J. H. On the Trelissick Elvan, with a proposed Classification of the Cornish Elvans. *Trans. Roy. Geol. Soc. Corn.*, vol. ix (1878), pp. 221-228.

1879. BONNEY, T. G. (a) Notes on some Ligurian and Tuscan Serpentines. *Geol. Mag.*, N.S., dec. 2, vol. vi, pp. 362-371.
(b) The Pre-Cambrian Rocks of Great Britain. *Proc. Birmingham Phil. Soc.*, vol. i, pp. 140-159.

1879. COLLINS, J. H. (a) Preliminary Note on the Stratigraphy of West Cornwall. *Trans. Roy. Geol. Soc. Corn.*, vol. x (1887), pp. 1-7.
(b) On the Geological Structure of the Northern Part of the Meneage Peninsula. *Trans. Roy. Geol. Soc. Corn.*, vol. x (1887), pp. 47-57.

1879. HOUGHTON, F. T. S. Note on an Olivine Gabbro (Forellenstein) from Cornwall. *Geol. Mag.*, N.S., dec. 2, vol. vi,. pp. 504-505.

1879. USSHER, W. A. E. (a) Historical Geology of Cornwall. *Geol. Mag.*, N.S., dec. 2, vol. vi, pp. 27-36, 74-81. Post-Tertiary Geology of Cornwall, pp. 102-110, 166-172, 203-211 ; Pleistocene Geology of Cornwall, pp. 251-263, 307-313.
(b) The Post-Tertiary Geology of Cornwall. Printed for private circulation. Hertford.

1880. BONNEY, T. G. On the Rocks of the Lizard District (Cornwall) *Proc. Camb. Phil. Soc.*, vol. iii, p. 85.

1880. PEACH, C. W. On Fossils from the Rocks of Cornwall, some of them New to the List. *Trans. Roy. Geol. Soc. Corn.*, vol. x (1887), pp. 90-97.

1881. COLLINS, J. H. (a) Recent Mineralogical Analyses from the Laboratory of the Royal Institution of Cornwall. *Journ. Roy. Inst. Corn.*, vol. vi, pp. 408-422.
(b) On the Geological Age of Central and West Cornwall. *Journ. Roy. Inst. Corn.*, vol. vii (1883), pp. 18-41.

1881. USSHER, W. A. E. " Prehistoric Europe "—Submerged Forests and Forest-Beds, Cornwall. *Geol. Mag.*, N.S., dec. 2, vol. viii, pp. 131-134.

1882. WHITLEY, N. The Evidence of Glacial Action in Cornwall and Devon. *Trans. Roy. Geol. Soc. Corn.*, vol. x (1887), pp. 132-141.

1883. BONNEY, T. G. (a) The Hornblendic and other Schists of the Lizard District, with some additional Notes on the Serpentine. *Quart. Journ. Geol. Soc.*, vol. xxxix, pp. 1-24.
(b) The Schists of the Lizard District. [Letter]. *Geol. Mag.*, N.S., dec. 2, vol. x, pp. 477-478.

1883. HUNT, T. STERRY. The Geological History of Serpentines, including Notes on pre-Cambrian Rocks. *Trans. Roy. Soc. Canada*, vol. ix, section 4, pp. 165-215. [Abstract in *Geol. Mag.*, N.S., dec. 3, vol. i (1884), pp. 276-281.]

1883. SOMERVAIL, A. On the Geological Structure and Age of the Strata of South Cornwall. *Journ. Roy. Inst. Corn.*, vol. vii, pp. 262-273.

1884. BONNEY, T. G. Remarks on Serpentine. *Geol. Mag.*, N.S., dec. 3, vol. i, pp. 406-412.

1884. CLARK, T. Volcanic Rocks of Cornwall. *Journ. Roy. Inst. Corn.*, vol. viii (1886), pp. 213-214.

1884. COLLINS, J. H. (a) On the Serpentine and associated Rocks of Porthalla Cove. *Quart. Journ. Geol. Soc.*, vol. xl, pp. 458-473.
(b) Remarks on Mr. Somervail's Paper " On the Geological Structure of South Cornwall." *Journ. Roy. Inst. Corn.*, vol. viii (1886), pp. 80-84.

1884. COLLINS, J. H. and H. F. On the Geological Age of Central and West Cornwall [2nd paper]. *Journ. Roy. Inst. Corn.*, vol. viii (1886), pp. 162-205.

1884. SOMERVAIL, A.   Prof. Bonney, F.R.S., and Mr. J. H. Collins, F.G.S., on the Serpentine of the Lizard District. [Letter]. *Geol. Mag.*, N.S., dec. 3, vol. i, pp. 479-480.

1885. BONNEY, T. G. (a) Cornish Serpentine.   [Letter].   *Geol. Mag.*, N.S., dec. 3, vol. ii, p. 431.
        (b) On Bastite-Serpentine and Troktolite in Aberdeenshire, with a Note on the Rock of the Black Dog. *Geol. Mag.*, N.S., dec. 3, vol. ii, pp. 439 448.
        (c) On the Archaean Rocks of Great Britain.   *Rep. Brit. Assoc.* for 1884, pp. 529-551. [Abstract in *Geol. Mag.*, N.S., dec. 3, vol. i (1884), pp. 521-522].

1885. COLLINS, J. H. On the Geological History of the Cornish Serpentinous Rocks. *Geol. Mag.*, N.S., dec. 3, vol. ii, pp. 298-302; also *Ibid.*, vol. iii (1886), pp. 359-367; also *Ibid.*, vol. iv (1887), pp. 220-226.

1885. SOMERVAIL, A., and H. Fox.   On the Occurrence of Volcanic Tuffs, Breccia, etc., in the Meneage District. *Trans. Roy. Geol. Soc. Corn.*, vol. x (1887), pp. 189-203.

1885. WHITLEY, N. Traces of a Great Post-Glacial Flood in Cornwall. *Journ. Roy. Inst. Corn.*, vol. viii (1886), pp. 240-242.

1886. BONNEY, T. G. (a) Presidential Address to the Geological Society. *Quart. Journ. Geol. Soc.*, vol. xlii, Proceedings, pp. 85-87.
        (b) The Foliation of the Lizard Gabbro. [Letter]. *Geol. Mag.*, N.S., dec. 3, vol. iii, pp. 575-576.

1886. BRENT, F. On the Occurrence of Flint Flakes, and Small Stone Implements in Cornwall. [1st paper]. *Journ. Roy. Inst. Corn.*, vol. ix (1889), pp. 58-61.

1886. CLARK, T. Roads and Road Metalling. *54th Ann. Rep. Roy. Corn. Poly. Soc.*, pp.103-110.

1886. TEALL, J. J. H. The Metamorphosis of the Lizard Gabbros. *Geol. Mag.*, N.S., dec. 3, vol. iii, pp. 481-489; see also *Rep. Brit. Assoc.* for 1886 (1887), pp. 668-669.

1886. WORTH, R. N. (a) On the Existence of a Submarine Triassic Outlier in the English Channel, off the Lizard. *Quart. Journ. Geol. Soc.*, vol. xlii, pp. 313-315.
        (b) The Rocks and Minerals of Cornwall and Devon. *54th Ann. Rep. Roy. Corn. Poly. Soc.*, pp. 70-88.

1887. BONNEY, T. G. (a) Note on Specimens of the Rauenthal Serpentine. *Geol. Mag.*, N.S., dec. 3, vol. iv, pp. 65-70.
        (b) Felspar in the Lizard Serpentine. [Letter]. *Geol. Mag.*, N.S., dec. 3, vol. iv, p. 239-240.
        (c) The Lizard Serpentines. [Letter]. *Geol. Mag.*, N.S., dec. 3, vol. iv, pp. 380-381.
        (d) Origin of certain Banded Gneisses. [Letter]. *Geol. Mag.*, N.S., dec. 3, vol. iv, pp. 573-574.

1887. FOX, H. The Porphyritic Rocks of the Lizard District. *55th Ann. Rep. Roy. Corn. Poly. Soc.*, pp. 48-50.

1887. McMAHON, C. A. Note on the Foliation of the Lizard Gabbro. *Geol. Mag.*, N.S., dec. 3, vol. iv, pp. 74-77.

1887. TEALL, J. J. H. (a) The Lizard Serpentines. [Letter]. *Geol. Mag.*, N.S., dec. 3, vol. iv, pp. 137-139.
        (b) On the Origin of certain Banded Gneisses. *Geol. Mag.*, N.S., dec. 3, vol. iv, pp. 484-493.

1887. WORTH, R. N. The Clays and Fictile Manufactures of Cornwall and Devon. *55th Ann. Rep. Roy. Corn. Poly. Soc.*, pp. 51-68.

1888. FOX, H. (a) On the Gneissic Rocks off the Lizard, with Notes on the Specimens by J. J. H. Teall. *Quart. Journ. Geol. Soc.*, vol. xliv, pp. 309-317.
        (b) Recent Geological Work at the Lizard. *Trans. Plymouth Inst.*, vol. x, pp. 113-119.

1888. Fox, H., and A. Somervail. On the Occurrence of Porphyritic Structure in some Rocks of the Lizard District. *Geol. Mag.*, N.S., dec. 3, vol. v, pp. 74-77; see also *Rep. Brit. Assoc.* for 1887, p. 708. [Abstract in *Geol. Mag.*, 1887, p. 518].

1888. Somervail, A. On a Remarkable Dyke in the Serpentine of the Lizard. *Geol. Mag.*, N.S., dec. 3, vol. v, pp. 553-555.

1888. Teall, J. J. H. British Petrography. London.

1888. Wünsch, E. A. The Problem of the Lizard Rocks. [1st paper] *Journ. Roy. Inst. Corn.*, vol. ix (1889), pp. 353-357.

1889. Bonney, T. G. (a) The Serpentine of the Lizard. [Letter]. *Geol. Mag.*, N.S., dec. 3, vol. vi, p. 44.
(b) Dyke in the Lizard Serpentine. [Letter]. *Geol. Mag.*, N.S., dec. 3, vol. vi, p. 189.

1889. Clark, T. The Basal Wrecks and Remnants of Extinct Volcanoes along the South-west Coast of Cornwall. *Journ. Roy. Inst. Corn.*, vol. ix, pp. 449-459.

1889. Collins, J. H. Sketch of the Geology of Central and West Cornwall. *Proc. Geol. Assoc.*, vol x, pp. 94-115.

1889. McMahon, C. A. Notes on the Hornblende-schists and Banded Crystalline Rocks of the Lizard. *Quart. Journ. Geol. Soc.*, vol. xlv, pp. 519-544.

1889. Rudler, F. W. Excursion to Cornwall. *Proc. Geol. Assoc.*, vol. x, pp. 196-216.

1889. Somervail, A. (a) The Serpentine of the Lizard. [Letter]. *Geol. Mag.*, N.S., dec. 3, vol. vi, p. 96.
(b) On a Breccia and an Altered Hornblende-Schist at Housel Cove, Lizard. *Geol. Mag.*, N.S., dec. 3, vol. vi, pp. 114-115.
(c) On the Greenstone and Associated Rocks of the Manacle Point Lizard. *Geol. Mag.*, N.S., dec. 3, vol. vi, pp. 425-427.

1889. Teall, J. J. H. (a) The Metamorphosis of Basic Igneous Rocks. *Proc. Geol. Assoc.*, vol. x, pp. 58-78. (Lizard rocks, pp. 72-78).
(b) Notes on some Minerals from the Lizard. *Mineralog. Mag.*, vol. viii, pp. 116-120.

1889. Wünsch, E. A. The Problem of the Lizard Rocks. [2nd paper]. *Journ. Roy. Inst. Corn.*, vol. ix, pp. 489-495.

1890. Bonney, T. G. (a) Note on the Effect of Pressure upon Serpentine in the Pennine Alps. *Geol. Mag.*, N.S., dec. 3, vol. vii, pp. 533-542.
(b) Mr. Somervail's Contributions to the Petrology of the Lizard. [Letter]. *Geol. Mag.*, N.S., dec. 3, vol. vii, pp. 573-574.

1890. Clark, T. Mineralogy of the rocks lying between the Black Head and Porthallow, N.E. of the Lizard District. *Journ. Roy. Inst. Corn.*, vol. x (1891), pp. 176-184.

1890. Collins, J. H. On the Origin and Development of Ore Deposits in the West of England. [1st paper]. *Journ. Roy. Inst. Corn.*, vol. x (1891), pp. 109-149.

1890. Fox, H. On the Junction of Hornblende Schist and Serpentine in the Ogo Dour District, and on the Occurrence of some Bands of Potstone North of Pol Cornick, with Mr. Teall's Notes thereon. *Trans. Roy. Geol. Soc. Corn.*, vol. xi (1895), pp. 213-220.

1890. McMahon, C. A. (a) On the Manufacture of Serpentine in Nature's Workshop. [Abstract of Lecture delivered to the Western Microscopic Club]. *Geol. Mag.*, N.S., dec. 3, vol. vii, pp. 33-34.
(b) Banded Rocks of the Lizard. [Letter]. *Geol. Mag.*, N.S., dec. 3, vol. vii, pp. 574-575.

1890. Reid, C. The Pliocene Deposits of Britain. *Mem. Geol. Surv.*

1890. RUTLEY, F. On a Specimen of Banded Serpentine from the Lizard, Cornwall. *Trans. Roy. Geol. Soc. Corn.*, vol. xi (1895), pp. 239-241.

1890. SOMERVAIL, A. (a) On the Schists of the Lizard District. *Geol. Mag.*, N.S., dec. 3, vol. vii, pp. 161-168.
    (b) On the Nature and Origin of the Banded Structure in Schists and other Rocks of the Lizard District. *Geol. Mag.*, N.S., dec. 3, vol. vii, pp. 505-513.

1890. TEALL, J. J. H. Metamorphism in the Hartz and West of England. *Trans. Roy. Geol. Soc. Corn.*, vol. xi (1895), pp. 221-238.

1891. BONNEY, T. G., and C. A. McMAHON. Results of an Examination of the Crystalline Rocks of the Lizard District. *Quart. Journ. Geol. Soc.*, vol. xlvii, pp. 464-499.

1891. ————. Reply to Mr. A. Somervail. [Letter]. *Geol. Mag.*, N.S., dec. 3, vol. viii, p. 89.

1891. CLARK, T. (a) Notes on the Lizard Rocks. *Journ. Roy. Inst. Corn.*, vol. x, pp. 393-398.
    (b) The Magnetic Rocks of the Lizard. *59th Ann. Rep. Roy. Corn. Poly. Soc.*, pp. 90-91.

1891. FOX, H. (a) On the Micaceous Schists of the Penolver District (the Lizard). *Trans. Roy. Geol. Soc. Corn.*, vol. xi (1895), pp. 327-333.
    (b) The Cavouga Boulder. *Trans. Roy. Geol. Soc. Corn.*, vol. xi (1895), pp. 334-335.
    (c) Picotite in Serpentine. *Trans. Roy. Geol. Soc. Corn.*, vol. xi (1895), pp. 336-337.

1891. HOLMES, T. V., and C. D. SHERBORN. Record of Excursions of the Geologists' Association. London. pp. 396-400.

1891. McMAHON, C. A. On the Manufacture of Serpentine in Nature's Laboratory. *Proc. Geol. Assoc.*, vol. xi, pp. 427-439.

1891. SOMERVAIL, A. Prof. Bonney and General McMahon on the Geology of the Lizard District. [Letter]. *Geol. Mag.*, N.S., dec. 3, vol. viii, pp. 46-47.

1891. USSHER, W. A. E. The Devonian Rocks as described by De la Beche. Interpreted in accordance with Recent Researches. *Trans. Roy. Geol. Soc. Corn.*, vol. xi (1895), pp. 273-326 ; see also *Rep. Brit. Assoc.* for 1890, pp. 801-802.

1892. COLLINS, J. H. On the Origin and Development of Ore Deposits in the West of England. [2nd paper]. *Journ. Roy. Inst. Corn.*, vol. xi (1895), pp. 111-184.

1892. FOX, H. On the Occurrence of an Aluminous Serpentine (Pseudophyte) with flint-like appearance near Kynance Cove. *Mineralog. Mag.*, vol. ix, pp. 275-277.

1892. McMAHON, C. A. The Manufacture of Serpentine in Nature's Laboratory. A Reply. *Geol. Mag.*, N.S., dec. 3, vol. ix, pp. 71-76.

1892. PRESTWICH, J. The Raised Beaches, and " Head " or Rubble-drift, of the South of England : their Relation to the Valley Drifts and to the Glacial Period; and on a late post-Glacial Submergence. *Quart. Journ. Geol. Soc.*, vol. xlviii, pp. 263-343.

1892. SOMERVAIL, A. Recent Observations on the Geology of the Lizard District, Cornwall. *Geol. Mag.*, N.S., dec. 3, vol. ix, pp. 364-367.

1893. CLARK, T. Paper and Sketch Map of Cornwall, shewing the locality of various Rocks possessing power to Deflect the Magnetic Needle. *Journ. Roy. Inst. Corn.*, vol. xi (1895), pp. 280-284.

1893. COLLINS, J. H. (a) On the Origin and Development of Ore Deposits in the West of England. [3rd paper]. *Journ. Roy. Inst. Corn.*, vol. xi (1895), pp. 327-377.
    (b) A Working List of the Palaeozoic Fossils of Cornwall. *Trans. Roy. Geol. Soc. Corn.*, vol. xi (1895), pp. 421-479.

1893. DAVISON, C. On the British Earthquakes of 1892. *Geol. Mag.*, N.S., dec. 3, vol. x, pp. 291-302.

1893. FOX, H., and J. J. H. TEALL. (*a*) Notes on some Coast-sections at the Lizard. *Quart. Journ. Geol. Soc.*, vol. xlix, pp. 199-210.

(*b*) On a Radiolarian Chert from Mullion Island; with a Note on the Radiolaria by G. J. Hinde. *Quart. Journ. Geol. Soc.*, vol. xlix, pp. 211-220.

1893. USSHER, W. A. E. The Devon and Cornish Granites. *Rep. Brit. Assoc.* for 1892, p. 709. [Abstract in *Geol. Mag.* for 1892, pp. 467-468].

1893. WORTH, R. N. The Age and History of the Granites of Devon and Cornwall. *Trans. Roy. Geol. Soc. Corn.*, vol. xi (1895), pp. 480-486.

1894. FOX, H. Presidential Addresses to the Royal Geological Society of Cornwall. *Trans. Roy. Geol. Soc. Corn.*, vol. xi (1895), pp. 495-511, 575-588.

1894. HUDLESTON, W. H. Presidential Address to the Geological Society. *Quart. Journ. Geol. Soc.*, vol. 1, Proceedings, pp. 131-135.

1894. McMAHON, C. A. Notes on some Trachytes, Metamorphosed Tuffs, and other Rocks of Igneous Origin on the Western Flank of Dartmoor. *Quart. Journ. Geol. Soc.*, vol. 1, pp. 338-366.

1894. SOMERVAIL, A. (*a*) The Origin and Relations of the Lizard Rocks. *Trans. Roy. Geol. Soc. Corn.*, vol. xi (1895), pp. 536-543; see also *Rep. Brit. Assoc.* for 1892 (1893), p. 719. [Abstract in *Geol. Mag.* for 1892, pp. 565-566].

(*b*) On the Probable Age of the Lizard Rocks. *Trans. Roy. Geol. Soc. Corn.*, vol. xi (1895), pp. 662-668.

1894. STEPHENS, F. J. (*a*) On some Remarkable Contortions of Rocks at Rosemullion Head. *Trans. Roy. Geol. Soc. Corn.*, vol. xi (1895), pp. 544-550.

(*b*) Some Notes on the Native Copper District of Lake Superior, and the occurrence of Copper in the Lizard Serpentine. *62nd Ann. Rep. Roy. Corn. Poly. Soc.*, pp. 108-118.

1894. TEALL, J. J. H. On Greenstones associated with Radiolarian Cherts. *Trans. Roy. Geol. Soc. Corn.*, vol. xi (1895), pp. 560-565.

1895. COLLINS, J. H. On the Origin and Development of Ore Deposits in the West of England. [4th paper]. *Journ. Roy. Inst. Corn.*, vol. xii (1896), pp. 49-75.

1895. FOX, H. Mullion Island. *Journ. Roy. Inst. Corn.*, vol. xii (1896), pp. 34-38.

1895. STEPHENS, F. J. (*a*) On a Supposed Resemblance between the Occurrence of Native Copper in the Lake Superior and Lizard Areas. *Trans. Roy. Geol. Soc. Corn.*, vol. xi, pp. 680-683.

(*b*) On a Discovery of Chert Beds in the Lower Palaeozoic rocks of St. David's. *63rd Ann. Rep. Roy. Corn. Poly. Soc.*, pp. 113-116.

1896. BONNEY, T. G. The Serpentine, Gneissoid, and Hornblende Rocks of the Lizard District. *Quart. Journ. Geol. Soc.*, vol. lii, pp. 17-51.

1896. FOX, H. The Radiolarian Cherts of Cornwall. *Trans. Roy. Geol. Soc. Corn.*, vol. xii (1905), I, pp. 39-70; see also *Rep. Brit. Assoc.* for 1893 (1894), pp. 771-772. [Abstract in *Geol. Mag.* for 1893, p. 558].

1896. HUNT, A. R. West Country Geological Problems. *Trans. Devon Assoc.*, vol. xxviii, pp. 507-530.

1896. STEPHENS, F. J. (*a*) Some Geological Notes for 1895. *Trans. Roy. Geol. Soc. Corn.*, vol. xii (1905), I, pp. 87-88.

(*b*) On certain Rocks in the Falmouth District. *64th Ann. Rep. Roy. Corn. Poly. Soc.*, pp. 62-63.

1897. HAMBLY, W. The Conglomerates of Cornwall and the Banket of South Africa. *65th Ann. Rep. Roy. Corn. Poly. Soc.*, pp. 97-103.

1897. HICKS, H. Presidential Address to the Geological Society. *Quart.*
Journ. Geol. Soc., vol. liii, Proceedings, p. lxxxix.

1897. RAISIN, C. A. On the Nature and Origin of the Rauenthal Serpentine. *Quart. Journ. Geol. Soc.*, vol. liii, pp. 246-268.

1897. STEPHENS, F. J. On the Occurrence of Radiolarian Chert and other
rocks between Trefusis Point and Penryn. *65th Ann. Rep. Roy.*
Corn. Poly. Soc., pp. 104-111.

1898. COLLINS, J. H. On the Origin and Development of Ore Deposits in
the West of England. [5th paper]. *Journ. Roy. Inst. Corn.*,
vol. xiii (1899), pp. 283-312.

1898. FOX, H. Notes on Veryan and other Limestones associated with
Radiolarian Cherts in South Cornwall. *Trans. Roy. Geol.*
Soc. Corn., vol. xii (1905), pp. 179-184.

1899. ————. Supplementary Notes on the Cornish Radiolarian Cherts
and Devonian Fossils. *Trans. Roy. Geol. Soc. Corn.*, vol. xii
(1905), pp. 278-282.

1899. HILL, J. B. (a) The Lower Palaeozoic Rocks of the South of Scotland,
viewed in connection with the Lower Palaeozoic Rocks of Cornwall. *Trans. Roy. Geol. Soc. Corn.*, vol. xii (1905), pp. 258-277.
    (b) Classification of the Lower Palaeozoic rocks of West
Cornwall. The Continuity of the Strata of Gerrans Bay with
those to the westward formerly coloured as Devonian. Summary
of Progress for 1898 (*Mem. Geol. Surv.*), pp. 97-103.

1899. HINDE, G. J. On Radiolaria in Chert from Chypons Farm, Mullion
Parish (Cornwall). *Quart. Journ. Geol. Soc.*, vol. lv, pp. 214-
219.

1899. STEPHENS, F. J. Recent Discoveries of Gold in West Cornwall,
Trans. Roy. Geol. Soc. Corn., vol. xii (1905), pp. 241-257.

1900. DAVISON, C. On the Cornish Earthquakes of March 29th to April
2nd, 1898. *Quart. Journ. Geol. Soc.*, vol. lvi, pp. 1-7.

1900. FOX, H. Geological Notes. *Trans. Roy. Geol. Soc. Corn.*, vol. xii
(1905), pp. 342-361.

1900. HILL, J. B. The Lower Silurian Strata of the neighbourhood of the
Helford River, and their correlation with those of Gerrans Bay.
Structures of the Killas. The Nare Point Conglomerate probably
represents an unconformity between the Upper and Lower Silu-
rians. Summary of Progress for 1899 (*Mem. Geol. Surv.*), pp.
88-95.

1900. LOWE, H. J. Natrolite from the Coverack District. *Trans. Roy.*
Geol. Soc. Corn., vol. xii (1905), pp. 336-337.

1901. BRENT, F. On the Occurrence of Flint Flakes, and Small Stone
Implements in Cornwall. [2nd paper]. *Journ. Roy. Inst.*
Corn., vol. xiv, pp. 417-419.

1901. FOX, H. Gunwalloe. *Trans. Roy. Geol. Soc. Corn.*, vol. xii (1905),
pp. 434-437.

1901. HILL, J. B. On some Geological Structures in West Cornwall. *Trans.*
Roy. Geol. Soc. Corn., vol. xii (1905), pp. 403-430.

1901. LOWE, H. J. The Sequence of the Lizard Rocks. *Trans. Roy. Geol.*
Soc. Corn., vol. xii (1905), pp. 438-466.

1902. HILL, J. B. (a) The Plutonic and other Intrusive Rocks of West
Cornwall in their Relation to the Mineral Ores. *Trans. Roy.*
Geol. Soc. Corn., vol. xii (1905), pp. 546-615.
    (b) Continuity of the Pillow Lavas of Gorran Haven with
those of Mullion Island. The Nare Point Conglomerates possible
line of demarcation between the Upper and Lower Silurian.
Summary of Progress for 1901 (*Mem. Geol. Surv.*), pp. 17, 18.

1902. LOWE, H. J. The Sequence of the Lizard Rocks. [2nd paper].
Trans. Roy. Geol. Soc. Corn., vol. xii (1905), pp. 507-534.

1903. COLLINS, J. H. Notes on the Principal Lead-bearing Lodes of the West of England. *Trans. Roy. Geol. Soc. Corn.*, vol. xii (1905), pp. 683-718.

1903. HILL, J. B. (*a*) The Grampound and Probus Conglomerate—probably represents an unconformity. Summary of Progress for 1902 (*Mem. Geol. Surv.*), p. 25.
(*b*) The Plutonic and other Intrusive Rocks of West Cornwall. *The Quarry*, vol. viii, pp. 533-538, 603-606.

1904. ADYE, E. H. The Twentieth Century Atlas of Microscopical Petrography. London.

1904. COLLINS, J. H. The Precious Metals in the West of England. *Journ. Roy. Inst. Corn.*, vol. xvi (1906), pp. 103-119. (Gold in Meneage, pp. 107, 108).

1904. FLETT, J. S. First Notes on the Petrography of Western Cornwall. Appendix to Summary of Progress for 1903 (*Mem. Geol. Surv.*), pp. 150-162.

1904. FOX, H. Geological Notes, No. 2. *Trans. Roy. Geol. Soc. Corn.*, vol. xii (1905), pp. 753-759.

1904. GREEN, U. (*a*) On the Discovery of Silurian Fossils of Ludlow Age in Cornwall. *Geol. Mag.*, N.S., dec. 5, vol. i, pp. 289-290.
(*b*) Note on the Correlation of some Cornish Beds with the Gedinnian of Continental Europe. *Geol. Mag.*, N.S., dec. 5, vol. i, pp. 403-407.

1904. PRIOR, G. T. Note on a Pillow-lava apparently forming a continuous horizon from Mullion Island to Gorran Haven in Cornwall. *Geol. Mag.*, N.S., dec. 5, vol. i, pp. 447-449.

1904. REID, C. On the probable Occurrence of an Eocene Outlier off the Cornish Coast. *Quart. Journ. Geol. Soc.*, vol. lx, pp. 113-119.

1904. USSHER, W. A. E. The Devonian Rocks of Cornwall. *Geol. Mag.*, N.S., dec. 5, vol. i, pp. 587-591.

1905. BONNEY, T. G., and C. A. RAISIN. The Microscopic Structure of Minerals forming Serpentine, and their Relation to its History. *Quart. Journ. Geol. Soc.*, vol. lxi, pp. 690-715.

1905. REID, C. The Lower Palaeozoic rocks of the Gorran Haven area and their relations to the Devonian. Probable correlation of rocks of West Cornwall with Lower and Middle Devonian. Fossils of the Silurian Limestone blocks and the Gorran Quartzite. Summary of Progress for 1904 (*Mem. Geol. Surv.*), pp. 23-25.

1905. RUDLER, F. W. A Handbook to a Collection of the Minerals of the British Islands, in the Museum of Practical Geology. (*Mem. Geol. Surv.*).

1906. GREEN, U., and C. D. SHERBORN. Lists of Wenlockian Fossils from Porthluney, Cornwall; Ludlowian Fossils from Porthalla; and Taunusian Fossils from Polyne Quarry, near Looe, Cornwall. *Geol. Mag.*, N.S., dec. 5, vol. iii, pp. 33-35.

1906. HILL, J. B., and D. A. MACALISTER. The Geology of Falmouth and Truro and of· the Mining District of Camborne and Redruth, with Petrological Notes by J. S. Flett. *Mem. Geol. Surv.*

1906. ————. (*a*) Geology of Cornwall. In " Victoria County History." London.
(*b*) On the Relation between the Older and Newer Palaeozoics of West Cornwall. *Geol. Mag.*, N.S., dec. 5, vol. iii, pp. 206-216.

1906. LOVEGROVE, E. J., J. S. FLETT, and J. A. HOWE. Attrition Tests of Road-making Stones. London. (Epidiorite from Porthoustock, p. 77).

1906. REID, C., and J. B. HILL. Lower Palaeozoic age of Portscatho, Falmouth and Mylor Series. Approximate succession of the Lower Palaeozoic rocks and their relations to the Devonian. Summary of Progress for 1905 (*Mem. Geol. Surv.*), pp. 24-26.

1906. STRUTT, R. J. On the Distribution of Radium in the Earth's Crust, and on the Earth's Internal Heat. *Proc. Roy. Soc.*, ser. A, vol. lxxvii, pp. 472-485.

1907 BATHER, F. A. The Discovery in West Cornwall of a Silurian Crinoid characteristic of Bohemia. *Trans. Roy. Geol. Soc. Corn.*, vol. xiii (1914), pp. 191-197.

1907. FLETT, J. S. Serpentine and associated Rocks of the Southern Lizard District. Summary of Progress for 1906 (*Mem. Geol. Surv.*), pp. 28-30.

1907. HILL, J. B. The Palaeozoic Rocks of the Northern Lizard District. Summary of Progress for 1906 (*Mem. Geol. Surv.*), pp. 30-33.

1907. REID, C. The Geology of the Country around Mevagissey, with Petrological Contributions by J. J. H. Teall. *Mem. Geol. Surv.*

1907. ————, and J. S. FLETT. The Geology of the Land's End District, with contributions by B. S. N. Wilkinson, E. E. L. Dixon, and W. Pollard. Mining Appendix by D. A. MacAlister. *Mem. Geol. Surv.*

1907. WHITLEY, D. G. The Head of Rubble on the Cornish Coast. *Journ. Roy. Inst. Corn.*, vol. xvii (1909), pp. 63-81.

1908. FLETT, J. S. Serpentine and associated Rocks of the Southern Lizard District. Summary of Progress for 1907 (*Mem. Geol. Surv.*), pp. 25-28.

1908. Fox, H. Trilobite in the Veryan Quartzite. (Note on a Specimen of *Calymene* from Veryan, by Philip Lake.) *Trans. Roy. Geol. Soc. Corn.*, vol. xiii (1914), pp. 233-236.

1908. RADLEY, E. G. Analyses of Cornish rocks. Pillow Lava from Tregidden, and Hornblende Schist from Lower Relowas. Summary of Progress for 1907 (*Mem. Geol. Surv.*), p. 58.

1908. WHITLEY, D. G. On the Occurrence of Trees and Vegetable Remains in the Stream Tin in Cornwall. *Trans. Roy. Geol. Soc. Corn.*, vol. xiii (1914), pp. 237-256.

1908. WORTH, R. H. The Dredgings of the Marine Biological Association (1895-1906), as a Contribution to the Knowledge of the Geology of the English Channel. *Journ. Marine Biolog. Assoc., U.K.*, N.S., vol. viii, pp. 118-188.

1909. FLETT, J. S. Lizard Rocks: The Man o' War Gneisses; the Treleague Quartzite. Summary of Progress for 1908 (*Mem. Geol. Surv.*), pp. 24-25.

1909. GREEN, U. On the Geological Structure of Western Cornwall. *Trans. Roy. Geol. Soc. Corn.*, vol. xiii (1914), pp. 284-296.

1909. ROGERS, W. (a) Note on a Polished Block of Quartzite in the Meneage Peninsula. *Trans. Roy. Geol. Soc. Corn.*, vol. xiii (1914), pp. 297-298.

(b) Notes on the Raised Beaches and Head of Rubble in the neighbourhood of Falmouth. *76th Ann. Rep. Roy. Poly. Soc. Corn.*, N.S., vol. i, pp. 91-95.

1909. TEALL, J. J. H. Quarter-inch Geological Survey map 21 and 25. Colour-printed.

1910. McLINTOCK, W. F. P. On Datolite from the Lizard district, Cornwall. *Mineralog. Mag.*, vol. xv, pp. 407-414.

1910. ROGERS, M. The Raised Beaches and Head of the Cornish Coast. *Trans. Roy. Geol. Soc. Corn.*, vol. xiii (1914), pp. 351-384.

1910. RUSSELL, A. Notes on the occurrence of zeolites in Cornwall and Devon. *Mineralog. Mag.*, vol. xv, pp. 377-384.

1910. USSHER, W. A. E.   The Geology of Cornwall, Devon, and West Somerset. In " Geology in the Field " (Jubilee Volume of the Geologists' Association), pp. 859-896.

1911. DEWEY, H., and J. S. FLETT.   On some British Pillow-lavas and the Rocks associated with them.   *Geol. Mag.*, N.S., dec. 5, vol. viii, pp. 202-209, 241-248.

1912. COLLINS, J .H. Observations on the West of England Mining Region. Plymouth. (*Trans. Roy. Geol. Soc. Corn.*, vol. xiv.)

1912. FLETT, J. S., and J. B. HILL.   One-inch Geological Survey map 359 (New Series), Lizard.   Colour-printed.

1912. GREEN, U., and C. D. SHERBORN.   Note on the Pollurian-Trewavas Coast Section, Cornwall.   *Geol. Mag.*, N.S., dec. 5, vol. ix, pp. 558-560.

1913. FLETT, J. S.   The Geology of the Lizard.   *Proc. Geol. Assoc.*, vol. xxiv, pp. 118-133.

1913. —————, and J. B. HILL.   Report of an Excursion to the Lizard, Cornwall.   *Proc. Geol. Assoc.*, vol. xxiv, pp. 313-327.

1913. GREEN, U., and C. D. SHERBORN.   On the General Geological Structure of Western Cornwall, with a Note on the Porthluney-Dodman Section.   *Geol. Mag.*, N.S., dec. 5, vol. x, pp. 70-73.

1913. HILL, J. B.   The Geology of Northern Meneage.   *Proc. Geol. Assoc.*, vol. xxiv, pp. 134-158.

1914. BONNEY, T. G.   The Crystalline Rocks of the Lizard. Some notes on their history and origin. Cambridge.

1916. LOWE, H. J.   Geologists' Association at the Lizard.   *Trans. Roy. Geol. Soc. Corn.*, vol. xv (1927), pp. 110-118.

1918. STILLWELL, F. L.   The Metamorphic Rocks of Adelie Land. Section I. Australian Antarctic Expedition 1911-1914, pp. 106-118.

1920. BONNEY, T. G.   Beerbachite at the Lizard.   *Geol. Mag.*, vol. lvii, pp. 339-340.

1921. McPHERSON, G., and T. Lamb.   Platinum-bearing Rocks in the Lizard District.   *Geol. Mag.*, vol. lviii, pp. 512-514.

1922. MILNER, H. B.   The Nature and Origin of the Pliocene Deposits of the County of Cornwall and their Bearing on the Pliocene Geography of the South-West of England.   *Quart. Journ. Geol. Soc.*, vol. lxxviii, pp. 348-377.

1923. BOSWELL, P. G. H.   The Petrography of the Cretaceous and Tertiary Outliers of the West of England.   *Quart. Journ. Geol. Soc.*, vol. lxxix, pp. 205-230.

1923. HENDRIKS, E. M. L.   The Physiography of South-West Cornwall, the Distribution of Chalk Flints, and the Origin of the Gravels of Crousa Common.   *Geol. Mag.*, vol. lx, pp. 21-31.

1925. DAVISON, E. H.   Platinum in the Lizard District.   *Mining Mag.*, vol. xxxiii, pp. 89-90.

1926. —————— Handbook of Cornish Geology.   Penzance.   2nd edition 1930.   Truro.

1926. HENDRIKS, E. M. L.   Serpentine from Gerrans Bay. Preliminary Account.   *Trans. Roy. Geol. Soc. Corn.*, vol. xv (1927), pp. 519-525.

1926. TEALL, J. J. H.   Quarter-inch Geological Survey map 21 and 25.   2nd edition.

1928. GHOSH, P. K.   The Mineral-Assemblage of the Falmouth Granite (Cornwall).   *Proc. Geol. Assoc.*, vol. xxxix, pp. 332-338.

1929. LANG, W. H.   On Fossil Wood (Dadoxylon Hendriksi, n.sp.) and other Plant-remains from the Clay Slates of South Cornwall.   *Annals of Botany*, vol. xliii, p. 663.

1929. LOVEGROVE, E. J., J. A. HOWE, and J. S. FLETT. Attrition Tests of British Road-stones. *Mem. Geol. Surv.*

1930. HALL, S. (a) The Geology of the Godolphin Granite. A study of the coastal geology between Perranuthnoe and Looe Pool. *Proc. Geol. Assoc.*, vol. xli, pp. 117-147; also Geologists' Association Handbook.
   (b) Field Meeting held at Helston, Whitsun, 1930. *Proc. Geol. Assoc.*, vol. xli, pp. 354-361.

1931. GUPPY, E. M., and H. H. THOMAS. Chemical Analyses of Igneous Rocks, Metamorphic Rocks and Minerals. *Mem. Geol. Surv.*

1931. HENDRIKS, E. M. L. The Stratigraphy of South Cornwall. *Rep. Brit. Assoc.* for 1930, p. 332.

1932. HARKER, A. Metamorphism. London. (pp. 317-319.)

1933. FLETT, J. S. The geology of the Meneage. Summary of Progress for 1932, part II, (*Mem. Geol. Surv.*), pp. 1-14.

1934. ————, and J. B. HILL. One-inch Geological Survey map 359 (New Series), Lizard. Revised edition.

1934. GHOSH, P. K. The Carnmenellis Granite: its Petrology, Metamorphism and Tectonics. *Quart. Journ. Geol. Soc.*, vol. xc, pp. 240-276.

1935. DEWEY, H. British Regional Geology: South-West England. *Mem. Geol. Surv.*

1937. BALSILLIE, D. The Girvan-Ballantrae Serpentine. [Letter]. *Geol. Mag.*, vol. lxxiv, p. 336.

1937. HENDRIKS, E. M. L. Rock succession and structure in South Cornwall: a revison. With notes on the Central European facies and Variscan folding there present. *Quart. Journ. Geol. Soc.*, vol. xciii, pp. 322-360.

1937. TILLEY, C. E. Anthophyllite-Cordierite-Granulites of the Lizard. *Geol. Mag.*, vol. lxxiv, pp. 300-309.

1938. SCRIVENOR, J. B. (a) Notes on the Geology of the Lizard Peninsula. No. 1. Some Mullion Rocks. *Geol. Mag.*, vol. lxxv, pp. 304-308.
   (b) Notes on the Geology of the Lizard Peninsula. No. 2. The Primary Hornblende-schists and Gneisses (The Lizard Hornblende-schists). *Geol. Mag.*, vol. lxxv, pp. 385-394.

The following papers on Lizard geology have been published while this Memoir was passing through the press:—

1938. SCRIVENOR, J. B. (c) Notes on the Geology of the Lizard Peninsula. No. 3. The Epidote Bands, Lenticles, and Veins. *Geol. Mag.*, vol. lxxv, pp. 515-526.

1939. ————. (a) Notes on the Geology of the Lizard Peninsula. No. 4. "The Devil's Frying Pan," Cadgwith. *Geol. Mag.*, vol. lxxvi, pp. 37-41.
   (b) Notes on the Geology of the Lizard Peninsula. No. 5 Porthallow and Neighbourhood: Folding: Tourmaline-bearing Rocks. *Geol. Mag.*, vol. lxxvi, pp. 97-109.

1939. HENDRIKS, E. M. L. The Start-Dodman-Lizard Boundary-Zone in Relation to the Alpine Structure of Cornwall. *Geol. Mag.*, vol. lxxvi, pp. 385-402.

1939. STUBBLEFIELD, C. J. Some Devonian and supposed Ordovician Fossils from South-West Cornwall. *Bull. Geol. Surv. Gt. Brit.*, No. 2, pp. 63-71.

ADDITIONAL BIBLIOGRAPHY 1940-1972

This list contains references relating wholly or in part to the geology of the Lizard and Meneage district, which were published during the period 1940–1972. Earlier works are listed in pages 179–92.

ALLAN, T. D. 1961. A magnetic survey in the western English Channel. *Q. Jnl geol. Soc. Lond.*, **117**, 157–70.

ARBER, MURIEL A. 1940. Outline of south-west England in relation to wave-attack. *Nature, Lond.*, **94**, 27–8.

—— 1949. Cliff profiles of Devon and Cornwall. *Geog. Jnl*, **114**, 191–7.

BALCHIN, W. G. V. [1966]. The denudation chronology of south-west England. *In* Present views of some aspects of the geology of Cornwall and Devon. *R. geol. Soc. Corn.*, Commem. Vol. for 1964, 267–81.

BELDERSON, R. H., KENYON, N. H. and STRIDE, A. H. 1971. Holocene sediments on the continental shelf west of the British Isles. *In* DELANY, F. M. (ed.). The geology of the East Atlantic continental margin. 2. Europe. *Rep. No. 70/14, Inst. geol. Sci.*, 157–70.

BOTT, M. H. P., DAY, A. A. and MASSON SMITH, D. 1958. The geological interpretation of gravity and magnetic surveys in Devon and Cornwall. *Phil. Trans. R. Soc. Lond.* (A), **251**, 161–91.

—— and SCOTT, P. [1966]. Recent geophysical studies in south-west England. *In* Present views of some aspects of the geology of Cornwall and Devon. *R. geol. Soc. Corn.*, Commem. Vol. for 1964, 25–44.

BROUWER, A. 1967. Caledonian movements and Devonian sedimentation in western Europe. *In* OSWALD, D. H. (ed.) *International Symposium on the Devonian System*, **2**, 1149–55. Calgary.

BUTLER, J. R. 1953. The geochemistry and petrology of rock weathering. (1) The Lizard area, Cornwall. *Geochim. et Cosmochim. Acta.*, **4**, 157–78.

COOMBE, D. E. and FROST, L. C. 1956. The nature and origin of the soils over the Cornish serpentines. *Jnl Ecol.*, **44**, 605–15.

CURRY, D., HAMILTON, D. and SMITH, A. J. 1970. Geological and shallow subsurface geophysical investigations in the Western Approaches to the English Channel, *Rep. No. 70/3, Inst. geol. Sci.* 12 pp.

—— —— —— 1971. Geological evolution of the western English Channel and its relation to the nearby continental margin. *In* DELANY, F. M. (ed.). The geology of the East Atlantic continental margin. 2. Europe. *Rep. No. 70/14, Inst. geol. Sci.*, 129–42.

DAY, A. A. 1958. The pre-Tertiary geology of the Western Approaches to the English Channel. *Geol. Mag.*, **95**, 137–48.

—— HILL, M. N., LAUGHTON, A. S. and SWALLOW, J. C. 1956. Seismic prospecting in the Western Approaches of the English Channel. *Q. Jnl geol. Soc. Lond.*, **112**, 15–44.

DEARMAN, W. R. 1963. Wrench-faulting in Cornwall and south Devon. *Proc. Geol. Ass.*, **74**, 265–87.

DEARMAN, W. R. 1969a. An outline of the structural geology of Cornwall. *Proc. geol. Soc. Lond.,* No. 1654, 33–9.

——— 1969b. The structural geology of Cornwall. *Proc. geol. Soc. Lond.,* No. 1654, 73–4.

——— 1969c. Tergiversate folds from south-west England. *Proc. Ussher Soc.,* **2,** pt 2, 112–5.

——— 1971. A general view of the structure of Cornubia. *Proc. Ussher Soc.,* **2,** pt 4, 220–36.

——— LEVERIDGE, B. E. and TURNER, R. G. 1969. Structural sequences and the ages of slates and phyllites from south-west England. *Proc. geol. Soc. Lond.,* No. 1654, 41–5.

DINES, H. G. 1956. The metalliferous mining region of south-west England. *Mem. geol. Surv. Gt Br.*

DODSON, M. H. 1961. Isotopic ages from the Lizard peninsula, south Cornwall. *Proc. geol. Soc. Lond.,* No. 1591, 133–6.

——— 1962. Potassium-argon ages of some south-western slates and phyllites. *Proc. Ussher Soc.,* **1,** pt 1, 13–4.

——— 1963. Further argon age determinations on slates from south-west England. *Proc. Ussher Soc.,* **1,** pt 2, 70–1.

——— and REX, D. C. 1971. Potassium-argon ages of slates and phyllites from south-west England. *Q. Jnl geol. Soc. Lond.,* **126,** 465–99.

EDMONDS, E. A., McKEOWN, M. C. and WILLIAMS, M. 1969. South-west England. *Brit. Reg. Geol., Geol. Surv. Gt Br.*

EVERARD, C. E., LAWRENCE, R. H., WITHERICK, M. E. and WRIGHT, L. W. [1966]. Raised beaches and marine geomorphology. *In* Present views of some aspects of the geology of Cornwall and Devon. *R. geol. Soc. Corn.,* Commem. Vol. for 1964, 283–310.

EXLEY, C. S. and STONE, M. [1966]. The granite rocks of south-west England. *In* Present views of some aspects of the geology of Cornwall and Devon. *R. geol. Soc. Corn.,* Commem. Vol. for 1964, 131–84.

FLOYD, P. A. 1972a. A model for the development of the greenstones and granites of S.W. England. *Proc. Ussher Soc.,* **2,** pt 5, 417–20.

——— 1972b. Geochemistry, origin and tectonic environment of the basic and acidic rocks of Cornubia, England. *Proc. Geol. Ass.,* **83,** 385–404.

FRYER, G. 1958. Evolution of the land forms of Kerrier. *Trans. R. geol. Soc. Corn.,* **19,** 122–53.

GEORGE, T. N. 1962. Devonian and Carboniferous foundations of the Variscides in north-west Europe. *In* COE, K. (ed.) *Some aspects of the Variscan fold belt,* 19–47. Manchester.

GOLDRING, R., HOUSE, M. R., SELWOOD, E. B., SIMPSON, S. and LAMBERT, R. ST. J. 1967. Devonian of southern Britain. *In* OSWALD, D. H. (ed.) *International Symposium on the Devonian System,* **1,** 1–14. Calgary.

GREEN, D. H. 1964a. The petrogenesis of the high-temperature peridotite intrusion in the Lizard area, Cornwall. *Jnl Petrol.,* **5,** 134–88.

——— 1964b. The metamorphic aureole of the peridotite at the Lizard, Cornwall. *Jnl Geol.,* **72,** 543–63.

——— [1966]. A re-study and re-interpretation of the geology of the Lizard Peninsula, Cornwall. *In* Present views of some aspects of the geology of Cornwall and Devon. *R. geol. Soc. Corn.,* Commem. Vol. for 1964, 87–114.

GREEN, J. F. N. 1943. The age of the raised beaches of south Britain. *Proc. Geol. Ass.,* **54,** 129–40.

HENDRIKS, E. M. LIND. 1949. The Gramscatho Series. *Trans. R. geol. Soc. Corn.,* **18,** 50–64.

——— 1959. A summary of present views on the structure of Cornwall and Devon. *Geol. Mag.,* **96,** 253–7.

HENDRIKS, E. M. LIND. 1966. Correlation of south and north Cornwall. *Proc. Ussher Soc.*, **I**, pt 5, 225–7.

——— 1970. Facies variations in relation to tectonic evolution in Cornwall. *Trans. R. geol. Soc. Corn.*, **20**, pt 2, 114–51.

HILL, M. N. and KING, W. B. R. 1953. Seismic prospecting in the English Channel and its geological interpretation. *Q. Jnl geol. Soc. Lond.*, **109**, 1–19.

——— and VINE, F. J. 1965. A preliminary magnetic survey of the Western Approaches to the English Channel. *Q. Jnl geol. Soc. Lond.*, **121**, 463–73.

HITCHCOCK, M. D. 1970. The origins of the surface relief in the area of Carnmenellis, Cornwall. *Trans. R. geol. Soc. Corn.*, **20**, pt 2, 152–62.

HOSKING, K. F. G. 1962. The relationship between the primary mineralization and the structure of south-west England. *In* COE, K. (ed.) *Some aspects of the Variscan fold belt*, 135–53. Manchester.

——— [1966]. Permo–Carboniferous and later primary mineralisation of Cornwall and south-west Devon. *In* Present views of some aspects of the geology of Cornwall and Devon. *R. geol. Soc. Corn.*, Commem. Vol. for 1964, 201–45.

HOUSE, M. R. and SELWOOD, E. B. [1966]. Palaeozoic palaeontology in Devon and Cornwall. *In* Present views of some aspects of the geology of Cornwall and Devon. *R. geol. Soc. Corn.*, Commem. Vol. for 1964, 45–86.

JAMES, H. C. L. 1968. Aspects of the raised beaches of south Cornwall. *Proc. Ussher Soc.*, **2**, pt 1, 55–6.

KING, W. B. R. 1954. The geological history of the English Channel. *Q. Jnl geol. Soc. Lond.*, **110**, 77–101.

LAMBERT, J. L. M. 1959. Cross-folding in the Gramscatho Beds at Helford River, Cornwall. *Geol. Mag.*, **96**, 489–96.

——— 1962. A reinterpretation of part of the Meneage crush zone. *Proc. Ussher Soc.*, **I**, pt 1, 24–5.

——— 1965. A reinterpretation of the breccias in the Meneage crush zone of the Lizard boundary, south-west England. *Q. Jnl geol. Soc. Lond.*, **121**, 339–57.

——— 1966. The structure of south west Cornwall: a study of tectonic facies. *Proc. Ussher Soc.*, **I**, pt 5, 218–20.

MIDGLEY, H. G. 1951. A serpentine mineral from Kennack Cove, Lizard, Cornwall. *Mineralog. Mag.*, **29**, 526–30.

MILLER, J. A. and GREEN, D. H. 1961a. Preliminary age-determinations in the Lizard area. *Nature, Lond.*, **191**, 159–60.

——— ——— 1961b. Age determinations of rocks in the Lizard (Cornwall) area. *Nature, Lond.*, **192**, 1175–6.

——— and MOHR, P. A. 1964. Potassium-argon measurements on the granites and some associated rocks from south-west England. *Geol. Jnl*, **4**, 105–26.

PHILLIPS, F. C. [1966]. Metamorphism in south-west England. *In* Present views of some aspects of the geology of Cornwall and Devon. *R. geol. Soc. Corn.*, Commem. Vol. for 1964, 185–200.

ROBSON, J. 1944. The recent geology of Cornwall. *Trans. R. geol. Soc. Corn.*, **17**, 132–63.

——— 1945. The structure of Cornwall. *Trans. R. geol. Soc. Corn.*, **17**, 227–46.

——— [1966]. The Cornish "greenstones". *In* Present views of some aspects of the geology of Cornwall and Devon. *R. geol. Soc. Corn.*, Commem. Vol. for 1964, 115–30.

ROTHSTEIN, A. T. V. 1971. A primary igneous texture from the Lizard peridotite, Cornwall. *Geol. Mag.*, **108**, 393–8.

SANDERS, L. D. 1955. Structural observations on the south-east Lizard. *Geol. Mag.*, **92**, 231–40.

SCRIVENOR, J. B. 1949. The Lizard-Start problem. *Geol. Mag.*, **86**, 377–86.

SEAGER, A. F. 1969.   Zeolites and other minerals from Dean Quarry, the Lizard,
          Cornwall. *Mineralog. Mag.*, **37**, 147–8.
——— 1970. Mineralisation and paragenesis at Dean Quarry, the Lizard, Cornwall.
          Trans. R. geol. Soc. Corn., **20**, pt 2, 97–113.
STONE, M. 1962.   Vertical flattening in the Mylor Beds, near Porthleven, Cornwall.
          Proc. Ussher Soc., **1**, pt 1, 25–7.
——— 1966. Fold structures in the Mylor Beds, near Porthleven, Cornwall. *Geol.
          Mag.*, **103**, 440–60.
——— and LAMBERT, J. L. M. 1956.   Shear-folding in the Mylor Slates, near Porth-
          leven, Cornwall. *Geol. Mag.*, **93**, 331–5.
STUBBLEFIELD, C. J. 1960.   Trilobites of south-west England. *Trans. R. geol. Soc.
          Corn.*, **19**, 101–12.
WOOLDRIDGE, S. W. 1950.   The upland plains of Britain: their origin and geograph-
          ical significance. *Adv. Sci.*, 162–75.

INDEX

120, 121, 122-123, 124, 135, 136 ; in sedimentary series, 38, 39, 40, 41, 44, 51, 52 ; Landewednack type, 15, 31, 34, 40, 42, 50, 51, 52 ; metamorphism, 15, 24, 29, 33, 42, 45, 46, 51, 52, 107, 124, 128 ; microscope slides, 53, 54, 123 ; origin, 13, 15, 51 ; petrography, 15, 45, 46, 47, 52, 53, 54, 123 ; photomicrographs, 55, 113 ; quarries, 39, 47, 48, 49, 53, 54, 64, 84, 108, 123, 134, 176 ; quartz veins, 46, 47, 167 ; relations with serpentine, 16, 17, 32, 33, 46, 47, 49, 50, 51, 52, 61, 63, 64, 66, 67, 68, 134 ; scenery, 4, 9, 50, 62 ; sketch-map, 12 ; soils, 48, 49, 173, 174 ; Traboe type, 15, 16, 42, 48, 49, 50, 51, 52, 53, 54 ; used for building and road-stone, 39, 47, 48, 175, 176 ; used for marl, 48, 115, 123 ; water supply, 175 ; weathering, 9, 47, 48, 50.

Horse, The, 8.
Hot Point, 15, 47.
HOUGHTON, F. T. S., 89.
Housel Bay, 6, 7, 9, 12 ; felsite, 31 ; hornblende-schist, 47, 50 ; Raised Beach, 171.
HUNT, T. S., 30.
HUTTON, J., 26.

Iron ore, mined, 176.

Jangye Ryn, 9, 144, 148.
Jointing, in epidiorite, 90, 156 ; in gabbro, 78 ; in granite, 69, 161, 162 ; in Kennack Gneisses, 108, 109 ; in serpentine, 8, 69, 70, 71, 72, 73, 108.
Jolly Town, 63.

Kennack, asbestos, 107 ; banded gneisses, 19, 20, 29, 61, 100, 101, 102, 103, 104, 105, 108, 110, 112, 113 ; epidiorite dykes, 19, 92, 93, 94, 95, 96, 98, 101 ; flint pebbles, 9 ; gabbro, 78 ; gabbro dykes, 82, 84, 92 ; granite-gneiss, 109, 110 ; granite vein, 111 ; Raised Beach, 10, 170, 171 ; scenery, 3, 7, 8, 10, 62 ; serpentine, 17, 29, 62, 65, 66, 67, 68, 71, 73, 93, 178 ; sketch-maps, 12, 99, 151.
Kennack Bay, 19, 69, 81, 108.
Kennack Cove, 3, 7, 8, 10, 93, 113, 171.
Kennack Gate, 82, 93, 96, 100, 103, 104, 105, 107.
Kennack Gneisses. *See* Banded gneisses and Granite-gneiss.

Kennack Sands, 3, 9, 10, 100, 101, 103, 105, 108, 109, 110.
Keratophyre, 130, 152, 154.
Kernewas, 49, 63, 64, 95.
Kestle, 164.
Kildown, 8, 99, 108.
Killas, age (early views), 22, 27, 28, 30, 31, 34, 35 ; contact-altered, 2, 13 ; faulting and folding, 9, 13, 114 ; for building, 175 ; in fault-breccia, 59, 115, 116, 117, 122, 123, 125, 126, 128, 129, 130, 134 ; origin, 114 ; outcrop, 13, 22 ; quartz veins, 5, 9, 22, 117, 165, 167, 173 ; scenery, 4, 9 ; soils, 173 ; water supply, 175 ; weathering, 5. *See* Gramscatho Beds *and* Mylor Beds.
Kilter, 98, 113.
KING, W., 29.
KINGSLEY, CHARLES, 2.
Kuggar, 27, 65, 100, 109, 110.
Kyanite, 14, 20, 34, 38.
Kynance, epidiorite dykes, 94, 96 ; gabbro dykes, 82, 84 ; granite dykes, 29, 108, 109, 111 ; Head deposit, 170 ; Kennack Gneisses, 32, 108 ; quartz and flint pebbles, 6, 166 ; Raised Beach, 171 ; scenery, 4, 6, 7, 62, 108 ; serpentine, 12, 17, 62, 63, 65, 66, 67, 68, 72, 73, 75, 76, 87, 178.
Kynance Cove, 6, 7, 108 ; sketch-maps, 12, 67, 72, 151.
Kynance Downs, 6, 67, 108, 173, 178.

Labham Reefs, 56, 57, 58.
Labham Rock, 56, 59.
Labradorite, 59, 89 (analysis).
Laden Ceyn, 111.
Ladock Beds, 22, 35, 153.
Lamprophyre, 25, 121, 164.
Lanarth, 174.
Landewednack, asbestos, 26 ; hornblende-schist, 28, 46. *See* Church Cove.
Landewednack type of hornblende-schist, distribution and outcrops, 15, 40, 46, 50, 52 ; foliation, 15, 46 ; metamorphism, 52 ; origin, 31 ; petrography, 15, 52, 53 ; relations and sequence, 34, 42, 51, 52 ; scenery, 50.
Landrivick, 123.
Landslips, 8, 72.
LANG, W. H., 22, 23, 36, 133, 135, 145, 151.
Lankidden Cove, 82, 86, 98.
Lanner Vean, 158.
Lawarnick Pit, 8, 72, 76, 111.
Lead mining, 176.

TEALL, J. J. H., banded gneisses, 32, 101, 103, 104 ; basic dykes, 21, 31, 82, 85, 94, 95 ; "British Petrography," 31, 59, 75, 76, 85, 87 ; gabbros, 21, 31, 87, 89 ; Man of War Gneiss, 56, 57, 59 ; pillowlavas and radiolarian cherts, 32, 34, 127, 130 ; Porthallow granitegneiss, 59, 60 ; quarter-inch map, 35 ; Raised Beach, 171 ; serpentine, 31, 75, 76 ; serpentine and schist complex (coast sections), 32, 33, 51, 82.
THOMAS, I., 126.
THOMAS, R., 163.
Thorny Cliff, 105.
TILLEY, C. E., 34, 38, 39, 41.
Tin, 1, 2, 10, 162,'171, 172, 176.
Tinstone, 73, 163.
Toll Point, 164.
Tonalite-gneiss, 56, 57, 59, 97.
Topaz, 161, 163.
Tor Balk, 72, 96, 178.
Tourmaline, in altered slate, 142, 143 ; in elvan, 162, 163 ; in granite, 160 ; in granite-gneiss, 60 ; in pebbles in Pliocene gravel, 167 ; in veins in granite, 73, 143 ; in veins in hornblende-schist, 54.
Traboe, hornblende-schist, 16, 48, 52, 53, 64, 67 ; quarry, 64 ; quartz pebbles, 166 ; serpentine, 16, 63, 64, 67, 75, 77, 178 ; sketch-maps, 12, 67, 151.
Traboe Cross Roads, 63, 166.
Traboe type of hornblende-schist, distribution and outcrops, 16, 48, 49, 50, 51, 52 ; foliation, 15, 48, 49, 50, 51 ; metamorphism, 52 ; petrography, 15, 48, 52, 53, 54 ; quarried, 49 ; relations to serpentine, 15, 16, 42, 48, 49, 50, 51, 52 ; scenery, 50 ; sequence, 34, 51, 52 ; soil, 48, 49, 174.
Trease, 41, 44.
Tregadra, 48, 64, 75.
Tregarne Mill, 41, 43.
Tregear Point, 140, 141, 142.
Tregidden, conglomerate, 133, 154 ; Lizard Boundary, 117 ; pillowlava and radiolarian chert, 113, 129, 130, 131, 176 ; quarry, 176 ; sedimentary schists, 40, 41 ; sketch-maps, 67, 151.
Tregithey, 122.
Treglossack, 117.
Tregonning Granite, 140. *See* Godolphin Granite.
Tregonwell, 123.
Trelan, 12, 16, 77.

Treleague, 21, 41, 42, 43, 55.
Treleague Quartzite, added to Lizard sequence, 33, 34 ; age, 21, 36, 42, 43, 52, 118, 119 ; epidiorite dykes in, 21, 34, 42, 52, 98 ; metamorphism, 21, 22, 42, 52, 118 ; microscope slides, 41, 43, 55 ; not found in Meneage Breccia, 121, 126, 135 ; outcrop, 12, 21, 41, 42 ; petrography, 21, 41, 42, 43, 126 ; photomicrograph, 55.
Trelease Mill, 43.
Trelowarren, 2, 24, 28, 41, 61, 126, 133.
Trembraze, 98.
Tremenhere, 98.
Tremolite, in gabbro, 29 ; in sand, 10 ; in serpentine, 17, 50, 62, 63, 64, 65, 66, 69, 74, 75, 77, 177 ; produced by action of granitic injections on serpentine, 106, 107, 111.
Tremolite-schist, 20, 62, 75, 77, 106.
Tremolite-serpentine, analysis, 76 ; distribution and outcrops, 12, 17, 50, 63, 68, 69, 72 ; fluxion structures, 64, 65, 66 ; for building and road-stone, 175, 176 ; microscope slides, 75, 76, 77 ; petrography, 17, 62, 64, 75 ; photomicrograph, 77 ; quarried, 50, 176 ; sequence, 64 ; weathering, 65.
Trenance, 44, 55, 134.
Trenoon, 110.
Trenoweth Mill, 43, 44.
Trerise, 110.
Trethevas, 80, 110, 178.
Trethewey, 117, 119, 128, 129, 131, 151.
Trevassack, 95.
Treveddon, 77.
Treviades, 143.
Trewennack, 159.
Treworgie, 129, 154.
Trewothack, 132.
Trezebal, 133.
Trezise, 67, 95.
Troctolite, analyses, 88, 89 ; distribution and outcrops, 81, 82, 83 ; forms of intrusion, 81, 83 ; petrography, 18, 73, 81, 82 ; sequence, 18, 33, 81, 84.
Tuffs, 130, 135, 148, 153.
Turwell, The, 24, 121, 125, 132, 151.

USSHER, W. A. E., 22, 34, 35.

Printed in England for Her Majesty's Stationery Office
by Ebenezer Baylis & Son Ltd, Leicester and London
Dd. 505918 K8